INTERNATIONAL SERIES OF MONOGRAPHS ON
PURE AND APPLIED BIOLOGY

Division: **MODERN TRENDS IN PHYSIOLOGICAL SCIENCES**

GENERAL EDITORS: P. ALEXANDER AND Z. M. BACQ

VOLUME 2

THE BIOCHEMISTRY OF DEVELOPMENT

THE BIOCHEMISTRY OF DEVELOPMENT

by

JEAN BRACHET

*Professor at the Faculté des Sciences, Université libre de Bruxelles,
Bruxelles, Belgium*

PERGAMON PRESS

OXFORD · LONDON · NEW YORK · PARIS

1960

90858

PERGAMON PRESS LTD.
Headington Hill Hall, Oxford
4 and 5 Fitzroy Square, London, W.1

PERGAMON PRESS INC.
122 East 55th Street, New York 22, N.Y.

GAUTHIER-VILLARS ED.
55 Quai des Grands-Augustins, Paris, 6ᵉ

PERGAMON PRESS G.m.b.H.
Kaiserstrasse 75, Frankfurt am Main

Copyright
©
1960
PERGAMON PRESS LTD.

Library of Congress Card Number 59–14176

*Printed in Great Britain by
The Anchor Press, Ltd.,
Tiptree, Essex*

To the Founder of Chemical Embryology

JOSEPH NEEDHAM

In memory of the good and evil days spent together

Contents

CONTENTS

Foreword

THE present monograph does not aim to replace classical treatises of Chemical Embryology such as J. Needham's *Chemical Embryology* (1931) and *Biochemistry and Morphogenesis* (1942), or the author's *Embryologie chimique* (1944, 1945, 1950), but to introduce the reader to the recent advances made in the field. A full treatment of the main problems which now face the chemical embryologist is entirely outside the scope of the present small book: such a long and important task would mean an almost complete re-writing of our previous *Embryologie chimique*. Pending such an extensive revision, it was felt that a much shorter discussion of the main problems which now lie ahead might be useful for many advanced students and teachers, especially since there has been no text-book in Chemical Embryology for almost 10 years. In fact, the material presented in this monograph is essentially the subject of the author's lectures to advanced students who are already familiar with his *Embryologie chimique*; it is a brief summary of the many advances made in a field which is becoming more and more active again, as indicated by the recent publication of a very important Symposium which was held in Baltimore in 1958 (*The Chemical Basis of Development*, edited by Mc Elroy and Glass).

Since no attempt is made towards completeness, the importance of the different chapters varies a good deal; the general plan of the book, however, remains, in a broad sense, that of the *Embryologie chimique*: development will be followed, as is natural, from the formation of the gametes to the differentiation of specialized organs such as lens or muscle. The accent, of course, is always placed on the more biochemical aspects of embryonic development; however, the recent morphological findings, made with the electron microscope, have not been left out, and we have tried to present one integrated morphological and biochemical picture of development. In view of the limited length of the present monograph, morphogenesis in other organisms than developing eggs (unicellular organisms or plants) had to be left out, despite its obvious interest.

If this monograph owes much to *Embryologie chimique*, it is also a development of certain chapters of the author's more recent *Biochemical Cytology*: the reader of this book will find unavoidable repetitions; the emphasis, in the present monograph is, however, continuously on the egg and the embryo.

No attempt has been made to cover the whole of the literature in the field. Most of the papers cited in the present monograph are either review articles or recent publications, in which references to older work can easily be found.

It is a great pleasure to express our warmest thanks to all those who helped us in preparing and writing this book: Drs. J. W. Legge (Melbourne), M. Nemer (Harvard University) and B. Sells (Montreal) kindly read the manuscripts and considerably improved the English. Drs. B. Afzelius, H. G. Callan, M. Durand, J. G. Gall, H. Gay, N. Kemp, D. Mazia, J. Pasteels, G. Reverberi, T. Yamada very kindly gave us a number of their photographs and allowed us to reproduce them; the book would have lost much without these beautiful illustrations. Invaluable help was obtained from Mrs. E. De Saedeleer and Y. Thomas for the preparation of the manuscript and from Professor H. De Saedeleer for that of many figures and the index. We are deeply grateful to all of them.

REFERENCES

BRACHET, J. (1944 and 1945): *Embryologie chimique*, Desoer, Liège, and Masson, Paris.
BRACHET, J. (1950): *Chemical Embryology* (trans. by L. G. Barth), Interscience Publishers, New York.
MC ELROY, W. D. and B. GLASS, Editors (1958): *A Symposium on the Chemical Basis of Development*. The Johns Hopkins Press, Baltimore.
NEEDHAM, J. (1931): *Chemical Embryology*. Cambridge University Press.
NEEDHAM, J. (1942): *Biochemistry and Morphogenesis*. Cambridge University Press

CHAPTER I

Gametogenesis

A. INTRODUCTORY REMARKS

GAMETOGENESIS, the process which leads to the formation of eggs and spermatozoa, consists in a highly specialized series of events: for instance, eggs should not be considered as ordinary cells, simply inflated with the deutoplasmic reserves (yolk, fat droplets, glycogen) which the embryo requires for further development. Eggs are much more than that: during oogenesis, the genetic material of the oocyte (which is contained in the large nucleus, the so-called germinal vesicle) has been actively at work and has exerted its influence on cytoplasmic organization and synthetic processes. All the potentialities required for further development and differentiation, including the capacity to initiate such biochemical processes as synthesis of new, specific proteins, are already present in the unfertilized egg. Even though haploidy is, as a rule, lethal, parthenogenetic embryos can develop to a large extent, without the participation of sperm cells. In Amphibians, for instance, experimentally produced parthenogenetic embryos may undergo normal cleavage, gastrulation, neural induction and differentiation of highly specialized organs such as eyes, brain, heart or kidney.

Spermatogenesis is, obviously, a still more specialized process, since it leads to the formation of the haploid, freely swimming spermatozoa. These very peculiar cells are apparently devoid of the high potentialities for development which are so characteristic of the egg: so far, nobody has obtained morphogenesis starting from a spermatozoon, even when it is placed in a complex nutritive medium.

Nevertheless, the spermatozoon is, from a genetic viewpoint, as important as the much larger egg; its tiny nucleus, which is so simplified as to have the structure of a crystal, contains all the paternal genes, i.e. all the potentialities for the expression, in the adult, of paternal characters. It should also be kept in mind that the production of gametes (as well as that of spores in plants) represents a very complicated mechanism from the genetic viewpoint: meiosis, in ovaries and testes, leads to the formation of haploid cells and to genetic segregation, through elaborate mechanisms, which will not be described here since so little is known about their chemical nature; fertilization is accompanied by the recombination of genes, which had been segregated at meiosis. The very fact that meiosis, a very specialized process, is always associated with gametogenesis in animals suffices to show that the haploid gametes are not cells in the usual sense of the term.

In the present chapter, oogenesis will be first studied, and we shall consider successively the cytoplasm and the nucleus of the oocyte; the end of the chapter will be devoted to spermatogenesis, from both the morphological and the biochemical viewpoints.

B. OOGENESIS

1. General metabolism

The metabolism of growing oocytes is directed toward the synthesis of the various reserve materials which will later be used by the developing embryo: these materials primarily include glycogen, lipids and proteins; the latter, which are present in the form of the microscopically visible yolk platelets, will be discussed later on in some detail.

Concerning *glycogen*, it is enough to say that it is usually present in the form of small granules or macromolecules; when the egg is rich in yolk, as is the case for amphibian or avian eggs for instance, most of the glycogen is found at the animal pole; a definite gradient, decreasing from the animal to the vegetal pole, can often be easily demonstrated by cytochemical methods. In the frog eggs, Brachet and Needham (1935) found part of the glycogen bound to proteins, in the form of desmo-glycogen.

The situation is somewhat more complicated in the case of *lipid* droplets: according to Holtfreter (1946), such free droplets do not exist in amphibian eggs; the lipid inclusions are surrounded by a thin protein coat and the oocyte contains therefore 'lipochondria', rather than free lipid droplets. Treatments which produce the denaturation of proteins (marked shifts in the pH of the surrounding medium, for instance) break down the protein coat which surrounds the lipids and set these free.

It is a well-known fact that synthesis of glycogen, lipids and proteins requires energy, and that the latter is provided by the oxidative phosphorylations, which have their main site in the mitochondria (see Brachet, 1957, for a more detailed study of this question). It is very unfortunate that extremely little is known about energy production and utilization in growing oocytes; energy is probably stored in the energy-rich phosphate bounds of adenosine triphosphoric acid (ATP) during oogenesis. But no study of the ATP content during oogenesis has ever been made and all that we know is that, according to Metscherskaja (1935), the oxygen consumption of growing frog oocytes is highest at the stage when yolk platelets, glycogen and lipids are being synthesized at the highest rate (i.e. in middle-sized oocytes). A much more complete and recent study of respiration during oogenesis is that of Gonse (1955, 1957), who worked on a very favourable material, the oocytes of *Phascolosoma*, which grow freely in the coelomic

fluid of the maternal organism. He found that respiration, when measured
in the coelomic plasma, shows two peaks, corresponding to periods of
accumulation of ribonucleic acid (RNA) in the cytoplasm. He also studied
in detail the effect of added substrates (succinate, pyruvate, glutamate,
etc.) on the respiration of these oocytes and came to the conclusion that the
Krebs (tricarboxylic acid) cycle functions normally in medium-sized cells.

While studies such as those of Metscherskaja (1935) and Gonse (1955,
1957) have obvious interest, it must be admitted that they will miss the
most important point until they are concerned with ATP production and
utilization, rather than oxygen consumption.

2. The role of follicle cells in yolk formation

There exists, at the present time, a good deal of evidence for the view
that intact blood proteins can cross the barrier formed by follicle cells and
directly get into the growing oocytes: the serological studies of Schechtman
(1947), Nace (1953), Flickinger and Rounds (1956) have clearly shown that,
in hen eggs, the yolk proteins bear very close resemblance with those of the
maternal blood (review by Schechtman, 1956). In the rather different case
of the Mammals also, the work of Brambell (1954, 1958) strongly suggests
that the placental barrier is permeable to proteins and that the latter can be
transferred as such from the blood to the embryo.

It is as yet not clear how this transfer of large molecules occurs; the
most likely explanation is that the follicle cells, as well as the cell surface
of the oocytes, play an active part in the protein transfer from blood to
the egg cells. There is scattered evidence in favour of such a viewpoint: for instance, Brachet and Ficq (1956) have found that follicle cells,
in amphibian ovaries, incorporate labelled amino acids very quickly,
although it is unlikely that they are the site of extensive protein synthesis.
In this respect, they strongly resemble kidney cells, which are also known
to be capable of protein resorption (Oliver et al., 1955).

It is very likely that the cell membrane of the oocyte itself is playing an
essential part in the process of blood protein resorption: electron microscope studies by Kemp (1956a, b) on amphibian oocytes have clearly
shown that the cell membrane of these oocytes forms 'micro-villi' (Fig. 1).*
It is very probable, although not absolutely certain, that these micro-villi
represent a mechanism of *pinocytosis*: the oocytes might, as amoebae or
fibroblasts in cell cultures, expand pseudopodia and 'swallow' or 'drink' the
protein-rich surrounding medium.

Such a process occurs on a grander scale in the ovaries of the insects,
since, as shown by Schrader and Leuchtenberger (1952) and by Colombo

* Micro-villi have also been found in the oocytes of the Mammals (Sotelo and
Porter, 1959, and Trujillo-Cenóz and Sotelo, 1959).

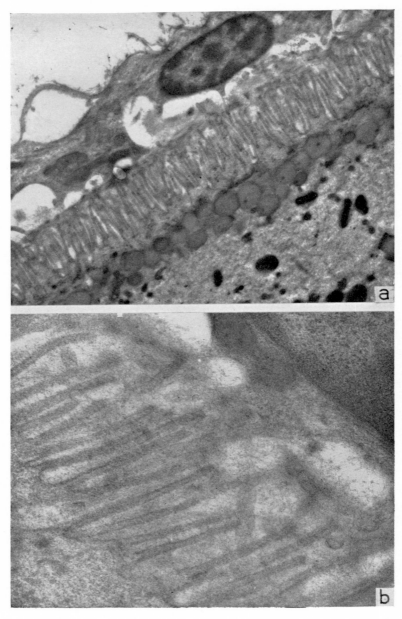

FIG. 1 (*a*). Surface of frog oocyte: below the follicle cells, the cortical layer contains the micro-villi and cortical granules (× 8750); (*b*). Micro-villi seen at a higher magnification (× 33,510) (courtesy of Dr. N. E. Kemp).

(1957) among others, whole follicle cells are engulfed into the growing oocytes and are assimilated by the egg cytoplasm.

3. The cytoplasm of the growing oocyte

(a) ERGASTOPLASM (ENDOPLASMIC RETICULUM)

The transparent, clear part of the cytoplasm (hyaloplasm) is known to be rich in *ribonucleic acid* (RNA) and to contain delicate and elaborate structures comparable to those known to electron microscopists as *ergastoplasm* or *endoplasmic reticulum*. It is impossible here to discuss adequately the significance and morphology of these RNA-containing structures; the interested reader will find an excellent summary of the question in the recent review by F. Haguenau (1958) and a less complete treatment of the question in the author's *Biochemical Cytology* (1957). In short, electron microscopy has shown that hyaloplasm, especially in gland cells, contains a network of double membranes of protein and phospholipid nature; small granules are imbedded in the membranes. This network, according to some electron microscopists, might play an essential part in the transfer of solutes from the cell membrane to the nucleus. There is good evidence for the view that the small granules (which are often called Palade's granules, since Palade first described them in 1955) are very rich in RNA; the latter, as shown many years ago by Caspersson (1941) and by the author (1942) and as repeatedly confirmed by many biochemists (see, for instance, Zamecnik *et al.*, 1956, or Brachet, 1957, for recent discussions of this question), plays a leading part in protein synthesis. The so-called 'microsomes' of the biochemists are nothing more than fragments of the ergastoplasm which has been broken down by extensive homogenization.

It is easy to detect RNA with cytochemical tests, either by combined staining with basic dyes and specific digestion with ribonuclease (Brachet, 1942), or by ultra-violet microspectrophotometry (Caspersson, 1941); it is also a relatively easy matter nowadays to study the ergastoplasm with the electron microscope in osmium-fixed ultra-thin sections.

In the following, we shall successively study the results obtained with the cytochemical and with the electron microscope techniques, restricting ourselves of course to the case of growing oocytes.

(a) *Cytochemical Studies on RNA Distribution With the Light Microscope*. It would be a worthless and almost impossible task to describe and discuss here *all* the papers which have dealt with RNA distribution in growing oocytes of all possible species. The main results have already been presented by us in 1942 and 1944 in the case of amphibian eggs; they can, *mutatis mutandis*, be extended to the ovaries of most animals.

The main findings can be briefly summarized as follows: young oocytes always contain large amounts of RNA in the cytoplasm and in the nucleoli.

During vitellogenesis, the yolk granules and the so-called yolk nucleus (*vide infra*) are poor in RNA: as a result, the observer often gathers the erroneous impression that there is a decrease in the RNA content during oogenesis (Fig. 2). In fact, there is no actual decrease in the RNA content, but a mere *dilution* of RNA in the oocyte which has tremendously increased in volume. A still more correct way to express things is to say that the RNA content increases during the whole course of oogenesis—but that, in late stages, the growth of the oocyte is faster than RNA synthesis. This can easily be demonstrated by two types of experiments (Brachet, 1941, 1942): (a) quantitative measurements of the RNA content of the oocyte at various stages of their growth clearly show that it increases continuously; (b) mild centrifugation of the ovary concentrates the RNA in the centripetal half of the oocytes: this part of the egg then becomes as basophilic as the young, yolk-free oocytes (Fig. 3). In many of the oocytes, however, an example being those of the Amphibians, part of the basophilic RNA-rich material is not displaced by centrifugation: a thin layer of this material is present, in the egg cortex, almost until the end of oogenesis; this is an interesting observation since it has often been assumed (but without experimental proof) by embryologists that substances which are not dis- placed by centrifugation are localized in the cortex (Brachet, 1947; Wittek, 1952). The role of this cortical, RNA-rich layer remains uncertain; it is likely that it plays a part in the synthesis of the egg proteins, at the expense of the amino acids present in the blood capillaries. The fact that this cortical layer of RNA disappears at the very end of oogenesis, when yolk formation stops (Wittek, 1952), supports such an interpretation. There is another RNA-rich region in the large oocytes: it is a thin perinuclear layer, which might represent a sign of nuclear intervention in cytoplasmic protein and RNA synthesis. Finally it should be pointed out that, in large oocytes such as those of the Amphibians, a very distinct polarity gradient in the RNA distribution can be observed: RNA is present in much larger amounts at the animal pole than at the vegetal end, with all the inter- mediaries in between.

Similar descriptions have been presented by many authors, working with very different materials; the interested reader will find many additional details in papers by Wittek (1952), Mulnard (1954), Urbani (1949, 1953), Bonhag (1955a, b), Yamamoto (1956), Cotronei and Urbani (1957), Fautrez-Firlefyn (1957), Colombo (1957), Cowden (1958), etc.; they deal mostly with oogenesis in Amphibians, Fishes, Insects and Crustaceans.

Since, as mentioned above, there is a close relationship between RNA content and protein synthesis, it is only to be expected that young oocytes, which are so rich in RNA, are important sites of protein synthesis. This expectation has been entirely fulfilled with the autoradiography studies of Brachet and Ficq (1956): they found that the incorporation of labelled

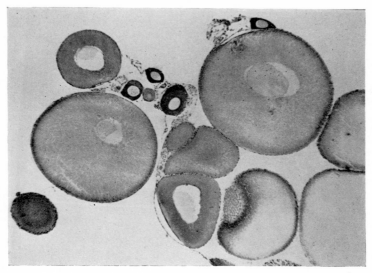

FIG 2. RNA distribution in amphibian oocytes (methyl green–pyronine staining method).

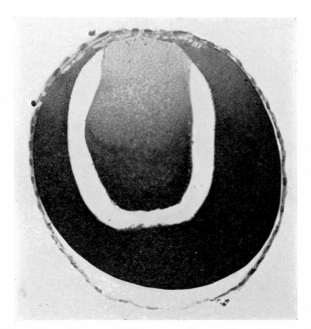

FIG. 3. Centrifuged oocyte of *Triturus*; sedimentation of the lampbrush chromosomes. Basophilia of the nucleus is due to the RNA present in the loops (Brachet and Ficq, 1956).

amino acids into proteins runs exactly parallel with the basophilia of the oocytes at the various stages of their growth.

It is perhaps a significant fact that the distribution of RNA in amphibian oocytes is apparently identical to the localization of macromolecules possessing the serological specificity of adult frog serum. Nace (1958) prepared antisera against adult female frog sera, conjugated them with fluorescein and used them as a stain for frog oocytes. The distribution pattern that he describes is strikingly similar to the well-known localization of RNA in amphibian ovaries. It would be of some interest to know whether the distribution pattern described by Nace (1958) remains the same when RNA has been removed from the sections by a digestion with ribonuclease.

Besides the obvious fact that growing oocytes actively synthesize yolk (i.e. proteins), there are reasons to believe that they contain all the equipment required for extensive protein synthesis: it is now accepted that the first stage of this process is the activation of amino acids by ATP, under the influence of soluble enzymes; as a result, the amino acyl-adenosinemonophosphate (AMP) compounds are formed. These amino acyl-AMP derivatives are, in a second stage, incorporated into soluble RNA and, in a third stage, into microsomal RNA (Hoagland et al., 1958). Finally, the synthesis of specific proteins apparently occurs in the microsomes themselves (or, more accurately, in the ergastoplasm of the intact cell). It is perhaps a significant fact that eggs have been found to contain both the amino acid-activating enzymes (Scarano and Maggio, 1957) and unusually large amounts of soluble RNA (Brachet and Jeener, 1944).

A last point should be mentioned concerning the RNA content of the cytoplasm in oocytes: it has been claimed by Caspersson and Schultz (1939) that this content is controlled by the genetic composition of the nucleus, in particular by the amount of heterochromatin present in the latter. Thus oocytes of females having a XXY chromosomal composition would have a higher RNA content than those of females having the normal XX complement, since the Y chromosome is largely heterochromatic. This question has been the subject of considerable work and discussion: according to Callan (1948), chemical estimations of the RNA content of XX and XXY eggs show no difference between them both; the reason for Caspersson and Schultz's (1939) observations might be, according to Callan (1948), unequal resorption of the RNA-rich nurse cells into the oocytes. More recently, N. Altorfer (1953) essentially confirmed Callan's (1948) findings; she observed, however, that normal males (having the XY composition) contain more RNA than the XX females: this fact suggests, again, a role of the heterochromatic Y chromosome in the control of the RNA content. Similar observations have been made by Patterson et al. (1954), who worked with isolated Drosophila salivary glands. More recent and extensive work by Schultz (1956) and by Levenbook et al. (1958) has solved to a

large extent the previous discrepancies: the presence of a Y heterochromo-
some does not modify the actual RNA content of the oocytes, but it changes
the composition (relative content in the various purine and pyrimidine
bases) of their RNA; it also modifies the composition of the acid-soluble
nucleotides, nucleosides and free bases pool. These very interesting studies
of Schultz and his co-workers (1956, 1958) clearly show how delicate is the
control exerted by the chromosomes (especially the heterochromosomes)
on the RNA content and composition of the egg.

(β) *Studies with the Electron Microscope.* The number of papers describing the ultra-structure of oocytes is growing sensibly; mention has
already been made of those of Kemp (1956 a, b) on amphibian eggs. Since
the ultra-structure of these large oocytes is difficult to study, in view of its
complexity, only smaller eggs, such as those of many marine Invertebrates,
will be considered here.

The eggs of the sea urchin and those of *Spisula* (*Mactra*) have been
studied in detail, with the electron microscope, respectively by Afzelius
(1957) and Rebhun (1956). Their main conclusion, which is also shared by
Pasteels *et al.* (1958, 1959a) and by Gross *et al.* (1958) is that the structure
of the hyaloplasm is much simpler in these eggs than in cells of liver or
pancreas. As shown in Fig. 4, no elaborate ergastoplasm or endoplasmic
reticulum can be found in sea urchin eggs. The RNA-rich hyaloplasm only
shows an abundance of granules with a diameter of about 150 Å, according
to Afzelius (1957). They presumably contain RNA and can be compared
to free Palade's small granules. Occasionally vesicles comparable to the
microsomes obtained after mechanical destruction of ergastoplasmic
lamellae in liver can be observed. There is no doubt that development of a
typical ergastoplasm occurs at a rather late stage of development, as a
result of a high order of structural, physiological and biochemical differentiation. It is interesting to note that a similar position exists in simple
organisms, when the ultra-structure of amoebae, for instance, is studied
with the electron microscope: like the eggs, they lack a well-defined
ergastoplasm (Brachet, 1958).

(b) MITOCHONDRIA

Mitochondria, in eggs, have the same ultra-structure and functions as
those of elsewhere (Fig. 4): morphologically, they are surrounded by a
double membrane and *cristae mitochondriales* protrude in the interior;
biochemically, they contain, as usual, a number of key respiratory enzymes,
such as cytochrome oxidase. We shall see, later on, that there is some reason
to believe that, in amphibian eggs at any rate, mitochondria undergo
progressive complications from both the morphological and the biochemical viewpoints.

Many oocytes contain, at early stages of their development, a so-called yolk nucleus; this microscopically visible structure is usually believed to be an accumulation of mitochondria; since the yolk platelets appear around this yolk nucleus, it is tempting to imagine that the mitochondria provide the energy required for the synthesis of some of the yolk proteins. Old work by Voss (1924) suggests that such an interpretation might well be correct for Amphibians: he found that the indophenoloxidase (or Nadi) reaction is given, in a specific way, by the yolk nucleus of young amphibian oocytes; there is little doubt that this reaction is a satisfactory index for cytochromeoxidase, a typical mitochrondrial enzyme.

In spiders, which contain a very elaborate yolk nucleus, Gabe (1956) has confirmed a previous finding of Jacquiert (1936) that —SH groups are abundant in this region of the oocyte; on the contrary, according to Gabe (1956), the yolk nucleus is poor in mucopolysaccharides, glycogen and RNA. Recent electron microscopy studies by André and Rouiller (1957) have confirmed that the yolk nucleus of spiders has a considerable degree of morphological complexity: it is formed of several layers, whose structure differs. Especially conspicuous is the abundance of mitochondria and Golgi elements in the outer layer, which is presumably the site of very active oxidative processes.*

A very different situation is found in sea urchin eggs, where the yolk nucleus is rich in RNA and is made of membrane pairs dotted with small granules or vesicles resembling microsomes (Afzelius, 1957).

It is obvious that very different structures, both morphologically and chemically, have been confused under the same name of yolk nuclei; a possible common denominator might, however, be their intervention in the synthesis of the yolk proteins, since protein synthesis requires the intervention of both microsomal RNA and ATP produced by the mitochondria.

(c) GOLGI ELEMENTS—HEAVY BODIES—METACHROMATIC GRANULES

If the situation regarding the yolk nuclei remains confuse, it is still worse in the case of other cell inclusions which are often found in oocytes: for instance, Dalcq (1957), Pasteels and Mulnard (1957) and Pasteels (1959b) have recently drawn attention to interesting granules or vacuoles which stain metachromatically with toluidine blue or brilliant cresyl blue. Immediately after the eggs are placed in contact with very dilute solutions of these dyes, small granules (the so-called α-granules) become visible; they soon enlarge and become transformed into 'β-granules'. Cytochemical tests show that they contain acid mucopolysaccharides and acid phosphatase. They have been found and studied in detail in the eggs of Ascidians, sea urchins and Molluscs. It is very likely that they have a still

---

* Comparable observations have been made by Millonig (1958) for the yolk nucleus of sea urchin oocytes.

wider distribution and that they play a significant role in morphogenetic processes.

It would be tempting to consider them as identical or similar to Golgi elements; the question remains, however, controversial: studies of Afzelius (1956), who carefully studied the Golgi apparatus in sea urchin

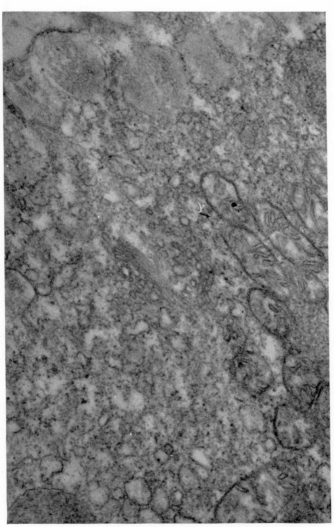

Fig. 4. General view of the cytoplasm of a sea urchin egg: mitochondria, Golgi body (at a central position in this photograph), cortical granules (on top), cell membrane (left top side); the cytoplasm is filled with small (150 Å) basophilic free granules and a few vesicles (courtesy of Dr. B. A. Afzelius).

eggs with the electron microscope, have shown that they contain a typical Golgi apparatus formed of classical dictyosomes (Figs. 4, 5). The latter possess an unusually great regularity and they multiply considerably during oogenesis.

There is obviously nothing in this description against the view that the metachromatic granules of Dalcq (1957) and Pasteels and Mulnard (1957)

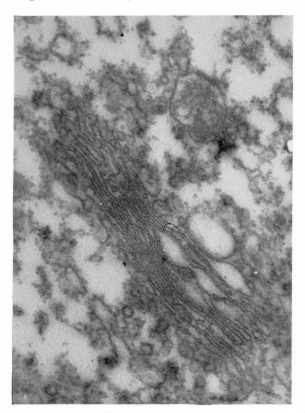

FIG. 5. Sea urchin oocyte. Dictyosome with a granular vacuole (Afzelius, 1956) (courtesy of Dr. B. A. Afzelius).

are typical dictyosomes and, therefore, constituents of the Golgi apparatus; but Afzelius (1957) has also described, in sea urchin eggs, a new type of particles, which he has called 'heavy bodies'. They are basophilic and they stain vitally with toluidine blue. The electron microscope shows that they have an envelope, which is very similar to the nuclear membrane in structure, and that they contain small inner granules. Afzelius (1957), Merriam (1958, 1959) and Swift (1958) consider a nuclear origin as very likely.

But later studies by Pasteels *et al.* (1958, 1959a, b) give a rather different picture for *fertilized* sea urchin eggs: comparing normal and centrifuged eggs, they found the envelopes of Afzelius' (1957) heavy bodies to be free and very numerous; they were very seldom found around the heavy bodies themselves. According to Pasteels *et al.* (1958, 1959), these envelopes—which they call *annulated lamellae*—represent a special form of the ergastoplasm (Fig. 6). The latter, as in Afzelius' (1957) studies, is atypical, being vesicular and rich in Palade's granules. Pasteels *et al.* (1958) conclude

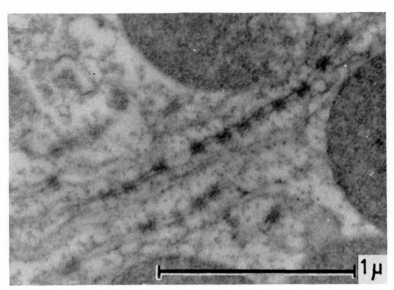

Fig. 6. Free annulated lamella resembling the nuclear membrane, in the cytoplasm of a fertilized sea urchin egg (Pasteels *et al.*, 1959a) (courtesy of Prof. J. J. Pasteels).

that, in centrifuged eggs, the metachromatic granules, the acid mucopolysaccharides and the acid phosphatase accumulate in a region which is the Golgi elements region.

It is thus impossible, for the time being, to draw any general conclusion from these observations: all that can be said is that a new and very exciting field is opening up. Hypotheses could be made and tested about the relationships existing between the metachromatic granules, the Golgi elements (dictyosomes), the 'heavy bodies', the nuclear membrane and other still mysterious particles, such as de Duve's (1957) *lysosomes*. The latter can be considered as small bags containing several hydrolytic enzymes (proteases, nucleases, etc.); the membrane surrounding these bags is of a lipoprotein nature; it apparently protects the cell against its own hydrolytic enzymes. There is some reason to believe that the lysosomes, as well as the metachromatic granules, might be the result of pinocytosis mechanisms (Straus, 1958); the pinocytosis could occur through the micro-villi present in the oocytes' membrane, as suggested above. More will be said later in this book about these intriguing questions.

(d) Yolk Platelets

The increasing use of the electron microscope in embryological studies has led to a revival of interest for these microscopically visible particles. They are classically considered as a simple reserve material, to be used by the embryos during development. Electron microscopy studies bear out this view in showing that yolk platelets and similar protein inclusions have a very regular, almost crystalline structure. This was found to be the case by Favard and Carasso (1957, 1958) in *Planorbis*, by Elbers (1957) in *Limnaea*, by Wischnitzer (1957) and by Karasaki and Komoda (1958) in *Triton* oocytes.

On the other hand, enzymatic studies have clearly shown that yolk platelets are less inert than had been thought before: in Amphibians, they contain enzymes capable of attacking the proteins of the platelets them-selves: one of them is phosphoprotein phosphatase (Brachet, 1944; Harris, 1946; Barth and Jaeger, 1950), which splits inorganic phosphate from phosphoproteins. Another is cathepsin: according to recent work by Deuchar (1958), yolk contains as much as 40 per cent of the total cathepsin in *Xenopus* eggs; she suggests that yolk breakdown, during embryogenesis, might be due to the action of cathepsin, followed by that of phospho-protein phosphatase.

A few words should be added about the chemical composition of the yolk platelets: the most recent studies, for Amphibians, are those of Flickinger and Schjeide (1957), who succeeded in a partial separation of vitellin, the yolk phosphoprotein, into two different fractions by ultra-centrifugation; the slower sedimenting component of vitellin is the phosphoprotein.

But it should be kept in mind that yolk platelets are, in fact, a very heterogeneous mixture and that chemical analysis of the total yolk can only give a crude idea of its composition. For instance, Panijel (1950) has been able to separate, by differential centrifugation, the small platelets from the large ones: the two fractions markedly differed in composition, especially in phosphorus-containing compounds (RNA, phosphoprotein content) and phosphoprotein phosphatase activity. This high degree of heterogeneity of yolk is also apparent in the recent electron microscopy studies of R. Bellairs (1958), who found three different types of yolk drops in hen eggs; it is especially interesting to note that, during development, some of them are found to contain intact mitochondria. Whether the latter originate from the yolk drops, as also suggested by Ranzi (1958) and by Lanzavecchia and Le Coultre (1958) for amphibian eggs, or migrate into them is not yet known; but there is no doubt about the general conclusion: yolk is not to be considered as a mere reserve of 'deutoplasm' or 'paraplasm'; it plays an *active* role in embryogenesis, as recently and correctly pointed out by Flickinger (1956, 1957).

4. The nucleus of the oocyte (germinal vesicle)

One of the main characteristics of the oocyte is the huge nucleus: the 'germinal vesicle' is characterized by the great increase in size or number

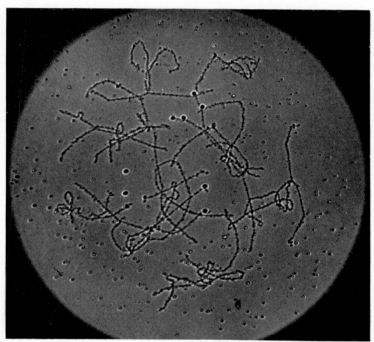

FIG. 7. Lampbrush chromosomes of *Triturus* oocyte; phase contrast; low magnification (courtesy of Prof. H. G. Callan).

of the nucleoli, by the abundance of the nuclear sap and, above all, by the peculiar structure of the chromosomes. The latter have a characteristically beaded appearance and, from each of the beads (or chromomeres), loops project in the nuclear sap; these enormous chromosomes have retained the name of 'lampbrush chromosomes', given to them by the cytologists of the last century. In many species, it is possible to dissect the germinal vesicle out of the oocyte and to study it under the microscope: Fig. 7 is a micro-photograph of such a germinal vesicle, isolated from an amphibian oocyte. It is even possible—but of course technically more difficult—to dissect chromosomes out of the previously isolated germinal vesicle. The latter, obviously, is a highly specialized type of nucleus: not only are the chromosomes paired in prophase, but the whole morphology of the germinal vesicle suggests that it plays an important role in the synthetic processes which are so characteristic of the surrounding cytoplasm.

In the following pages, we shall successively describe and discuss the nuclear membrane, the lampbrush chromosomes, the nucleoli and the

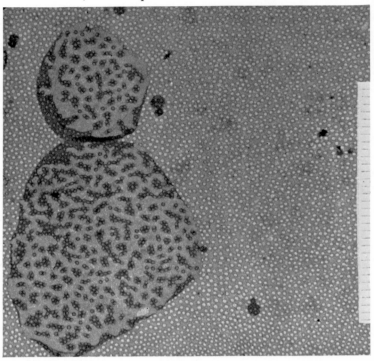

FIG. 8. Pores in the isolated membrane of *Triturus* oocytes ($\times$ 17,000) (courtesy of Dr. J. G. Gall).

nuclear sap of the germinal vesicle from the morphological and the biochemical viewpoints.

(a) THE NUCLEAR MEMBRANE

Almost all of our present knowledge about the nuclear membrane comes from electron microscopy and from experiments on its permeability: although it is possible to separate nuclear membranes from isolated germinal vesicles, no attempt has yet been made to ascertain their chemical nature. Cytochemical tests indicate, however, that the nuclear membrane of the oocyte is mainly of a protein nature.

The ultra-structure of the nuclear membrane has been first studied by Callan and Tomlin in 1950, working on nuclear membranes isolated from broken germinal vesicles dissected out of amphibian oocytes. They found that they are formed of two sheets: an inner layer which is continuous and an outer layer which is reinforced by annuli (Figs. 8, 9). According to Callan and Tomlin (1950), the role of this outer layer would be to increase the mechanical strength of the nuclear membrane.

The development of methods for ultra-thin sectioning has allowed a

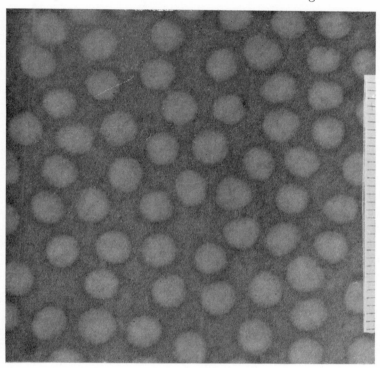

FIG. 9. Same as Fig. 8, but at a higher magnification (× 140,000) (courtesy of Dr. J. G. Gall).

more precise study of the fine structure of the nuclear membrane in oocytes, but the main conclusions of Callan and Tomlin (1950) remain valid. One question remains, however, highly controversial: are the annuli, which are present in the outer layer, pores or not? Afzelius (1955a) and Rebhun (1956), who worked on oocytes of marine Invertebrates, as well as Anderson and Beams (1956) who studied oogenesis in *Rhodnius*, believe that the nuclear membrane is really perforated by pores, which would allow free passage of substances or even of nucleolar material

c

between the nucleus and the cytoplasm. A more cautious view is adopted by Kemp (1956b), who concludes that, in *Rana pipiens* oocytes, it is impossible to decide whether the ring-shaped structures he observed are really pores permitting direct continuity of cytoplasm and nuclear sap or just inhomogeneities in the structure of the nuclear membrane.*

Physiological experiments on the permeability of the germinal vesicle make it rather unlikely that its membrane is really perforated with pores large enough to allow an easy passage for large macromolecules: Callan (1948b) and Battin (1959) found that germinal vesicles isolated from frog oocytes are permeable to salts, sugars and polypeptides, but not to proteins. However, Holtfreter (1954) observed quick penetration of haemoglobin in the same material. But the results obtained with isolated nuclei are always open to question, since the very act of isolation might possibly lead to deep changes in permeability. For this reason, the results obtained by Harding and Feldherr (1958) on whole frog oocytes seem to be more trustworthy: their conclusion is that molecules with a molecular weight of 34,500 to 40,000 do *not* penetrate in the germinal vesicle. There is no doubt, however, that proteins of a small molecular weight can cross the nuclear membrane: ribonuclease (mol. wt.: 13,000), for instance, quickly penetrates into the germinal vesicle of starfish oocytes (Ficq and Errera, 1955; unpublished observations of K. Nair).

Before leaving the subject of the nuclear membrane, it should be recalled that many electron microscopists believe that it contributes, by a process of delamination, to the formation of the ergastoplasm: we have already seen that Rebhun (1956), Afzelius (1957), Swift (1958) and Pasteels *et al.* (1958) found structures strongly resembling the nuclear membrane in the cytoplasm of the eggs of several marine Invertebrates.

(b) The Lampbrush Chromosomes

There are excellent reviews on the subject by several of the cytologists who have contributed most to our recent knowledge of the structure of lampbrush chromosomes (Gall, 1954, 1956, 1958; Alfert, 1954; Callan, 1955). We shall therefore devote little space to the problems of fine structure and concentrate on the composition and metabolism of the lampbrush chromosomes.

(a) *Structure.* As shown in Fig. 10, the characteristic structure of the lampbrush chromosome is the chromomeric appearance and the presence of loops, which originate from the chromomeres and protrude in the nuclear sap. It is generally believed that the loops can be sloughed off from the chromomeres and that they are set free in the nuclear sap. The relationship between the chromomeres, the loops and the nucleoli (which are very

* Wichnitzer (1958) believes that the walls of the annuli contain eight microcylinders, which he calls sub-annuli.

numerous in middle-sized amphibian oocytes) remains obscure. At the end
of oogenesis, the giant lampbrush chromosomes contract and shrink back

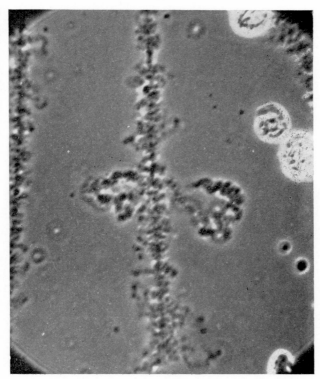

FIG. 10. Lampbrush chromosomes of *Triturus* oocyte; phase contrast;
high magnification (courtesy of Prof. H. G. Callan).

FIG. 11. Diagram of structure of a chromosome and its attached loop
pair (J. G. Gall, 1956).

to the centre of the germinal vesicle; at the same time, the number of the
the nucleoli considerably decreases.

There is now fairly general agreement about the fine structure of the
lampbrush chromosomes: as indicated in Fig. 11 and as suggested by Gall
(1956, 1958), each homologue consists of two chromatids of enormous

length (several centimetres), but very thin (a few hundred Å in diameter only). These chromatids become very tightly wound at places, which are the microscopically visible chromomeres. At these same places, each chromatid would form a very delicate lateral extension, corresponding to the axis of the loops. The most recent electron microscopy study of lampbrush chromosomes, that of Lafontaine and Ris (1958), is in substantial agreement with such a view: they conclude that the axes of the whole chromosome, chromomeres and loops included, are formed by two continuous chromonemata. We shall soon find additional support for such a conclusion.

Before we leave the morphology of the lampbrush chromosomes, one additional and interesting remark should be made: as found by Callan and Lloyd (1956), loop pairs at homologous chromosome loci may be non-identical: one pair of loops may be present at a particular locus of one chromosome and absent on the partner chromosome. Callan and Lloyd (1956) suggest, as an explanation, that 'different alleles of a given gene may produce loops of differing morphology'.

(β) *Chemical Composition and Metabolism.* It is now unanimously accepted that the chromomeres present in the lampbrush chromosomes contain deoxyribonucleic acid (DNA): they always give a positive Feulgen reaction, which is characteristic of this nucleic acid (Brachet, 1940; Painter and Taylor, 1942; Dodson, 1948; Gall, 1952). Sometimes, however, the chromomeres are so scattered in the nuclear sap that it becomes difficult to decide whether the Feulgen reaction is positive or not. In some of these cases (the frog, for instance), the chromomeres may be packed at the centrifugal pole of the nucleus by centrifugation of the oocytes at sufficient speed: they then give a clearly positive Feulgen test (Brachet, 1940).

Cytochemical methods, especially staining with basic dyes combined with specific digestion with ribonuclease, have also very clearly demonstrated that the loops of the lampbrush chromosomes contain RNA (Painter and Taylor, 1942; Dodson, 1948; Gall, 1952, 1954) associated with proteins. Cytochemical studies on centrifuged ovaries confirm this view: as already shown in Fig. 3, the RNA-containing material is displaced at the centrifugal end of the germinal vesicle, together with the Feulgen-staining chromosomes (Brachet and Ficq, 1956).

Only the chromomeres give a positive Feulgen reaction; but, if the views expressed above concerning the structure of the lampbrush chromosomes are correct, the axes of the loops should also contain DNA. The fact that the axis cannot be seen in sections stained with Feulgen is however not surprising, since this axis is so thin as to be beyond the resolution of the light microscope. But Callan and Macgregor (1958) have recently brought very elegant proof that the axes, as well as the chromomeres, contain DNA: working with lampbrush chromosomes isolated from germinal vesicles of amphibian oocytes, they have treated them with a number of proteolytic and nucleolytic enzymes: they found that pepsin, trypsin and ribonuclease bring about the solution of loop matrix material, without destroying the linear integrity of the chromosomes.* On the other hand, deoxyribonuclease (the enzyme which breaks down DNA) produces, in a few minutes, a dramatic and drastic disruption of the chromosomes. Callan and Macgregor (1958) conclude that deoxyribonucleic acid runs throughout the lengths of lampbrush chromosomes, including the axes of their lateral loops.

Having satisfied ourselves that DNA is present in the lampbrush chromosomes, our next question will be a *quantitative* one: how much DNA is there in the germinal vesicle as compared to a haploid cell, such as a spermatozoon? The answer is a difficult one, because of the limitations of the present methods. The standard technique is to attach a photocell to the microscope's ocular and to measure the intensity of the stain obtained after treatment of the cells with the Feulgen reaction. These 'histophotometric' measurements can yield valid and quantitative values, provided the apparatus is satisfactory from a technical viewpoint. The method might fail unless the DNA-containing bodies were packed by centrifugation. A second method is to isolate germinal vesicles and to estimate their DNA content with straight biochemical methods; the validity of this method, of course, entirely depends on the specificity of the assay technique. Finally, incorporation of a labelled precursor of DNA, which can be studied autoradiographically, also provides a useful index of DNA synthesis: it is generally believed that there is very little turnover of DNA in resting cells (see Brachet, 1957, for a more complete discussion of this question) and that labelling of DNA with a radioactive precursor is thus a good sign of net synthesis. For technical reasons, thymidine labelled with tritium is, for the time being, the favourite DNA precursor for such studies. It is, however, dangerous to believe too seriously in the absolute specificity of this test since, as we shall see, thymidine, or a portion of it, is sometimes incorporated in cytoplasmic structures which probably contain very little, if any, DNA. It should be kept in mind that exchange reactions between tritium and hydrogen are possible and that thymidine can, as well as any other substance, be metabolized by cells in such a way that tritium becomes incorporated into other substances than DNA. Additional tests, digestion by a specific deoxyribonuclease for instance, are required before conclusions can be drawn.

With these reservations in mind, we shall now examine the available data: using the Feulgen reaction and different histophotometric devices, Alfert (1950), Pasteels and Lison (1951), Govaert (1953) and Van de

* It is worth mentioning that, according to Amarose (1959), colchicin exerts the same effect.

Kerckhove (1959) have come to the same conclusion: the DNA content, in growing oocytes, remains essentially constant and corresponds, as one would expect, to four times the value found in the spermatozoon. In other

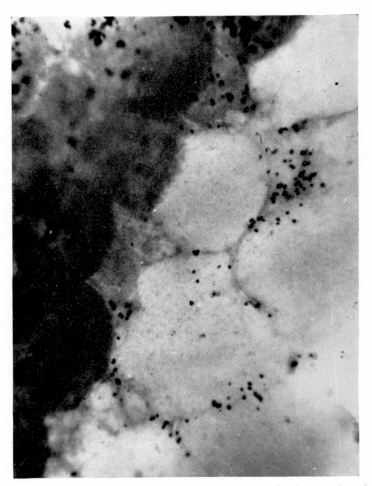

FIG. 12. Incorporation of tritium-labelled thymidine in the cytoplasmic network of *Gryllus* oocytes (Durand, 1958) (courtesy of Dr. M. Durand).

words, the oocyte is a tetraploid cell, preparing for division; during its two meiotic divisions, its DNA content first falls from tetraploidy to diploidy and then from diploidy to haploidy.

The significance of the results becomes more obscure when the second method, i.e. chemical analysis of the DNA content of isolated germinal vesicles, is used: Marshak and Marshak (1955) found that the DNA content of isolated oocyte nuclei is, in the case of the starfish, several times higher than one would have expected. Due to polyploidy or polyteny, these germinal vesicles might contain as much DNA as 16 spermatozoa. But, on the other hand, perfectly normal results have been obtained, in frog oocytes, by England and Mayer (1957): germinal vesicles isolated from homogenates of frog ovaries contain only four times as much DNA as the spermatozoon from the same species.

The results given by the third technique—autoradiography studies of the incorporation of tritium-labelled thymidine—are still more open to question, because extensive labelling of the cytoplasm (although it does not give a positive Feulgen reaction) is sometimes observed (Durand, 1958, in the case of insect oocytes: Fig. 12). The whole question of cytoplasmic DNA in eggs will be discussed, in detail, in Chapter III. For our present purpose, it is enough to say that, so far, no labelling of the lampbrush chromosomes has ever been described, after treatment of oocytes with tritium-labelled thymidine: the results therefore strongly suggest that there is no, or very little, DNA synthesis during oogenesis.

Taken together, the present data, obtained with a variety of independent techniques, lead to a common conclusion: DNA is not synthesized to a large extent during the growth of the oocytes, although the latter are the site of extensive RNA, protein, lipid and glycogen synthesis. If polyploidy or polyteny occur at all during oogenesis, it is only on a very limited scale.

We have already seen that the loops of the lampbrush chromosomes contain RNA; electron microscopy suggests that this RNA is localized in small granules, less than 300–400 Å in diameter (Gall, 1956; see Fig. 11). It has been suggested by Gall that the RNA-containing small granules present in the loops might be related to the ergastoplasmic small granules (Palade's granules), which also contain RNA. Further observations and experiments are required before this suggestion can be accepted; but there is an alternative (and not exclusive) explanation for the presence of RNA in lampbrush chromosomes: RNA might play a part in *chromosome pairing* during meiosis. This idea has been suggested independently by Huskins (1948) and Montalenti (1948); more recent work of Kaufmann and his associates (1957) on the effects of ribonuclease and of versene, a heavy metal-chelating agent, on pollen formation strongly suggests that RNA plays an active part in chromosome pairing, meiotic division and crossing over.

Finally, a few words should be said about the *metabolic properties* of lampbrush chromosomes: autoradiography techniques are the only possible ones in this case. As shown by Ficq (1955a), by Brachet and Ficq (1956) and by Gall (1958), who studied both normal and centrifuged oocytes, the incorporation of radioactive adenine into RNA occurs almost entirely in the loops of the chromosomes: as shown in Fig. 13, the incorporation of the labelled purine base is especially strong in the sedimented lampbrush chromosomes, after centrifugation of whole oocytes. The incorporation of labelled amino acids, phenylalanine for instance, is also stronger in the lampbrush chromosomes than in the nuclear sap (Brachet and Ficq, 1956); the differences in activity between chromosomes and nuclear sap is, however, not as great as in the case of adenine.

While these experiments provide valuable hints in favour of the view

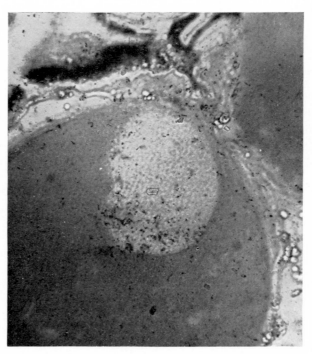

Fig. 13. Incorporation of labelled adenine into RNA, in centrifuged *Triturus* oocyte: strong incorporation in the loops of the sedimented lampbrush chromosomes (autoradiograph by Brachet and Ficq, 1956).

that there is an active metabolism in the lampbrush chromosomes, it should be kept in mind that the elegant autoradiography method still has its limitations. Until we know how much of the precursor was accessible to the structure studied, and until we know the exact content of the same precursor in this structure, it will be impossible to measure specific radio-activity and thus to make quantitative measurements. Nobody should be surprised if adenine, for instance, is strongly incorporated in structures which, like the nucleoli or the loops of the lampbrush chromosomes, are rich in RNA; or if phenylalanine is not incorporated in a protein which contains little or none of this amino acid. Unfortunately, we still know very little indeed about the amino acid composition of the proteins which make up the cellular main structures.

(c) THE NUCLEOLI

Very useful reviews about the morphology, chemistry and possible role of the nucleoli in growing oocytes have been recently published by Vincent (1955, 1957a) and by Stich (1956).

Regarding first the fine structure of the nucleolus, it must be admitted that electron microscopy—which has been such a powerful tool in the examination of mitochondria and ergastoplasm—has added relatively little to previous knowledge. The nucleolus is apparently made of small granules, which resemble Palade's small granules in the ergastoplasm. According to Estable and Sotelo (1955), nucleoli are made of two distinct parts: a filamentous *nucleolonema* and a *pars amorpha*. Similar structures have been observed by Bolognari (1957a, 1958) in the nucleoli of mollusc oocytes, but only at certain stages of the growth cycle.

Observations with the light microscope or with phase contrast clearly show that, in oocytes, the nucleolus contains many vacuoles; according to Vincent and Huxley (1954), who used the interference microscope and worked on starfish oocytes, these vacuoles contain very little dry matter; on the contrary, the matrix of the same nucleoli contains as much as 40–85 per cent dry matter, depending on the stage of oogenesis. The question of the intranucleolar vacuoles has been taken up again recently by Serra (1958): using cytochemical methods for lipid detection, he comes to the conclusion that the vacuoles result from a partial separation of two different phases and that they do not represent permanent nucleolar structures. Similar conclusions have been drawn by Bolognari (1957a, b). Nothing is known, unfortunately, about the chemical nature of these vacuoles, which give negative tests for nucleic acids and proteins; it is likely that they contain water-soluble products of the metabolic activity of the nucleoli. It has been reported by Duryee (1950) that, in frog oocytes, nucleoli some-times evert their contents when they are in contact with the nuclear membrane; this might be a process for the transmission of nucleolar material to the cytoplasm. Bolognari (1957b) also observed that, in *Mytilus* oocytes, the nucleolar volume undergoes marked changes, which are apparently due to the synthesis and elimination of substances.

There has been a good deal of discussion on the question whether whole nucleoli can be extruded in the cytoplasm during oogenesis. Although nobody seems to have observed such a phenomenon in normal, living oocytes, so many cytologists have described it on sections that its reality seems very probable. Elimination of nucleoli is apparently the result of a pinching off of expansions of the nuclear membrane. Among recent papers describing elimination of whole nucleoli, mention should be made of those of Wittek (1952), Fautrez and Fautrez-Firlefyn (1953), Scholtysek (1954) and Yamamoto (1956).

We can now go into the *chemical composition of nucleoli*, beginning with cytochemical studies and following with work done on isolated nucleoli.

Cytochemical methods have quickly disclosed the presence of RNA in the nucleoli of all cells (Caspersson and Schultz, 1939; Brachet, 1942). There is no doubt that both the volume and the RNA content of the nucleolus change during oogenesis (Vincent, 1955; Bolognari, 1956, 1957a): relative nucleolar size and RNA content are highest just before yolk formation starts and they are lowest at the very end of oogenesis. There is thus an excellent correlation between nucleolar development and RNA content on one hand, and cytoplasmic protein synthesis on the other; such a correlation is in agreement with the views expressed by Caspersson (1941) on the role of the nucleolus in protein synthesis.

RNA is, of course, associated with proteins in the nucleoli, which give strong cytochemical reactions for arginine (Serra and Queiroz-Lopes, 1944) and stain with the usual reagents for cytochemical detection of proteins (Millon reaction, staining with bromophenol blue or naphthyl yellow, etc.). Despite the strong arginine reaction, it is doubtful, as we shall soon see, that the nucleoli contain basic proteins of the histone type.

Another element which is said to be accumulated in appreciable concentration in the nucleoli of oocytes (in marine Invertebrates) is zinc: cytochemical observations (Fujii, 1954) and autoradiography studies on the uptake of ^{65}Zn (Miura *et al.*, 1957) are in agreement on this point. But the role of Zinc, in nucleoli, remains completely obscure.

While the bulk of the nucleolus contains no DNA and therefore is Feulgen negative, small Feulgen positive inclusions have been repeatedly described in large nucleoli such as those of the oocytes: the question has been studied in greatest detail by Mulnard (1956), who believes that the DNA-containing granules correspond to chromosome strands which penetrate into the nucleoli. Similar observations have been made by Bolognari (1956, 1957a), who worked on the oocytes of various Molluscs; his interpretation is, however, somewhat different from that of Mulnard (1956).

Much of our knowledge on the chemical composition of nucleoli comes from work done on *isolated nucleoli*: it is the merit of Vincent (1952) to have succeeded first in isolating in bulk starfish oocytes nucleoli. A somewhat improved method of isolation has been described later by E. Baltus (1954). These methods, as shown in Fig. 14, give remarkably clean preparations of isolated nucleoli.

Detailed description of the biochemical work performed on isolated starfish nucleoli can be found in two reviews by Vincent (1955, 1957a);

only the main findings will be summarized here. First, the biochemical studies have confirmed the presence of RNA in isolated nucleoli (Vincent, 1952; Baltus, 1954). According to Baltus (1954), RNA represents about 5 per cent of the total weight of the nucleolus; such a figure is to be taken as a minimum, because losses of RNA during isolation remain an obvious possibility. The danger of losses of an easily soluble RNA is especially great, as pointed out by Vincent (1952). He found the base composition of nucleolar RNA to be different from that of the cytoplasm. In later work (1957a, b, 1958), he showed that starfish nucleoli contain at least two different fractions when incorporation of ^{32}P into RNA is studied: one of

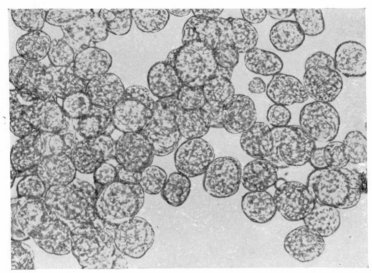

FIG. 14. Nucleoli isolated from starfish oocytes (courtesy of Dr. E. Baltus).

them is more easily soluble and considerably more active metabolically than the other. Still more recently, Vincent *et al.* (1958) found that starfish nucleoli first incorporate inorganic phosphate in an unbound form; in a second stage, the radioactive phosphate is incorporated into the nucleolar RNA itself.

We owe to Vincent (1952, 1957a) and to Baltus (1954) interesting studies on the protein and enzyme content of isolated nucleoli; according to Vincent (1952), no basic protein of the histone type can be extracted when isolated nucleoli are treated with dilute acids. The bulk of the nucleolar proteins is apparently a phosphoprotein (Vincent, 1952, 1957a, b); it is interesting to note that phosphoproteins are, as a rule, characteristic of yolk and it is therefore tempting to speculate about possible relationships between nucleolar and yolk phosphoproteins. Recently, Vincent (1958) has concluded from N-terminal end-groups analyses that the nucleoli contain only two major species of proteins; one of them accounts for only 5–10 per cent of the total nitrogen of the nucleolus and seems to be associated with the metabolically most active RNA fraction; it has histidine as its N-terminal end-group. The identity of the terminal end-group in the other protein, which represents 90 per cent of the nucleolus, remains unknown.

Nucleoli cannot, however, be made of two single proteins since they contain several enzymes: if dipeptidase, alkaline phosphatase and cytochrome c reductase cannot be detected in isolated nucleoli, acid phos-

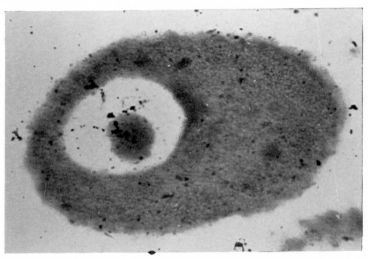

Fig. 15. Strong incorporation of adenine into ribonucleoproteins of the starfish oocyte nucleolus. Autoradiography Method (A. Ficq, 1955b).

phatase (Vincent, 1952), nucleoside phosphorylase and the enzyme which synthesizes diphosphopyridine nucleotide (DPN) at the expense of ATP and nicotinamide mononucleotide are present (Baltus, 1954). In fact, the two enzymes studied by Baltus (1954) are much more concentrated in the nucleoli than in the cytoplasm; these interesting observations strongly suggest that nucleoli play a very important part in the synthesis of nucleotides and co-enzymes.

However important the work done on isolated nuclei might be, it is necessary to corroborate it with metabolic studies made *in situ*, i.e. on *intact* oocytes: this can now be best achieved with autoradiography. Experiments on the incorporation of RNA and protein precursors lead to the general conclusion that the activity of the nucleolus in both RNA and protein metabolisms is very high. In particular, the work of A. Ficq (1955a, b), on amphibian and starfish oocytes, has shown that incorporation of adenine into RNA and, to a lesser extent, that of glycine into protein is unusually fast in the nucleolus (Fig. 15). More recent observations of Pantelouris (1958) on *Triton* ovaries have essentially confirmed Ficq's conclusions: before yolk synthesis begins, protein precursors, such as methionine and glycine, quickly migrate towards the nucleus and accumulate in the nucleolus. At later stages of oogenesis, when vitellogenesis proceeds actively, the reverse situation is observed and a transfer of macromolecules from nucleolus to cytoplasm becomes then a possibility.

More experiments, made with a larger variety of precursors, are however required before definitive conclusions can be drawn: the reason for this caution is that, in recent and still unpublished experiments, Dr. A. Ficq found that medium-sized starfish oocytes strongly incorporate phenylalanine in their cytoplasm; there is no measurable incorporation of this amino acid in young and old oocytes. But the most striking result is that *no radioactivity is found in the nucleolus* whatever the stage of oogenesis. The reason for this lack of uptake of phenylalanine in the nucleoli might simply be, as pointed out before, the absence of this amino acid in nucleolar proteins; analysis of the amino acid composition of these proteins, which could be performed on isolated nucleoli, should help to solve the present uncertainties.

In summary, it can be concluded that the nucleolus certainly plays an essential role in nucleotide metabolism at all possible levels (synthesis of mononucleotides, dinucleotides, co-enzymes and polynucleotides such as RNA). It probably is also an important organite for protein synthesis, as suggested long ago by Caspersson (1941); however, its importance in protein metabolism, as indicated by autoradiography studies, is not as conspicuous as in the case of RNA synthesis.

Much more work will be required before conclusions instead of hypotheses can be made about the role of the nucleolus: it might be, as suggested by Vincent (1957), that the nucleolus receives and stores genetic information from the lampbrush chromosomes, and transmits it to the cytoplasm. Before accepting such a hypothesis, one would like, however, to know the answer to an important question: is there a serological relationship between nucleolar and cytoplasmic proteins? It should be possible to solve this important question with the immunological techniques, such as those of Ouchterlony and of Coons, which exist at present. One would also welcome a study of the effects of a localized U.V. irradiation of the nucleolus on RNA and protein synthesis: such an irradiation could presumably destroy nucleolar RNA; it would be very interesting to follow the consequences with autoradiography methods.

In short, the nucleolus remains a fascinating mystery: but, whatever its real functions might be, there is no doubt that they are of the utmost importance for the life of the cell and that they deserve very close scrutiny.

(d) THE NUCLEAR SAP

Very little is known, unfortunately, about the composition and the role of the sap which fills the largest part of the germinal vesicle. It is obviously mostly made of water and protein, although RNA and glycoproteins have been detected at certain stages of oogenesis (Stich, 1956).

In many species, the basophilia of the nuclear sap becomes very intense when the nuclear membrane breaks down at the time of maturation: the free mixing of nuclear sap and surrounding cytoplasm results in the appearance of a very strong basophilia in the sap (Fig. 16), at the

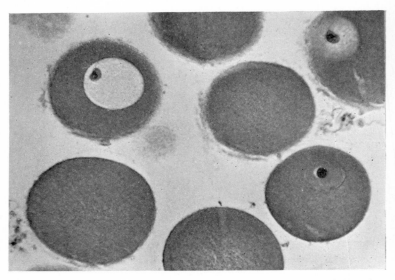

FIG. 16. Maturation begins in the starfish oocyte on the right; the basophilia of its nuclear sap has increased in contrast to the oocyte on the left.

time the nucleolus disappears. The reason for these changes in stainability of the nuclear sap is not known, but it is not unlikely that they have something to do with the onset of meiosis, since we shall meet with similar changes when we study prophase during early cleavage.

Another striking peculiarity of the nuclear sap, in oocytes, is its high content in —SH groups, after denaturation of the proteins by a fixative such as trichloroacetic acid. This seems to be a rather general feature, since the same results have been found in Echinoderms (Dulzetto, 1931; Brachet, 1939), in several Molluscs (Ries, 1937; Brachet, 1939; Raven, 1949) and in Amphibians (Brachet, 1939; Gersh, 1940). The reason for this accumulation of —SH-containing proteins in the nuclear sap is also unknown; but, again, one might speculate about a relationship between nuclear sap and mitosis: we shall see later that, during cleavage, asters and spindles are rich in protein-bound —SH groups.

The nuclear sap stains positively with the usual reactions for protein detection, including the Millon reaction; but the intensity is usually lower than in the surrounding cytoplasm. The presence of protein in the nuclear sap has been undoubtedly proven by Brown *et al.* (1950), who isolated a large number of frog germinal vesicles, broke them down by gentle homogenization and spun down the nuclear membranes and the nucleoli by centrifugation; the supernatant, which contained the nuclear sap, was hydrolysed and gave a number of amino acid spots on paper chromatograms. It certainly would be rewarding to repeat and to extend these experiments; but still more interesting would be a study of the homogeneity of nuclear sap proteins, in view of the fact that the lampbrush chromosomes are literally bathing in this sap: one might therefore expect nuclear sap to contain a number of direct products of gene activity.

Enzymatic studies on germinal vesicles isolated from frog oocytes strongly suggest that the nuclear sap contains a large number of different specific proteins; however, there is no formal proof that the enzymes found so far are strictly localized into the nuclear sap itself: they might equally well be localized to the lampbrush chromosomes, the nucleoli or the nuclear membrane. At any rate, a number of hydrolases have been found in isolated germinal vesicles (Brachet, 1939, 1944; Duspiva, 1942): dipeptidase, polypeptidase, ribonuclease, alkaline phosphatase and esterase are among them. In no case was the enzymatic activity higher in the germinal vesicle than in an equivalent amount of cytoplasm; but caution is needed here, since Duspiva (1942) has shown that one of the above-mentioned enzymes, namely dipeptidase, is easily leached out from isolated nuclei. Duspiva's experiments (1942) have been done under experimental conditions which precluded the diffusion of cell sap protein in the surrounding cytoplasm; his experiments have led to the interesting conclusion that, while a correlation exists between dipeptidase content of the cytoplasm and yolk synthesis, no such correlation can be found in the case of nuclear dipeptidase. It could certainly be worth while to extend Duspiva's studies to a number of enzymes, especially those concerned with protein and nucleic acid synthesis.

Cytochemical tests for oxidative enzymes (oxidases, dehydrogenases, peroxidases) are negative in the isolated germinal vesicles which have a very low oxygen consumption; in fact, removal of the nucleus with a minimal loss of cytoplasm has no measurable effect on the respiration of frog oocytes (Brachet, 1939). It is therefore likely that the germinal vesicle is dependent on the cytoplasm for the production of the energy required for nuclear synthetic processes; autoradiography studies on the effects of a number of metabolic inhibitors on cytoplasmic and nuclear RNA and protein synthesis might throw some light on this question.

Regarding the latter processes, the autoradiography work of Brachet and Ficq (1956) on centrifuged amphibian oocytes should be recalled here: it showed that appreciable incorporation of amino acids into proteins occurs in the nuclear sap, while incorporation of purines into RNA is a more specific function of the lampbrush chromosomes and the nucleoli. But this lack of RNA metabolism in the nuclear sap is not surprising since, according to Brown *et al.* (1950), it contains no nucleotides in Amphibians.

C. SPERMATOGENESIS

Since the subject of this book is Embryology and not Genetics, much less will be said about spermatozoa than eggs: while the male pronucleus is genetically as important as the female one, the embryologist cannot forget that, besides natural parthenogenesis which leads to full development, primary morphogenesis usually occurs after artificial parthenogenesis.

Spermatogenesis, especially spermiogenesis, i.e. the transformation of the spermatids into spermatozoa, is, however, a most fascinating subject for electron microscopists. It is entirely outside the scope of this book to describe in detail the results of their work and we shall restrict ourselves to a few references for the interested reader: there is, first of all, the very complete and recent review of Fawcett (1958), who describes and discusses in detail all the parts of the highly complex mammalian spermatozoon (the nucleus, the head cap, the acrosome, the perforatorium, the post-nuclear cap, the cytoplasmic sheath, which are all in the sperm head; the neck; the axial fibre bundle, the mitochondrial helix and the annulus of the middle piece; the fibrous sheath and the axial fibre bundle of the principal piece; and, finally, the axial fibre bundle of the end piece) (Fig. 17).*

In Invertebrates, the most interesting work has been done on Insects: one should especially mention the papers by Gay (1955, 1957), Grassé *et al.* (1956), Yasuzumi *et al.* (1957), Rebhun (1957), Gall and Bjork (1958). Startling features of spermiogenesis, in this especially favourable material, are the curious aspects of the *Nebenkern* (which is of mitochondrial origin, as shown by Gay, 1957) (Fig. 18) and the fascinating evolution of the nucleus: the nuclear contents are first fibrous; the fibres then form plates or lamellae; finally, there is a coalescence of the lamellae into a crystalline body (Gall and Bjork, 1958; Figs. 19, 20 and 21).

After these very incomplete indications about the existing literature on

* One should also mention the recent work of Cleland and Rothschild (1959) on the structure of the tail in the bandicoot spermatozoon

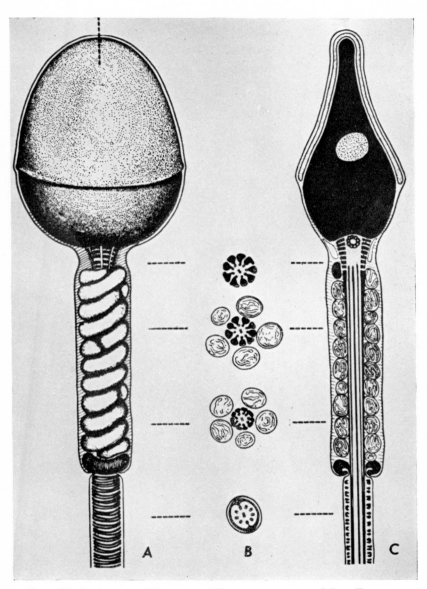

FIG. 17. Structure of the mammalian spermatozoon (after Fawcett, 1958).

D

spermiogenesis, a little more will be said about the structure and chemical embryology of ripe spermatozoa.

1. The acrosome

The acrosome, which is usually believed to originate from the Golgi elements (dictyosomes) of the spermatid, is a dense granule lying inside a

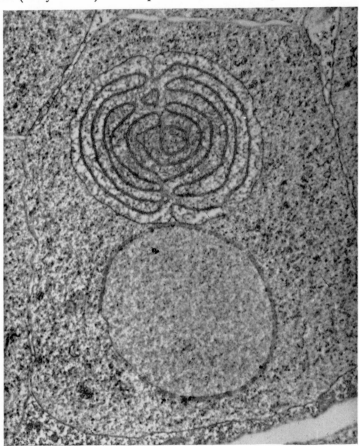

Fig. 18. Ultra-structure of the Nebenkern in a *Drosophila* spermatocyte (courtesy of Dr. H. Gay).

vacuole (the acrosomal vacuole of Fawcett, 1958). In the sea urchin spermatozoon, which has been studied by Afzelius (1955b, 1959), the acrosomal globule remains a simple homogeneous sphere.

From the cytochemical viewpoint, the acrosome is characterized by its high content in polysaccharides: in sea urchins as well as in Mammals, it gives an intensive periodic acid Schiff (PAS) reaction (Wislocki, 1949;

Leblond, 1950; Monné and Hårde, 1951; Clermont *et al.*, 1955, etc.);
several of the sugars entering in the constitution of the acrosomal polysaccharides have been identified by Clermont *et al.* (1955).

It has been suggested by Leuchtenberger and Schrader (1950) that the
acrosome might contain hyaluronidase; but one must admit that their

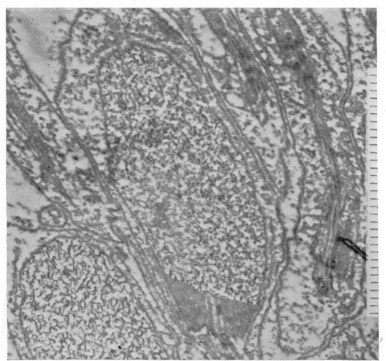

FIG. 19. Early spermatid of *Melanoplus*. Fibrillar nuclear structure
(courtesy of Dr. J. G. Gall).

evidence was mainly indirect and that this interesting suggestion is still
far from proven.

Much of the present interest in the acrosome is due to the so-called
acrosomal reaction, which occurs at fertilization in several Invertebrates:
the acrosomal globule is first projected to the outside of the cell membrane
of the spermatozoon; this projection is followed by the formation of a
long acrosomal filament. More will be said about the acrosomal reaction
in the next chapter.

2. The nucleus

As already mentioned, the nucleus of the ripe spermatozoon has a
crystalline organization; X-ray diffraction studies by Wilkins and Randall

(1953) have shown that this organization is due to the parallel orientation of deoxyribonucleoprotein molecules in the sperm nucleus.

Chemically, the nucleus of the spermatozoon is made of DNA associated with basic proteins. During spermatogenesis, as in oogenesis, the DNA content of the cell decreases in the expected way if one assumes that it is

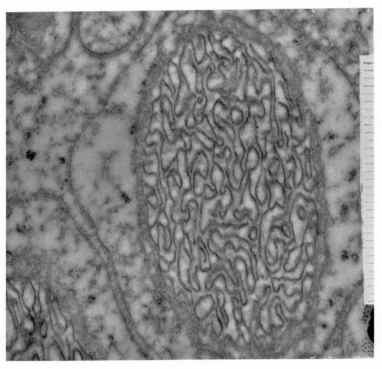

FIG. 20. Middle period spermatid of *Melanoplus*. Lamellar nuclear contents (courtesy of Dr. J. G. Gall).

constant per chromosome set: late primary spermatocytes contain, just before meiosis, four times as much DNA as spermatids or spermatozoa.*

It has been known for a long time that the spermatozoa of certain species of Fishes contain a very simple type of basic protein: the usual histones are replaced by protamines, which are exceedingly rich in arginine and have a low molecular weight (2000–12,000). Despite this apparent simplicity of the protamines, they display species-specificity according to Felix (1952); his calculations indicate that there are as many as five million

—————————

* However, according to C. and R. Leuchtenberger (1958), the amount of DNA is frequently diminished in the spermatozoa of infertile men and bulls.

molecules of nucleoprotamines in a single trout spermatozoon (Felix *et al.*, 1956, 1958).

The old question of the replacement of histones by protamines during spermatogenesis in Fishes has been taken up again recently by Vendrely *et al.* (1957, 1958): they conclude that this replacement occurs at the very end of spermatogenesis, probably at the time the sperm nucleus becomes crystalline. They also found that protamines are present in

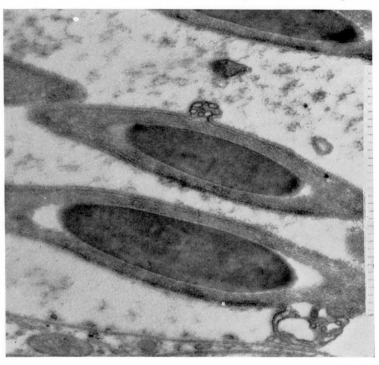

Fɪɢ. 21. Late spermatid of *Melanoplus*. Condensation of the nuclear material (courtesy of Dr. J. G. Gall).

certain species of Fishes only; other species retain the histones, while an intermediary composition of the basic protein is found in a third group.

It is certainly an odd thing that the sperm nucleus, which obviously contains all the paternal genes, is unusually simple from both the morphological and the biochemical points of view; it is possible that this apparent simplicity represents, in reality, a way to keep intact the genetic information contained in the DNA of the spermatozoon.

A last oddity of sperm cells, which is directly or indirectly linked to their nucleus, is the fact, reported by Lindahl (1958), that it is possible to separate from each other, by counter-streaming centrifugation, the spermatozoa which have the X or the Y chromosome. This finding is curious enough to warrant further biochemical study.

3. The middle piece

It has been known for a long time that the middle piece of spermatozoa contains mitochondria; recent electron microscopy studies (cf. Fawcett, 1958) have shown that the middle piece is formed by an axial bundle of fibrils (the axial filament) which extends in the tail, and a surrounding mitochondrial helix.

Cytochemical work of Restivo and Reverberi (1957) has confirmed the presence of oxidative enzymes characteristic of mitochondria (cytochrome oxidase), as well as of glycogen, in the middle piece of *Patella* and *Ciona* spermatozoa. Thus, in the middle piece, the fibrils are immediately surrounded with a layer of energy-producing mitochondria, in close contact with natural substrates, such as glycogen or phospholipids. However, according to Humphrey and Pollak (1954), respiration of the head is higher than that of the tail in oyster spermatozoa.

4. The tail

The tail, according to Fawcett (1958), is to be divided into the 'principal piece', and the 'end piece'. The principal piece, which is the proximal part of the tail, is thought to play the main part in sperm movements. It is formed of a fibrous sheath, surrounding the same axial fibre bundle as in the middle piece. This axial fibre bundle is still present in the end piece of the tail; but the fibrils are now embedded in a minimum of cytoplasmic matrix. The axial fibre bundle has a very typical (and now classical) organization in both the middle piece and the tail; it is formed of nine (sometimes double) fibrils disposed in a cylinder around a central pair (Bradfield, 1955; Fawcett, 1958). It has been suggested by Bradfield (1955) that the two central fibrils might play a role in conduction, while the nine outer fibrils could be contractile.

Some evidence for this view can be found in a recent study of Nelson (1957), who combined electron microscopy with cytochemistry: he believes that adenosine triphosphatase (ATPase), the enzyme which is so closely associated with myosine (the contractile protein of muscle), is strictly localized in the nine outer fibrils of the sperm tail.

More recently, Nelson (1958, 1959) has presented evidence, based again on combined cytochemical and electron microscopical studies, for the view that these nine outer fibrils of the sperm tail contain succinic dehydrogenase as well as ATPase: if so, energy produced by succinic dehydrogenase would be converted *in situ* into phosphate bond energy.

There are other reasons to believe that close analogies between muscle contraction and sperm movement really exist: for instance, Engelhardt and Burnashava (1957) and Burnashava (1958) were able to isolate from spermatozoa a contractile protein which they called *spermosin*; like acto-myosin from muscle, it displays strong ATPase activity. The isolation of a contractile protein from spermatozoa has also been reported by Bishop (1958a, b).

5. The metabolism of spermatozoa

The metabolism of mammalian sperm has been extensively studied by T. Mann (reviews in 1954 and 1957); the emphasis, in this case, must be placed on the importance of carbohydrate metabolism, especially that of fructose which is present in semen. The utilization of fructose, which is obviously an exogenous substrate, is an anaerobic process and mammalian spermatozoa remain therefore motile for a long time in anaerobiosis.

Another important constituent of seminal plasma, in ram sperm, is sorbitol, which can be converted into fructose, or vice versa, according to the following reversible reaction, which is catalysed by a sorbitol dehydrogenase present in the spermatozoa:

$$\text{Sorbitol} + \text{DPN}^+ \rightleftharpoons \text{fructose} + \text{DPNH} + \text{H}^+ \text{ (King and Mann, 1958)}.$$

The situation is very different in the sea urchin spermatozoa studied by Rothschild and Cleland (1952): in contradiction with earlier beliefs, they demonstrated that the energy for movement is not provided by the breakdown of intracellular carbohydrates, but by that of phospholipids. The latter, as pointed out before, are located in the middle piece and are thus in close neighbourhood of the mitochondria, which contain the required respiratory machinery.*

One would expect from these observations a high ATP content of spermatozoa: recent work from Hultin (1958) has confirmed this expectation, in the case of the sea urchin. But this work of Hultin (1958) led him to an unexpected finding: there is no decrease in the ATP content of sea urchin spermatozoa in three hours, although motility is lost by that time. It should thus be concluded that exhaustion of the ATP store is not the cause of the loss of motility.

We shall end this brief survey of the chemical embryology of spermatozoa with a few words about protein and nucleic acids metabolism: although, according to Malkin (1953), mature sea urchin sperm might be able to incorporate glycine and adenine into DNA, it is more probable that the DNA of spermatozoa is, as a rule, metabolically very stable. For instance, Sirlin (1958) and Sirlin and Edwards (1958) found that mammalian

---

* In ram spermatozoa also, endogenous metabolism occurs at the expense of phospholipids (plasmalogens), according to Hartree and Mann (1959).

spermatozoa do not become labelled for 30–40 days after precursors such as adenine or thymidine are injected in the intact animal. Similar results had been obtained earlier by Pelc (1957), who got some evidence for the view that the DNA of the spermatozoa might take its origin from RNA. In any event, these *in vivo* experiments suggest that adenine and thymidine are only incorporated into DNA by young sperm cells (spermatogonia, for instance) and not by mature ones. It might be added that many attempts have been made, in the author's laboratory, to label mature frog spermatozoa with adenine or thymidine: they have so far failed completely.

Similar conclusions can be drawn for the incorporation of labelled amino acids into the proteins of mature sperm cells: a definite uptake of amino acids into bull spermatozoa has been observed by Bhargava (1957); but autoradiography studies by Martin and Brachet (1959) have shown that the incorporation does not occur in the spermatozoa themselves, but in cell 'débris' which are presumably contaminated with bacteria Bhargava's results (1957), if true, would have been especially interesting. since bull spermatozoa contain no detectable RNA, a substance which is usually required for protein synthesis. In the experiments of Martin and Brachet (1959), it was found that only the young, RNA-containing, testis cells are the site of measurable incorporation; they concluded therefore that spermatozoa, far from being an exception, reinforce the theory that RNA is required for protein synthesis. It is interesting to note, in this respect, that both Pelc (1957) and Martin and Brachet (1959) found that the RNA which is, during spermiogenesis, extruded from the spermatozoa does not become labelled: only genuine, intracellular RNA is metabolically active and capable to play its part in protein synthesis.

The general conclusion therefore is that spermatozoa have a very high catabolism: they are rich in substrates and mitochondria, and they have a very active respiration. But their protein and nucleic acids anabolism, on the other hand, is exceedingly low, if it exists at all.

REFERENCES

Afzelius, B. A. (1955a): *Exp. Cell Res.* **8**, 147.
Afzelius, B. A. (1955b): *Z. Zellforschg. mikrosk. Anat.* **8**, 147.
Afzelius, B. A. (1956): *Exp. Cell Res.* **11**, 67.
Afzelius, B. A. (1957): *Z. Zellforschg.* **45**, 660.
Afzelius, B. A. (1959): *J. biophys. biochem. Cytol.* **5**, 269
Alfert, M. (1950): *J. cell. comp. Physiol.* **36**, 381.
Alfert, M. (1954): *Internat. Rev. Cytol.* **3**, 131.
Altorfer, N. (1953): *Experientia* **9**, 463.
Amarose, A. P. (1959): *Nature* **83**, 975.

ANDERSON, E. and H. W. BEAMS. (1956): *J. biophys. biochem. Cytol.* suppl. **2**, 439.
ANDRÉ, J. and C. ROUILLER. (1957). *J. biophys. biochem. Cytol.* **3**, 977.
BALTUS, E., (1954): *Biochim. biophys. Acta* **15**, 263.
BARTH, L. G. and L. JAEGER. (1950): *J. cell. comp. Physiol.* **35**, 413, 437.
BATTIN, W. T. (1959): *Exp. Cell Res.* **17**, 59.
BELLAIRS, R. (1958): *J. Embryol. exp. Morphol.* **6**, 149.
BHARGAVA, P. M. (1957): *Nature* **179**, 1120.
BISHOP, D. W. (1958): *Federation Proc.* **17**, 15.
BISHOP, D. W. (1958): *Nature* **182**, 1638.
BOLOGNARI, A. (1956): *Acta histochemica* **2**, 229.
BOLOGNARI, A. (1957a): *Bull. Soc. ital. Biol. sper.* **33**, 46.
BOLOGNARI, A. (1957b): *Arch. Zool. ital.* **42**, 229.
BOLOGNARI, A. (1958): *Bull. Soc. ital. Biol. sper.* **34**, 245.
BONHAG, P. F. (1955a): *J. Morph.* **96**, 381.
BONHAG, P. F. (1955b): *J. Morph.* **97**, 283.
BRACHET, J. (1939): *Arch. exp. Zellforschg.* **22**, 541.
BRACHET, J. (1940): *Arch. Biol.* **51**, 151.
BRACHET, J. (1941): *Enzymologia* **10**, 87.
BRACHET, J. (1942): *Arch. Biol.* **53**, 207.
BRACHET, J. (1944a): *Enzymologia* **11**, 336.
BRACHET, J. (1944b): *Embryologie chimique.* Desoer, Liège and Masson, Paris.
BRACHET, J. (1947): *Experientia* **3**, 329.
BRACHET, J. (1957): *Biochemical Cytology.* Academic Press, N.Y.
BRACHET, J. (1958): *Exp. Cell Res.*, suppl. **6**, 78.
BRACHET, J. and A. FICQ. (1956): *Arch. Biol.* **67**, 431.
BRACHET, J. and R. JEENER. (1944): *Enzymologia* **11**, 196.
BRACHET, J. and J. NEEDHAM. (1935): *Arch. Biol.* **46**, 821.
BRADFIELD, J. R. G. (1955): *Sympos. Soc. exp. Biol.* **9**, 306.
BRAMBELL, F. W. R. (1958): *Biolog. Rev.* **33**, 488.
BRAMBELL, F. W. R. and W. A. HEMMINGS. (1954): *Sympos. Soc. exp. Biol.* **8**, 476.
BROWN, G. L., H. G. CALLAN and G. LEAF. (1950): *Nature* **165**, 600.
BURNASHAVA, S. A. (1958): *Biokhimiya* **23**, 558.
CALLAN, H. G. (1948a): *Nature* **161**, 440.
CALLAN, H. G. (1948b): *Ricerca scientif.* **18**, 3.
CALLAN, H. G. (1955): In : *Fine Structure of Cells*, p. 89. Interscience Ltd., N.Y.
CALLAN, H. G. and L. LLOYD. (1956): *Nature* **178**, 355.
CALLAN, H. G. and H. C. MACGREGOR. (1958): *Nature* **181**, 1479.
CALLAN, H. G. and S. G. TOMLIN. (1950): *Proc. Roy. Soc.* B**137**, 367.
CASPERSSON, T. (1941): *Naturwissensch.* **29**, 33.
CASPERSSON, T. and J. SCHULTZ. (1939): *Nature* **143**, 602, 609.
CLELAND, K. W. and LORD ROTHSCHILD. (1959): *Proc. Roy. Soc.* B**150**, 24.
CLERMONT, Y., R. E. GLEGG and C. P. LEBLOND. (1955): *Exp. Cell Res.* **8**, 453.
COLOMBO, G. (1957): *Arch. ital. Zool.* **62**, 309.
COTRONEI, G. and E. URBANI. (1957): *Pubbl. Staz. zool. Napoli* **29**, 15.
COWDEN, R. R. (1958): In : *The Chemical Basis of Development*, p. 404. Johns Hopkins Press, Baltimore.
DALCQ, A. (1957): *Bull. Soc. zool. Fr.* **82**, 296.
DE DUVE, C. (1957): *Sympos. Soc. exp. Biol.* **10**, 50.
DEUCHAR, E. M. (1958): *J. Embryol. exp. Morphol.* **6**, 223.
DODSON, E. O. (1948): *Univ. Calif. Publ. Zool.* **53**, 281.

DULZETTO, F. (1931): *Arch. Biol.* **41**, 221.
DURAND, M. (1958): *Exp. Cell Res.* **15**, 257.
DURYEE, W. R. (1950): *Ann. N.Y. Acad. Sci.* **50**, 920.
DUSPIVA, F. (1942): *Biol. Zentralbl.* **62**, 403.
ELBERS, P. F. (1957): *Proc. koninkl. Akad. Wetensch. Amsterdam*, **C**, **60**, 96.
ENGELHARDT, V. A. and S. A. BURNASHAVA. (1957): *Biokhimiya* **22**, 554.
ENGLAND, M. C. and D. T. MAYER. (1957): *Exp. Cell Res.* **12**, 249.
ESTABLE, C. and J. R. SOTELO. (1955): In: *Fine Structure of Cells*, p. 170. Interscience. Ltd., N.Y.
FAUTREZ, J. and N. FAUTREZ-FIRLEFYN. (1953): *C. R. Soc. Biol.* **147**, 351.
FAUTREZ-FIRLEFYN, N. (1957): *Arch. Biol.* **68**, 249.
FAVARD, P. and N. CARASSO. (1957): *C. R. Acad. Sci. Paris* **245**, 2547.
FAVARD, P. and N. CARASSO. (1958): *Arch. Anat. micr. Morphol. génér.* **47**, 211.
FAWCETT, D. (1958): *Internat. Rev. Cytol.* **7**, 195.
FELIX, K. (1952): *Experientia* **8**, 312.
FELIX, K., A. GOPFOLD-KREKELS and H. LEHMANN. (1958): *Zeitschr. f. physiol. Chemie* **312**, 57.
FELIX, K., H. FISCHER and A. KREKELS. (1956): *Biochim. biophys. Acta* **6**, 1.
FICQ, A. (1955a): *Exp. Cell Res.* **9**, 286.
FICQ, A. (1955b): *Arch. Biol.* **66**, 509.
FICQ, A. and M. ERRERA. (1955): *Arch. internat. Physiol.* **63**, 259.
FLICKINGER, R. A. (1956): *J. exp. Zool.* **131**, 307.
FLICKINGER, R. A. (1957): *Amer. Naturalist* **91**, 337.
FLICKINGER, R. A. and D. E. ROUNDS. (1956): *Biochim. biophys. Acta* **22**, 38.
FLICKINGER, R. A. and O. A. SCHJEIDE. (1957): *Exp. Cell Res.* **13**, 312.
FUJII, T. (1954): *Nature* **174**, 1108.
GABE, M. (1956): *Ann. Histochim.* **1**, 160.
GALL, J. G. (1952): *Exp. Cell Res.*, suppl. **2**, 95.
GALL, J. G. (1954): *Sympos. Soc. exp. Biol.* **9**, 358.
GALL, J. G. (1956): *J. biophys. biochem. Cytol.*, suppl. **2**, 393.
GALL, J. G. (1958): In: *The Chemical Basis of Development*, p. 103. Johns Hopkins Press, Baltimore.
GALL, J. G. and L. B. BJORK. (1958): *J. biophys. biochem. Cytol.* **4**, 479.
GAY, H. (1955): *Proc. nat. Acad. Sci. Wash.* **41**, 370.
GAY, H. (1957): *Carnegie Inst. Washington Year Book* **56**, 378.
GERSH, M. (1940): *Z. Zellforschg. u. mikr. Anat.* **30**, 483.
GONSE, P. H. (1955): *Exp. Cell Res.* **8**, 550.
GONSE, P. H. (1957): *Biochim. biophys. Acta* **24**, 267, 520.
GOVAERT, J. (1953): *Nature* **172**, 302.
GRASSÉ, P. P., N. CARASSO and P. FAVARD. (1956): *Ann. Sc. nat. Zool.* **18**, 340.
GROSS, P. R., S. NASS and W. PEARL. (1958): *Federation Proc.* **17**, 62.
HAGUENAU, F. (1958): *Internat. Rev. Cytol.* **7**, 425.
HARDING, C. V. and C. FELDHERR. (1958): *Nature* **182**, 676.
HARRIS, D. L. (1946): *J. biol. Chem.* **165**, 541.
HARTREE, E. F. and T. MANN. (1959): *Biochem. J.* **71**, 423.
HOAGLAND, M. B., M. L. STEPHENSON, J. F. SCOTT, L. L. HECHT and P. C. ZAMECNIK. (1958): *J. biol. Chem.* **231**, 241.
HOLTFRETER, J. (1946): *J. exp. Zool.* **101**, 355.
HOLTFRETER, J. (1954): *Exp. Cell Res.* **7**, 95.
HULTIN, T. (1958): *Exp. Cell Res.* **14**, 633.
HUMPHREY, G. F. and J. K. POLLAK. (1954): *Austral. J. exp. Biol. Med.* **32**, 587.

HUSKINS, C. L. (1948): *J. Heredity* **39**, 311.
JACQUIERT, C. (1936): Thesis. Le François. Paris.
KARASAKI, S. and T. KOMODA. (1958): *Nature* **181**, 407.
KAUFMANN, B. P., H. GAY, N. D. DE and Y. YOSHIDA. (1957): *Carnegie Inst. of Washington Year Book* **56**, 373.
KEMP, N. E. (1956a): *J. biophys. biochem. Cytol.* suppl. **2**, 187.
KEMP, N. E. (1956b): *J. biophys. biochem. Cytol.* **2**, 281.
KING, T. E. and T. MANN. (1958): *Nature* **182**, 868.
LAFONTAINE, J. G. and H. RIS. (1958): *J. biophys. biochem. Cytol.* **4**, 99.
LANZAVECCHIA, G. and A. LE COULTRE. (1958): *Arch. ital. Anat. Embroil.* **63**, 445.
LEBLOND, C. P. (1950): *Amer. J. Anatomy* **86**, 1.
LEUCHTENBERGER, C. and F. SCHRADER. (1950): *Proc. nat. Acad. Sci. Wash.* **36**, 677.
LEUCHTENBERGER, C. and R. LEUCHTENBERGER. (1958): *Zeitschr. f. physiol. Chemie* **313**, 130.
LEVENBOOK, L., E. C. TRAVAGLINI and J. SCHULTZ. (1958): *Exp. Cell Res.* **15**, 43.
MANN, T. (1954): *The Biochemistry of Semen*, Methuen, London.
MANN, T. (1957): *Biochem. Soc. Sympos.* no. **7**, 11.
MARSHAK, A. and C. MARSHAK. (1955): *Exp. Cell Res.* **8**, 126.
MARTIN, F. and J. BRACHET. *Exp. Cell Res.* (in press).
MERRIAM, R. W. (1958): *Biol. Bull.* **115**, 329.
MERRIAM, R. W. (1959): *J. biophys. biochem. Cytol.* **5**, 117.
METSCHERSKAJA, K. A. (1935): *Arch. russes Anat. Hist. Embryol.* **14**, 656.
MILLONIG, G. (1958): *Mikroskopie* 13, 239
MIURA, Y., T. FUJII and T. MIZUNO. (1957): *C. R. Soc. Biol.* **151**, 1460.
MONNÉ, L. and S. HÅRDE. (1951): *Arkiv Zool.* **1**, 487.
MONTALENTI, G. (1948): *Atti Accad. naz. Lincei* **8**, 466.
MULNARD, J. (1954): *Arch. Biol.* **65**, 261.
MULNARD, J. (1956): *Arch. Biol.* **67**, 485.
NACE, G. W. (1953). *J. exp. Zool.* **122**, 423.
NACE, G. W. (1958): In : *The Chemical Basis of Development*, p. 91. Johns Hopkins Press, Baltimore.
NELSON, L. (1957). *Biochim. biophys. Acta* **27**, 634.
NELSON, L. (1958): *Biol. Bull.* **115**, 326.
NELSON, L. (1959): *Exp. Cell Res.* **16**, 403.
OLIVER, J., W. STRAUS, N. KRETSCHMER, Y. C. LEE, H. W. DICKERMAN and F. CHEROT. (1955): *J. Histochem. Cytochem.* **3**, 277.
PAINTER, T. S. and A. J. TAYLOR. (1942): *Proc. nat. Acad. Sci. Wash.* **28**, 311.
PALADE, G. (1955): *J. biophys. biochem. Cytol.* **1**, 59.
PANIJEL, J. (1950): *Biochim. biophys. Acta* **5**, 343.
PANTELOURIS, E. M. (1958): *Exp. Cell Res.* **14**, 584.
PASTEELS, J. (1959): *Arch. Biol.* **69**, 591
PASTEELS, J., P. CASTIAUX and G. VANDERMEERSCHE. (1958): *J. biophys. biochem. Cytol.* **4**, 575.
PASTEELS, J., P. CASTIAUX and G. VANDERMEERSCHE (1959): *Arch. Biol.* **69**, 627.
PASTEELS, J. and L. LISON. (1951): *Nature* **167**, 948.
PASTEELS, J. and J. MULNARD. (1957): *Arch. Biol.* **68**, 115.
PATTERSON, E. K., H. M. LANG, M. J. DACKERMAN and J. SCHULTZ. (1954): *Exp Cell Res.* **6**, 181.
PELC, S. R. (1957): *Exp. Cell Res.* **12**, 320.
RANZI, S. (1958): *Acta Embryol. Morphol. exp.* **2**, 102.
RAVEN, C. P. (1949): *Arch. néerl. Zool.* **7**, 353.

REBHUN, L. I. (1956): *J. biophys. biochem. Cytol.* **2**, 93.
REBHUN, L. I. (1957): *J. biophys. biochem. Cytol.* **3**, 509.
RESTIVO, F. and G. REVERBERI. (1957): *Acta Embryol. Morphol. exp.* **1**, 164.
RIES, E. (1937): *Pubbl. Staz. zool. Napoli* **16**, 364.
ROTHSCHILD, LORD and K. W. CLELAND. (1952): *J. exp. Biol.* **29**, 66.
SCARANO, E. and R. MAGGIO. (1957): *Exp. Cell Res.* **12**, 403.
SCHECHTMAN, A. M. (1947): *J. exp. Zool.* **105**, 329.
SCHECHTMAN, A. M. (1956): *Internat. Rev. Cytol.* **5**, 303.
SCHOLTYSEK, E. (1954): *Nature* **173**, 40.
SCHRADER, F. and C. LEUCHTENBERGER. (1952): *Exp. Cell Res.* **3**, 136.
SCHULTZ, J. (1956): *Cold Spring Harbor Sympos.* **21**, 307.
SERRA, J. A. (1958): *Nature* **181**, 1544.
SERRA, J. A. and A. QUEIROZ-LOPES. (1944): *Naturwissensch.* **32**, 47.
SIRLIN, J. L. (1958): *Exp. Cell Res.* **15**, 250.
SIRLIN, J. L. and R. G. EDWARDS. (1958): *J. exp. Zool.* **137**, 363.
SOTELO, J. R. and K. R. PORTER (1959): *J. biophys. biochem. Cytol.* **5**, 327.
STICH, H. (1956): *Experientia* **12**, 7.
STRAUS, W. (1958): *J. biophys. biochem. Cytol.* **4**, 541.
SWIFT, H. (1958): In : *The Chemical Basis of Development*, p. 174. Johns Hopkins Press, Baltimore.
TRUJILLO-CENÓZ, O. and J. R. SOTELO (1959): *J. biophys. biochem. Cytol.* **5**, 347.
URBANI, E. (1949): *Bull. di. Zool.* **16**, 151.
URBANI, E. (1953): *Rendic. Accad. naz. Lincei* **15**, 308.
VAN DE KERCKHOVE, D. (1959): *Nature* **183**, 329.
VENDRELY, R., A. KNOBLOCH and C. VENDRELY. (1957): *Exp. Cell Res.* suppl. **4**, 279.
VENDRELY, R., A. KNOBLOCH and C. VENDRELY. (1958): *C. R. Acad. Sci. Paris* **246**, 2679, 3128.
VINCENT, W. S. (1952): *Proc. nat. Acad. Sci. Wash.* **38**, 139.
VINCENT, W. S. (1955): *Internat. Rev. Cytol.* **4**, 269.
VINCENT, W. S. (1957a): In : *The Beginnings of Embryonic Development*, p. 1, A.A.A.S. Publ. No. 48, Washington.
VINCENT, W. S. (1957b): *Science* **126**, 306.
VINCENT, W. S. (1958): In : *The Chemical Basis of Development*, p. 153. Johns Hopkins Press, Baltimore.
VINCENT, W. S., B. BENSHAM and A. BENSHAM. (1958): *Biol. Bull.* **115**, 342.
VINCENT, W. S. and A. H. HUXLEY. (1954): *Biol. Bull.* **107**, 290.
VOSS, H. (1924): *Arch. mikrosk. Anat.* **100**, 560.
WILKINS, M. H. A. and J. T. RANDALL. (1953): *Biochim. biophys. Acta* **10**, 192.
WISCHNITZER, S. (1958): *J. ultrastruct. Res.* **1**, 201.
WISLOCKI, G. B. (1949): *Endocrinology* **44**, 167.
WITTEK, M. (1952): *Arch. Biol.* **63**, 133.
YAMAMOTO, K. (1956): *Embryologia* **3**, 131.
YAMAMOTO, K. (1956): *J. Fac. Sci. Hokkaido Univ.*, Ser. VI, **12**, 375.
YASUZUMI, G., W. FUJIMURA and H. ISHIDA. (1957): *Exp. Cell Res.* **14**, 268.
ZAMECNIK, P. C., E. B. KELLER, J. W. LITTLEFIELD, M. B. HOAGLAND and R. B. LOFTFIELD. (1956): *J. cell. comp. Physiol.* **47**, supp. **1**, 81.

CHAPTER II

Fertilization

IN recent years, there has been a considerable revival of interest in many of the problems of fertilization. This revival is largely due to better observation and understanding of the early phases of fertilization (acrosome reaction, surface changes in the egg), and to extensive studies on the nature and mechanism of action of the *gamones*: these substances are produced by the gametes and released in the surrounding medium. Progress, although appreciable, has not been made to the same extent in the field of the chemical embryology, *sensu stricto*, of fertilization. This is very unfortunate, since fertilization is of course much more than surface reactions between the two gametes: it starts embryonic development, but experimental parthenogenesis can do the same. However, parthenogenetic haploids are seldom viable. One of the main results of fertilization is thus the reestablishment of diploidy, which has far-reaching consequences: genetic recombination, inheritance of paternal characters, sex determination are fundamental events for the future life of the fertilized egg. They really take place when the two pronuclei fuse at amphimixis, long after the fertilization membrane is lifted after contact with the spermatozoon.

These remarks are not to be taken as a criticism of the beautiful work which has been done recently on the mechanism of fertilization; they only mean that the topic is so important in the field of general biology that it deserves the keenest interest of embryologists as well as biochemists.

The above revival of interest in fertilization has had a happy consequence: one book (Rothschild, 1956) and several reviews (Runnström, 1956, 1957; Runnström *et al.*, 1959; Tyler, 1957; C. B. Metz, 1957; J. Dan, 1956; A. and L. Colwin, 1957; A. Monroy, 1957; R. Allen, 1958, etc.) have recently been devoted to the subject by leading workers in the field. Since the subject of the present book is Chemical Embryology, we shall largely refer to these excellent reviews when we deal with the more morphological aspects of the fertilization problem. A last remark should be made: most of the recent work on fertilization has been done with sea urchin eggs; it is only natural that, in the following, a major place be given to this very convenient experimental material. But the interested reader can find an excellent account of fertilization in fish eggs in a recent review by Rothschild (1958a): he will see that they behave very much like those of the sea urchins.

1. Morphological changes at fertilization

(a) THE ACROSOME REACTION

This phenomenon, which was first described accurately by J. Dan in 1952, has been the subject of the before-mentioned reviews of Dan (1956) and A. and L. Colwin (1957). J. Dan (1952) found that the spermatozoa of several marine Invertebrates, including sea urchins, undergo deep changes when they are stimulated by contact with unfertilized eggs or sea water in which such eggs have been left for some time (*egg water*); these changes, which constitute the so-called acrosome reaction are, however, not of a specific nature: they can also be induced by treatment of sperm with alkaline sea water or by simple contact with solid surfaces. The acrosome reaction is essentially the breakdown of the acrosome membrane, immediately followed by the protrusion of a thin filament, the so-called *acrosome filament* (Fig. 22). The length of this filament may

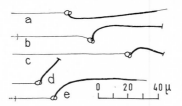

FIG. 22. Reacted spermatozoa showing acrosome filament, from photographs of living specimens (Colwin and Colwin, 1956).
a–c, Thyone briareus; d–e, Asterias forbesii; a, in egg water (35 microns); *b*, at egg surface (48 microns); *c*, in alkaline sea water (75 microns) (position of distal part of flagellum modified for reasons of space); *d*, in inseminated culture but directed away from egg (15 microns); *e*, at egg surface (22 microns).

vary from 1μ in the sea urchin (Dan, 1952; Afzelius and Murray, 1957) to 25μ in the starfish (Dan, 1954) and it reaches more than 55μ in the case of *Thyone* (Colwin and Colwin, 1956). The existence of the acrosome reaction has been confirmed in many species of Molluscs and Echinoderms (see the review of Colwin and Colwin, 1957, for additional details); in many cases, alkaline sea water is a better stimulant than egg water.

The acrosome filament is usually rather straight and rigid; its length is correlated with the thickness of the jelly coat surrounding the unfertilized eggs. As shown in Fig. 23, the long known *fertilization cone* rises around the acrosome filament, which enters the egg intact as the most anterior part of the sperm head (Colwin and Colwin, 1957).

The exact role of the acrosome filament in fertilization is not yet well understood: present studies show that the movement of the spermatozoon into the egg is *not* due to a contraction of the acrosome filament, nor to the retraction of the fertilization cone. According to Wada *et al.* (1956), the acrosome of *Mytilus* spermatozoa contains a substance which dissolves the egg membrane (egg membrane lysine); this suggestion is reminiscent of that of Leuchtenberger and Schrader (1950): as already mentioned in Chapter I, these authors believe that the acrosome contains the enzyme hyaluronidase, which attacks mucopolysaccharides.

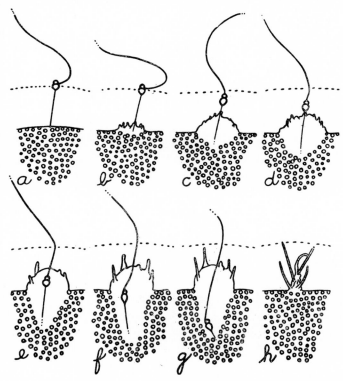

FIG. 23. Diagrammatic representation of successive stages of sperm entry as seen in the living egg of *Holothuria atra* (Colwin and Colwin, 1957).

(b) MORPHOLOGY OF CORTICAL CHANGES DURING THE FERTILIZATION OF SEA URCHIN EGGS

Figure 24, taken from Runnström (1958), shows the different surface layers of the unfertilized egg: under the *jelly coat* is the *vitelline membrane*, which is apparently formed of two layers (Rothschild, 1958b); below the latter, the *cortical layer* of the cytoplasm contains the co-called *cortical granules.*

A few words should be said about these various constituents of the surface layers: the jelly coat, as demonstrated by Vasseur (1952) is of the nature of a glycoprotein. It contains 20 per cent of amino acids (presumably as a protein) and 80 per cent polysaccharides; the latter are esterified with sulfate, as in acid mucopolysaccharides, but there are apparently no amino sugars. The vitelline membrane is about 100 Å thick; since it is sensitive to proteolytic enzymes, it is probably made of proteins. The cortical layer is $1·5-2\mu$ thick and is very rigid; its uppermost surface yields cytochemical reactions for acid mucopolysaccharides (Runnström and Immers, 1956). Finally, the cortical granules are about 1μ in diameter and number approximately 30,000 in an egg; in the oocyte, these granules are scattered in the interior of the cytoplasm; after the breakdown of the germinal vesicle, they form a uniform layer in the cortex of the egg (Monné and Hårde, 1951).

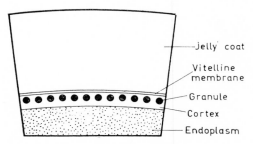

FIG. 24. Diagram showing the different surface layers of the sea urchin egg (Runnström, 1958).

Little is known about the biochemical reactions which lead to the rupture of the germinal vesicle. Experiments of Goldstein (1953) in the worm *Chaetopterus*, suggest, however, that the dissolution of the nuclear membrane results from the activation of a proteolytic enzyme by Ca^{++} ions.

Going back to the cortical granules, the cytochemical work of Monné and Hårde (1951) strongly suggests that they contain acid mucopolysaccharides, while the electron microscope studies of Afzelius (1956) show that they have a very complicated ultra-structure, which varies with the species studied. According to Allen (1957), it is possible to isolate the cortical granules from homogenates of unfertilized sea urchin eggs; it certainly would be rewarding to study them from the biochemical viewpoint more closely than has been done so far.

The formation of the *fertilization membrane* is a complicated process, which has been analysed in detail by Runnström (1952, 1958), Runnström *et al.* (1959), Rothschild (1956), etc. The vitelline membrane is lifted from the egg cortex, so that the perivitelline space, containing the perivitelline fluid, appears between the membrane and the cortex. It is the existence of the perivitelline fluid which allows the rotation of the fertilized egg under the influence of gravity. But the cortical granules take an important part in the formation of the fertilization membrane: they are expelled from the cortex and they fuse with the inner surface of the vitelline membrane, as shown in Fig. 25. The resulting fertilization membrane is about 500 Å thick. Soon after its formation, a thin extra-cellular layer appears on the surface of the egg: it is the so-called hyaline layer, which is believed by Hagström and Hagström (1954a) and by Hagström and Runnström (1959) to play an important role in preventing the penetration of more than one spermatozoon into the egg (block to polyspermy).

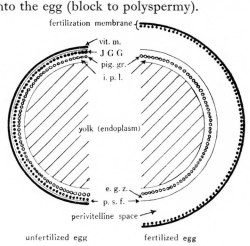

FIG. 25. Diagram of the structure of the sea urchin egg; left half, unfertilized egg; right half, fertilized egg.

e.g.z. extra-granular zone, *i.p.l.* inner protoplasmic layer, JGG, Janus green granule layer, *pig.gr.* pigment granule layer, *p.s.f.* morphological protoplasmic surface film, *vit.m.* vitelline membrane (after Motomura, 1941).

All these surface changes occur in a short time and their exact sequence is not yet perfectly known; according to a recent experimental study of Allen and Griffin (1958), fertilization begins with a latent period of 17 seconds before the cortical reaction becomes visible. This latent period is apparently limited by chemical processes, while the cortical reaction itself (i.e. the breakdown of the cortical granules) seems to be limited by diffusion processes; this conclusion is based on the effects of temperature changes on fertilization (Allen and Griffin, 1958).

It would be a mistake, however, to believe that the changes attending fertilization in sea urchin eggs are purely cortical: as shown repeatedly

E

in Runnström's (1952, 1958, 1959) laboratory, the structure of the endo-plasm is also modified. For instance, the structure of the unfertilized egg is coarser than that of the fertilized egg, whose yolk granules give stronger polysaccharide cytochemical reactions (Immers, 1957).

Nevertheless, the cortical changes are probably the most important ones for the process of fertilization itself: treatments which inhibit or slow down the cortical changes have far-reaching consequences for the future of the egg.

Many agents which interfere with the elevation of the fertilization membrane induce polyspermy. More recently it has been shown that a variety of treatments (lack of calcium, proteolytic enzymes, urea, acids), which inhibit membrane formation, permit the refertilization of an already fertilized egg at practically any interval after the first insemination (Sugiyama, 1951; Hagström and Hagström, 1954b; Tyler, Monroy and Metz, 1956; Nakano, 1956; Hagström and Runnström, 1959). Finally it should be noted that removal of the jelly coat can, in certain cases, con-siderably increase the percentage of cross-fertilization between different species of sea urchins; this finding of Harding and Harding (1952) has practical importance for chemical embryologists, since it now provides them with the possibility of working with large quantities of inter-species hybrids.

2. Physical changes at fertilization

Only methods which are capable of recording very short events can give information about physical changes occurring during the cortical reaction: for instance, Runnström et al. (1944) and Mitchison and Swann (1952) have been able to follow changes in the *birefringence* of the cortex and the fertilization membranes. There is also a sudden and transient rise in *stiffness* of the cortex at fertilization, according to Mitchison and Swann (1955), who built a special instrument, the 'cell elastimeter', for these measurements. These authors believe that, in contradiction with the ideas often expressed by Heilbrunn (1915, 1953), calcium ions play little part in the rigidity of the cortex of fertilized eggs. Another very fast change occurring after fertilization is that of the *membrane potential*: according to the recent measurements of Tyler et al. (1956) and Hiramoto (1959), there is a potential difference of 30–60 mV between the outside and the inside, the latter being negative. The potential difference decreases momentarily just after insemination of about 10 mV; after 10 to 20 seconds, it reverts to the initial value.

The membrane potential also undergoes a series of charges upon ferti-lization of fish eggs (Hori, 1958): as a result of the cortical changes, there is a depolarization of the membrane and an increase of the permeability to ions. Before leaving the subject of the membrane of fish eggs, one should mention the recent work of Zotin (1958) who has studied the hardening of their membrane after fertilization and found it to be linked to the release from the egg surface of a 'hardening enzyme'. The hardening would be due to an initiated chain polymerization of substances within the membrane.

We can now come to changes in *viscosity* and *permeability*: since very variable results are obtained, even by the same authors when working on different materials, little will be said here on this subject. A very complete and critical account of the work published up to 1955 will be found in Rothschild's (1956) book and in Monroy's (1957) review.

Regarding first *viscosity*, it is generally accepted that fertilization is followed by cytoplasmic gelation: according to Heilbrunn (1915, 1952), this phenomenon is similar to the clotting of blood and calcium would play an essential role in both processes. More will be said about this question at the end of this chapter.

Coming now to *permeability*, there is recent evidence that permeability to water (Ishikawa, 1954) and to K^+ (Tyler and Monroy, 1956) both markedly increase immediately after fertilization. The uptake of ^{32}P is also strongly increased by fertilization (Abelson, 1948; Brooks and Chambers, 1948; Lindberg, 1948), but there are notable exceptions in this case (*Urechis caupo*: Brooks and Chambers, 1954, for instance). There has been a good deal of speculation about the role of adenosine triphosphatase (ATPase) in phosphate uptake by unfertilized and fertilized eggs: estimations of ATPase activity show that it increases after fertilization (Connors and Scheer, 1947; Monroy, 1957). This increase in activity is probably due to the release of the previously bound enzyme to mitochondria (Monroy, 1957) rather than to true synthesis. What we should study, of course, is the 'ecto-ATPase', i.e. the function of the enzyme which might be present in the membrane itself. But we do not even know whether eggs have an ecto-ATPase; in fact, unpublished experiments from the author's laboratory have failed to disclose any measurable ecto-ATPase activity in amphibian eggs.

3. The sperm–egg interacting substances (gamones)

Considerable work has been done, in recent years, on the biological role and chemical composition of the substances produced by spermatozoa and eggs of many species. Since the subject has been extensively reviewed by Rothschild (1956), C. B. Metz (1957) and Runnström *et al.* (1959), only a brief summary of the main facts will be given here.

(a) FERTILIZIN

The field opened up with the well known discovery of *fertilizin* by F. R. Lillie in 1912, when he found that 'egg water' agglutinates spermatozoa; Lillie quickly realized that this agglutination reaction is of the type of an antigen–antibody specific reaction and that fertilizin reacts with an *antifertilizin* present in sperm heads. As shown later by Lillie (1914) and Tyler (1940), eggs also contain an antifertilizin.

Fertilizin is identical with the jelly coat: it is thus a mucopolysaccharide, with a high sulfur content. It exerts many important effects on the spermatozoa: it induces the acrosome reaction, it activates and prolongs the motility and it produces the agglutination of the heads. In contradiction to earlier belief, it is now admitted that it exerts no chemotatic influence on the spermatozoa. According to a recent study of Hagström (1959), the overall activity of the jelly coat is to reduce the fertilizing power of the spermatozoa and thus to prevent polyspermy.

Fertilizin also increases the oxygen consumption and prolongs the life of the spermatozoa; but, according to Rothschild and Tyler (1954), these are rather unspecific effects, possibly due to chelation of heavy metals which exerted a depressive action on the respiration of the sperm suspension.

While there is no doubt that fertilizin might play an important part in fertilization, it should be pointed out that its presence has been demonstrated in a small number of species only and that fertilizin-free eggs can be fertilized. The presence of fertilizin is therefore not an absolute prerequisite for successful fertilization. C. B. Metz (1957) concludes from a careful analysis of the existing literature that 'fertilizin at the egg surface facilitates fertilization whereas the same agent in solution, by virtue of its combination with sperm, acts as a barrier to fertilization'.

Little is known about the groups present in the fertilizin molecules which specifically react with antifertilizin: they are destroyed by oxidation with H_2O_2 or periodate, not by reducing agents. It has been suggested (cf. Metz, 1957) that adjacent hydroxyl groups of carbohydrates, or sulphate groups (or both) might be essential.

(b) ANTIFERTILIZIN FROM EGGS

F. Lillie (1914) discovered that egg water from cytolyzed eggs does not agglutinate spermatozoa strongly: the eggs must therefore contain an agent which neutralizes fertilizin. This agent, which has been called antifertilizin from eggs, has been isolated in active form by Tyler (1940).

Antifertilizin is a protein, since it can be inactivated by digestion with proteases. According to Monroy and Runnström (1952) it is bound to small granules, from which it can be released by treatment with ribonuclease (Runnström *et al.*, 1955). It is therefore likely that it is present in small ribonucleoprotein granules, similar to the microsomes. Its exact role in fertilization remains unsettled.

(c) ANTIFERTILIZIN FROM SPERM

This is the specific receptor for fertilizin on the sperm surface; it can be extracted by various means from sperm and, if in solution, it neutralizes fertilizin. Chemically, it is a small protein, with a molecular weight of less than 10,000 and an acidic isoelectric point. This protein has once been confused by Hultin (1947) with the basic proteins of the sperm nucleus (protamines, histones), which agglutinate sperm and eggs easily. But anti-fertilizin from sperm is more specific in its action than the basic proteins: it agglutinates only eggs, not spermatozoa. Its exact role in fertilization remains unclear.

(d) LYSINE FROM SPERM

Sperm sometimes contains agents which have a lytic action on the membranes which surround the eggs; the most important of these membrane lysines is probably hyaluronidase, an enzyme which attacks mucopolysaccharides and is present in Mammalian sperm. Membrane lysines have also been found in the sperm of various Molluscs. While it is tempting, as already pointed out before, to imagine a relationship between these lysines and the acrosome, nothing certain in this respect is known at present.

(e) RECENT IMMUNOLOGICAL STUDIES ON FERTILIZATION

P. Perlmann (1954, 1956, 1957) and his co-workers (P. and H. Perlmann, 1957; P. Perlmann and Hagström, 1957) have carried out extensive studies on the effects of antisera obtained from rabbits injected with homogenates of unfertilized eggs, sperm and jelly substance. The results show that the situation is a very complex one and only the main conclusions will be summarized here.

First, homologous anti-egg serum produces the precipitation of the jelly coat and parthenogenetic activation of the eggs. Further analysis shows that there are a number of different antigen–antibody reactions, since four different antigens have been detected in the eggs of *Paracentrotus*. A special F-antigen is responsible for the precipitation of the jelly; this F-antigen is a carbohydrate, present in the jelly coat as an integral part. A second antigen, the A-antigen, is responsible for the parthenogenetic activation; it is present in the egg cortex, but can also be found in the jelly; it is apparently a mucopolysaccharide. A third antigen (C-antigen) is a protein, probably located in the cortex: when it reacts with the antibody cortical damage occurs. Finally, an F-antigen seems to be a specific, sperm-recepting carbohydrate of the egg cortex.

One can conclude from all this important and interesting work that the egg cortex has a highly complicated antigenic structure, which is different from that of the jelly coat.

Finally, mention should be made of a curious observation of Tyler and Brookbank (1956), although it is not really related to our present topic:

they found that antisera prepared against fertilizin block cell division in the early development of sea urchin eggs. These antisera also immediately immobilize hatched blastulae or gastrulae; it can therefore be concluded that surface antigens from the unfertilized egg persist until these stages of development.

4. Metabolic changes at fertilization

(a) ENERGY PRODUCTION

The consequences of fertilization on the oxygen consumption of the egg are highly variable: as shown first by Whitaker (1933), fertilization can

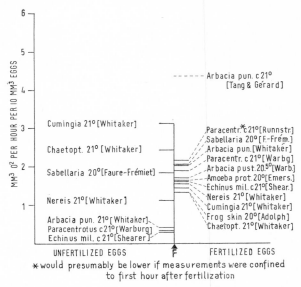

FIG. 26. Absolute rates of oxygen consumption, per unit volume. (Compiled by Whitaker, 1933.) Where temperature is preceded by the letter c, a temperature correction has been made.

produce either an increase in the respiratory rate (this was known to occur for sea urchin eggs since Warburg's (1908) pioneer work), or a decrease (*Cumingia, Chaetopterus*) or finally no change at all (*Sabellaria*, for instance). In frog eggs there is no appreciable difference in the oxygen consumption of unfertilized and fertilized eggs (Brachet, 1934); on the other hand, fertilization substantially increases the respiration of ascidian eggs (Tyler and Humason, 1937; Minganti, 1957).

The meaning of these highly variable results has been made clear by Whitaker (1933): as shown in Fig. 26, if the rate of the oxygen consumption is expressed for the same volume of eggs, it is almost the same for the fertilized eggs of several marine Invertebrates; on the contrary, the respiration rates of the unfertilized eggs are widely different. The conclusion is inescapable: fertilization exerts a *regulatory* (and not necessarily a stimulatory) effect on the oxidation rate. What is abnormal is the respiration of the unfertilized egg; the latter should be considered as an intoxicated or anaesthesized cell.

Later work by Lindahl and Holter (1941) has brought additional and important support for this view: they followed, with a very sensitive method (the so-called Cartesian diver), the oxygen consumption of sea urchin eggs during maturation and found that it strongly decreases at that time. Figure 27 summarizes their results: it shows that ootids have a much lower rate of respiration than primary oocytes: it looks as if, during maturation, the oxidations of the oocyte became progressively inhibited. Fertilization brings respiration back to its high initial rate: the oxygen consumption of the fertilized sea urchin egg is thus of the same order of magnitude as that of the primary oocyte. It is the exceedingly low oxygen uptake of the ripe, unfertilized egg (which is at the oocyte stage), and not the high respiration of the fertilized egg, which is abnormal in this case.

Later work by Borei (1948, 1949) has essentially substantiated Lindahl and Holter's (1941) conclusions, although his experiments suggest that the matter might be somewhat more complicated than it was thought before. Borei (1948, 1949) showed, among other things, that there probably would be no increase in oxygen uptake if one could measure the respiration of

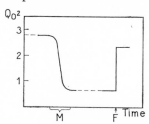

FIG. 27. Change in oxygen consumption in relationship to maturation (M) and fertilization (F) in sea urchin eggs (Lindahl and Holter, 1941).

unfertilized sea urchin eggs immediately after shedding and fertilize them immediately; he also found that, in the eggs of a starfish, respiration increases, apparently as a result of the breakdown of the germinal vesicle.

The dramatic increase in respiration at fertilization in sea urchin eggs has attracted much attention in the past, but few papers have been devoted to the subject recently. A fundamental piece of work remains that of Runnström (1930), who showed that specific inhibitors of cytochrome-oxidase (KCN, CO in the dark) have no effect on the oxygen consumption of unfertilized eggs; but they strongly inhibit the respiration of fertilized eggs. Cytochrome oxidase is, however, present in both unfertilized and fertilized eggs. Runnström has proposed two hypotheses in order to explain this apparent contradiction: one is that, in the unfertilized egg, cytochrome oxidase may not be in direct contact with the other members of the electron transfer chain (Runnström, 1930); the other, that fertilization might introduce in this chain an intermediary carrier which was missing in the unfertilized egg (Runnström, 1935).

Recent work makes this second interpretation rather unlikely, because sea urchin eggs apparently contain a complete cytochrome system: Maggio and Ghiretti (1958) and Rapoport *et al.* (1958) were able to detect cytochromes a_3, a, b and c in their mitochondria. A cytochrome system also exists, according to Rothschild and Tyler (1958) in *Urechis* eggs: their respiration is sensitive to KCN and CO, and components a and c of the cytochrome system could be demonstrated.

It is still impossible to explain with certainty why oxygen consumption so suddenly increases on fertilization in sea urchin eggs. For the writer, two explanations appear attractive: the first is the one which was proposed by Runnström (1930) almost 30 years ago, i.e. that cytochrome oxidase is not in direct contact with other members of the respiratory chain in unfertilized eggs. Such an explanation is more plausible than ever, now that we know that certain members of the respiratory chain (cytochrome oxidase in particular) are bound to mitochondria, while others are not: we have already seen that cytoplasmic structure undergoes visible changes upon fertilization and it can easily be imagined that these changes might lead to better contact between mitochondria and substrates or hydrogen carriers. The second explanation is that the unfertilized egg might contain an inhibitor of cellular oxidations: the production or retention of such an inhibitor would easily explain why Lindahl and Holter (1941) and Borei (1948, 1949) found a progressive inhibition of respiration during ageing of unfertilized eggs. We know that the latter have a very low permeability and it is conceivable that they cannot release in the outer medium the hypothetical respiratory inhibitor; the sudden increase of permeability which accompanies fertilization would allow the elimination of this inhibitor and lead to normal functioning of the cytochrome system.

That such an explanation is not an unlikely one will be obvious to all those who noticed the strong smell of H_2S which occurs when sea urchin eggs of certain species are homogenized. However, many other possibilities should also be taken into account: the recently disclosed fact that fertilized *Urechis* eggs can oxidize CO into CO_2 (Samuel *et al.*, 1958) shows that the situation, regarding the use of respiratory inhibitors as an analytical tool, might be more complicated than was first believed. There is no ready explanation either for a recent observation of Krane and Crane (1958), who found a considerable increase in the reduced triphosphopyridine nucleotide (TPNH) level after fertilization. The main purpose of this discussion lies in the hope that more experimental work will be done on a question which remains almost as baffling as when, 50 years ago, Warburg (1908) made his first major discovery.

Fertilization, in the sea urchin, is accompanied with a quick and short burst in CO_2 production, as indicated in Fig. 28 taken from a paper of Laser and Rothschild (1939): as a result, the apparent respiratory quotient (CO_2/O_2) is highly abnormal. But this burst in CO_2 production is essentially the consequence of another phenomenon, an acid production (Runnström, 1933) immediately after fertilization. In a recent study, Allen *et al.* (1958) have measured this acid formation with a pH meter and found that it is a very fast phenomenon; it is not fast enough, however, to explain the block to polyspermy; but it should be kept in mind that the method

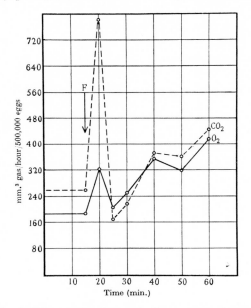

FIG. 28. Total CO_2 production and O_2 consumption expressed as mm^3 gas/hour, plotted against time. F: fertilization (Laser and Lord Rothschild, 1939).

used can measure the acid only when it is present in the outside medium. Allen *et al.* (1958) found also that the acid is not eliminated all at once when the cortical granules break down; but it goes into the surrounding medium by the time the changes in the cortical granules become visible.

There has been a good deal of discussion and speculation about the chemical nature of the acid (or acids) produced: it is usually believed that it is a mixture of acids resulting from carbohydrate catabolism (Lindberg, 1941), presumably as a result of glycogen breakdown and direct oxidation of glucose-6-phosphate. According to a recent study of Akata (1957), lactic acid, which was thought to be ruled out as a possible candidate, increases at fertilization in sea urchin eggs; Akata (1957) believes that this lactic acid originates from a polyose different from glycogen.* The most likely conclusion is that proposed by Runnström et al. (1959): changes in acid polysaccharides, occurring during fertilization, probably contribute to the acid production, which precedes the rise in oxygen consumption; but, since the acid formation outlasts the cortical changes, it certainly reflects a still unknown enzymatic process.

Since, as a general rule, phosphorylations leading to the synthesis of ATP are closely linked to respiration, one could expect the ATP content to increase when sea urchin eggs are fertilized: this expectation is, however, not fulfilled. As shown by Chambers and Mende (1935a, b), there is no appreciable change in the ATP content of the eggs upon fertilization: this negative result might of course be due to increased utilization of ATP balancing, after fertilization, increased synthesis.

After this discussion of the changes in energy production undergone by the egg after fertilization, we shall examine successively carbohydrate, lipid and nucleoprotein metabolism. Again, much information about earlier work will be found in Brachet (1950) and most of the evidence will come from sea urchin eggs.

(b) Carbohydrate Metabolism

It is well established, since Örström and Lindberg's (1940) pioneer work, that there is a marked utilization of glycogen during the 10 minutes which follow fertilization; the rate of glycogenolysis, after this initial period, is essentially the same in fertilized and unfertilized eggs for several hours.

There has been a good deal of discussion about the metabolic pathway of glycogen breakdown in sea urchin eggs: while Lindberg and Ernster (1948) emphasized the importance of direct oxidation of glucose-6-phosphate to 6-phosphogluconate, Cleland (1950, in the eggs of the rock-oyster) and Cleland and Rothschild (1952, in those of the sea urchin) have obtained evidence for a classical glycolytic system and a tricarboxylic acid cycle. Both systems probably co-exist in sea urchin eggs as in most cells, but their relative importance is not yet clear: after a thorough discussion of the problem, Rothschild (1956) concludes that 'the lack of answers to these questions indicates, as usual, the need for more experiments'. Of special interest, perhaps, might be experiments on the utilization and oxidation of glucose labelled with ^{14}C in different positions.

There is nothing mysterious either about carbohydrate metabolic pathways in amphibian eggs: according to A. I. Cohen (1954, 1955) and

---

* According to a more recent paper of Rothschild (1958c), the 'fertilization acid' is definitely *not* lactic acid.

S. Cohen (1954), the usual glycolytic and tricarboxylic acid systems are predominant.

(c) Lipid Metabolism

According to Öhman (1945), about 30 per cent of the free cephalin becomes bound to proteins during the 10 minutes which follow fertilization. The total lipid content of sea urchin eggs decreases during 7 hours after fertilization. Free cholesterol increases at fertilization, according to Monroy and Ruffo (1945).

Although, as can be seen, very little is known about lipid metabolism at fertilization, even in sea urchin eggs, Monroy (1953a, b; 1957) has drawn attention to the fact that lipids are abundant in the cortex: thus, they might possibly play a part in the reaction between sperm and egg cortex. Monroy (1953a, b) has therefore postulated that the spermatozoon, when it penetrates the egg cortex, might split the lipoprotein cortical complex. Model experiments showed that addition of sea urchin sperm to a lipoprotein from hen egg yolk (the so-called lipovitelline) produces first an increase, then a decrease in free phospholipids (Monroy, 1956). Monroy (1956) found that the released phospholipids are attacked by phospholipases with, as a result, the production of hemolytic lysophosphatides.

Going back from these model experiments to the sea urchin egg, Monroy (1956, 1957) has proposed the following scheme: the spermatozoon would react with the cortex and split the lipoproteins which it contains; the liberated phospholipids would be split with the transient appearance of a lytic activity. The release of lysophosphatides would be the key reaction of the activation of the egg.

Monroy's (1956, 1957) hypothesis certainly deserves attention, since it explains many facts and is plausible; but model experiments never carry complete conviction and the hypothesis should ultimately be tested on the eggs themselves.

(d) Protein Metabolism

The fundamental paper in this field remains that of Örström (1941), who found a transient production of ammonia after fertilization of sea urchin eggs. This ammonia, according to Örström (1941), results from the deamination of amino purines, still attached to RNA. Both fertilized and unfertilized eggs are capable of splitting glutamine into glutamic acid and ammonia; but the reverse reaction of glutamine synthesis is only possible in fertilized eggs. Finally, Örström (1941) found that sea urchin eggs are very rich in free amino acids, especially glycine, which might play a part in keeping constant the internal pH of the eggs. During the first 10 minutes after fertilization, free amino acids increase and Örström (1941) concluded that penetration of the spermatozoon induces a transient proteolysis in the egg; this proteolysis is followed by a resynthesis of proteins.

Many points of Örström's (1941) work have been confirmed by later workers: for instance, Hultin (1950) observed a maximum rate of ammonia uptake at the time of the formation of the fertilization membrane, and Pasquinelli (1954) found that freshly fertilized eggs take up five times as much ammonia as the unfertilized eggs. The latter confirmed that ammonia is used, to a large extent, for glutamine synthesis in fertilized eggs. However, the source of the ammonia produced at fertilization is not RNA, but adenylic acid (Ishihara, 1956).

Ricotta (1956) has confirmed that there is an appreciable increase in non-protein nitrogen during the 5 or 10 minutes which follow insemination. By far the most extensive work in the field of amino acids metabolism in developing sea urchin eggs is that of Kavanau (1953, 1954a, b): he observed cyclical changes in the amino acid concentration throughout development and came to the conclusion that there is an abrupt change of amino acid metabolism at fertilization. He suggests that yolk synthesis stops and an intense protein degradation begins, and further that proteins could be used, by the fertilized eggs, as an important energy source. In later development also, splitting of yolk and synthesis of embryonic proteins alternate in a cyclical manner. On the whole, Kavanau's (1953, 1954a, b) results are in substantial agreement with those of Örström (1941), but his interpretation is slightly different and more elaborate.

We now come to another important aspect of protein metabolism at fertilization: is the egg, at that time, the site of protein synthesis or protein rearrangement? The greatest part of the available evidence indicates that fertilization is characterized by considerable rearrangement of the existing egg proteins, while protein synthesis is a much later process in development.

Let us now consider the experimental evidence on which this conclusion is based: it is one of the merits of Mirsky (1936) to have shown that, in sea urchin eggs, fertilization leads to important changes in the solubility of the proteins: a protein fraction markedly decreases in solubility during the 10 minutes which follow insemination, perhaps as a result of a reversible denaturation.

More recent work by Monroy (1950) has confirmed and considerably extended Mirsky's (1936) finding: using electrophoresis, Monroy (1950) could detect, besides a decrease in solubility of one component immediately after fertilization, the transient appearance of a new component resulting from the splitting of a component already present in unfertilized eggs. Further work done in Monroy's laboratory (Giardina and Monroy, 1955; Céas et al., 1955) has dealt with the effects of various agents (trypsin, heat denaturation, urea, etc.) on the sea urchin egg proteins; it has confirmed the general conclusion that there is a difference between the proteins of unfertilized and fertilized eggs: proteins obviously undergo some sort of internal rearrangement after fertilization of sea urchin eggs (Monroy, 1957). This conclusion, which is in agreement with Kavanau's (1953, 1954a, b) already discussed results, is also accepted by Runnström *et al.* (1959), who state that 'fertilization means an unchannelling of the metabolic processes in the egg'.

A valuable method for the analysis of protein anabolism is, of course, study of the incorporation of labelled amino acids into proteins. It should however, be clearly pointed out that incorporation of a precursor into a biochemical component of the cell is not necessarily indicative of a net *synthesis*: it might indicate a mere turnover or, even, a rather unspecific attachment of the precursor to a side chain of the macromolecule under study.

The most important work on incorporation of amino acids into the proteins of fertilized and unfertilized sea urchin eggs is undoubtedly that of Hultin (1953): he found stronger incorporation of labelled glycine or alanine in the insoluble proteins of fertilized eggs than in the soluble ones. He concluded that, soon after fertilization, there is a 'rebuilding or multiplication of small cytoplasmic granules containing RNA'. Although this conclusion of Hultin (1953) is probably correct, a reserve should be made: as will be shown later, incorporation of amino acids occurs predominantly in the nuclei (and not in the microsomes) of amphibian eggs during early cleavage. In view of the small size of the nuclei in sea urchin eggs, it is not impossible that they might contaminate to an appreciable extent the small cytoplasmic granules fraction studied by Hultin (1953). Further work, especially with autoradiographic methods, should clarify this point; in the meantime, we can still conclude that Hultin's (1953) results are in good agreement with the general idea that fertilization leads, among other things, to a rebuilding of the egg proteins.

Recent work by Nakano and Monroy (1958), Giudice and Monroy (1958) and by Nakano *et al.* (1958) has brought out interesting results: these authors succeeded in labelling unfertilized eggs with ^{35}S-methionine. After fertilization or induction of parthenogenesis with butyric acid, it was found that an appreciable portion of the acid soluble amino acid became incorporated into the proteins of the mitochondria: thus, unfertilized sea urchin eggs hardly incorporate any methionine into proteins, while fertilization (or parthenogenetic activation) leads to appreciable incorporation. It is tempting to suggest that this incorporation of the amino acid into proteins is linked to the production, after fertilization, of the new protein component detected by Monroy (1950) with electrophoretic methods.

Before jumping to such a conclusion, one should, however, remember what has just been said about the difficult interpretation of incorporation experiments; furthermore, one would like to know whether amino acids other than methionine behave in the same way.

There is a last fruitful approach to the problem of protein synthesis or rearrangement at fertilization: comparative enzymatic studies on fertilized and unfertilized eggs. It has been suggested by Runnström (1949) that the cortex of the unfertilized sea urchin egg might contain an inhibitor-enzyme complex; activation under the influence of either sperm or parthenogenetic agents, would result in the breakdown of this complex and

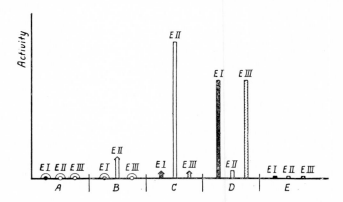

FIG. 29. Changes in the proteolytic activity of three proteolytic enzymes of the sea urchin egg: (*A*) before fertilization, (*B*) at fertilization, (*C*) at membrane elevation, (*D*) immediately after membrane elevation, (*E*) ten minutes or more after membrane elevation (Lundblad, 1954).

the removal of the inhibitor; the latter might possibly be a mucopoly-saccharide closely related to the jelly coat.

Experimental work by Lundblad (1949, 1950, 1954) and Lundblad and Hultin (1954) has brought extremely important and interesting support in favour of Runnström's (1949) hypothesis: studying proteases, they found that sea urchin eggs contain at least three different proteolytic enzymes (E I, E II, and E III) which become strongly activated at fertilization. As shown in Fig. 29, the activity of protease E II tremendously increases at the time of membrane elevation; marked activation of proteases E I and E III occurs just a little later, i.e. immediately after the elevation of the fertilization membrane. It is an especially striking fact that, after this enormous burst of activity, the three proteases come back to the initial, low level of activity about ten minutes after membrane elevation (Lundblad, 1954). *In vitro* experiments of Lundblad and Hultin (1954) have further shown that, in homogenates of unfertilized eggs, proteases E I and E III are activated by ribonuclease. The Swedish authors believe therefore that fertilizing spermatozoon might activate egg ribonuclease; the latter, in turn, activate proteases E I and E III.

Recent work by Maggio (1957) is in good agreement with these experiments and conclusions. According to Maggio (1957), protease is present in both the cytoplasm and the mitochondria of unfertilized sea urchin eggs; after fertilization, the activity of the cytoplasmic enzymes increases at the expenses of the mitochondrial ones. On the whole, Maggio's (1957) experiments confirm that protease activity increases in the cytoplasm upon fertilization.

It should be added that the reverse changes in cytoplasmic and mitochondrial activity have been found to occur, upon fertilization of sea urchin eggs, for another enzyme, ATPase (Monroy, 1957): mitochondrial ATPase undergoes an increase upon fertilization.

These modifications in mitochondrial enzymatic activity favours the view, expressed by Monroy (1953b), that mitochondria might be involved in the very early changes which follow fertilization: physiological, or ultrastructural, rearrangements might take place in the mitochondria of sea urchin eggs upon fertilization.

We shall see, in the final discussion of the present chapter, that there are, however, other possibilities of explanation.

(e) NUCLEIC ACID METABOLISM

We have seen, in Chapter I, that the nuclear DNA content of the two gametes undergoes the expected changes during meiosis. It falls from the value characteristic for cells which prepare for cell division (i.e. four times the DNA content of a spermatozoon) to the amount present in the spermatozoon. As shown by Swift (1953), amphimixis brings back the nuclear DNA content to the expected value (twice that found in the spermatozoon). Also, as expected, the DNA value of the zygote nucleus doubles quickly and reaches again the 'tetraploid' level. This doubling of the DNA content of course reflects the preparation of the egg nucleus for the first cleavage mitosis.

Less is known about possible changes in the RNA content of the egg upon fertilization: the most recent work on the subject is that of Elson *et al.* (1954), which indicates the existence of a transient drop in RNA when sea urchin eggs are fertilized. The meaning of this drop is by no means understood; but this abrupt change in RNA content might well deserve more careful inquiry. There is no doubt that fertilization shows analogies with infection of a sensitive bacterium by a bacteriophage: in both cases, DNA is, so to speak, injected in the receiving cell (see Hershey and Chase, 1952, for experiments and discussion in the case of phage). It is also a well established fact that, in the bacterium-phage system, inoculation of viral DNA is followed by increased RNA and protein anabolism (Hershey,

64   THE BIOCHEMISTRY OF DEVELOPMENT

1953, 1955; Volkin and Astrachan, 1956; Burton, 1955; Jeener, 1959, etc.): it looks as if the infected cell builds up new RNA and new protein in order to make the synthesis of phage DNA possible. It would be very interesting to know whether a similar situation holds for fertilization in eggs: we have already seen that a new protein can be detected, after fertilization of sea urchin eggs, by electrophoretic and isotopic methods. We now find that there is an abrupt and transient change in the RNA content of the same eggs upon fertilization. It would be important, from the standpoint of general biology, to know whether enhanced ^{32}P incorporation into RNA and synthesis of a specific protein are prerequisites of DNA synthesis in both systems; all that we know for the time being is that, as mentioned earlier in this chapter, the ^{32}P uptake in the egg increases suddenly after insemination in many species. It is unfortunate that nobody has so far tried to establish whether this fast ^{32}P uptake is actually linked with increased RNA turnover; if so, fertilization would bear analogies with phage infection and induced enzyme synthesis (Chantrenne, 1956). Since fertilization is, as well as these two processes, a very fast phenomenon, the general biologist cannot help wondering about possible resemblances and differences.

5. Conclusions

In the preceding pages, we have already indulged in speculations, in the hope that analogies might be found between such apparently different phenomena as fertilization, phage infection and induced enzyme synthesis; one might (and perhaps should) add to this list genetic recombination in bacteria, through mating, transduction or transformation. The tremendous development of bacterial genetics during the past few years is sufficient excuse. But if, for the purpose of a discussion, we go back to theories of fertilization, we first meet on our way the great old names of Frank Lillie, Eugène Bataillon and Jacques Loeb: something should be said about their ideas and how they stand now.

In F. Lillie's (1919) theory, the emphasis was of course placed on fertilizin by its discoverer: alteration of the spermatozoon by the egg and fusion of the gametes would be the result of the interaction between sperm and egg substances. We have seen, in the present chapter, that there is no doubt about the existence of sperm–egg interacting substances and that a good deal is already known about their chemical composition. However, none of these substances has so far been proven to be of an absolute necessity for successful fertilization; therefore, the criticisms of Dalcq (1928), who rightly pointed out that fertilizin can, at most, only explain 'external fertilization' (i.e. the meeting of the gametes) remain valid: fertilization, as pointed out earlier, is much more than that from the viewpoints of both the embryologist and the geneticist.

Bataillon (1910, 1912, 1929a, b) has put the emphasis on the progressive intoxication of the unfertilized egg, leading to its progressive inertness. Fertilization or parthenogenesis, in inducing the elevation of the fertilization membrane, would eliminate the toxic substances accumulated in the unfertilized egg. For Bataillon (1910–1929), fertilization is essentially a *réaction d'épuration*, the increase in permeability leading to the disintoxication of the egg.

There is no doubt that there is a good deal of truth in these ideas: increase in permeability at fertilization is a very frequent phenomenon; we have seen that the experiments of Whitaker (1938), Lindahl and Holter (1941) and Borei (1948, 1949) on the oxygen consumption changes at fertilization all agree with the view that the unfertilized egg is an inhibited cell. In fact, we have concluded from our analysis that a very likely explanation for the low oxygen consumption of unfertilized sea urchin eggs is the presence of a respiratory inhibitor.

But fertilization is a complicated process, which has too many different aspects to be explained in one simple, single way: the theory of Loeb (1913) is very different from that of Bataillon; nevertheless, it has also retained a good deal of truth and explicative value. Struck by the fact that, in sea urchin eggs, two successive treatments are required in order to provoke parthenogenetic development, Loeb (1913) has proposed the following theory: in a first stage, lysis of the egg cortex, accompanied by abnormal oxidations, would occur; in a second stage, a 'correcting' factor would save the egg from complete cytolysis and bring its respiration back into the normal road.

There is no doubt that the theory fails as a general one: as pointed out by Dalcq (1928), successful parthenogenesis can be obtained, in certain species, by a single treatment of the unfertilized eggs. It is also certain that the oxidative changes at fertilization do not always follow the course that one would expect according to the theory. But, if we concentrate on the sea urchin egg, on which Loeb (1913) based his theory, one cannot help to admire the insight of this great biologist: breakdown of cortical granules, transient release of proteolytic enzymes, breakdown of large molecules (glycogen, proteins), possible intervention of lysophosphatides in the cortical reaction, transient changes in the value of the respiratory quotient (even if they are due to acid production rather than to a change in the nature of the substrates which are oxidized), the rechannelling of metabolic processes observed by Runnström et al. (1959) are all in perfect agreement with Loeb's (1913) ideas.

Before leaving the subject, a few words should be said about two more recent theories of fertilization, those of Heilbrunn (1915, 1952, 1956) and Runnström (1949).

As already mentioned in this chapter, Heilbrunn (1952, 1956) has

F

developed many times the idea that calcium plays a fundamental role in fertilization, as well as in blood clotting. The importance of calcium for fertilization has also been stressed by Dalcq (1928), but without going so far as Heilbrunn (1915–1956) in believing that release of calcium is the main phenomenon in fertilization. There is no doubt that Heilbrunn's view is somewhat one-sided and that it is impossible to explain all the complexities of fertilization by analogies between cytoplasmic gelation and blood coagulation. On the other hand, it is highly probable that calcium release is one of the many important events which occur upon fertilization. Recent evidence for this view can be found in the fact that, according to Harding (1951), heparin and other mucopolysaccharides, which inhibit blood clotting also inhibit parthenogenesis in frog eggs. It is an interesting and perhaps a significant fact that the mucopolysaccharides of the sea urchin eggs jelly coat (fertilizin) inhibit blood clotting (Immers, 1949). Furthermore, it has been shown by Shaver (1953) that inoculation of mitochondria and microsomes from various sources into unfertilized frog eggs leads to parthenogenetic development, and that there is a certain degree of correlation between the parthenogenetic activity of these cytoplasmic granules and their ability to enhance blood clotting. These few hints are interesting enough to deserve further studies; they definitely suggest that, as proposed by Heilbrunn (1915–1956), calcium and processes similar to blood coagulation play an important role in cytoplasmic gelation, especially in aster formation. However, present evidence does not carry enough weight to be entirely convincing. It is an open question, as pointed out by Rothschild (1956), whether calcium release is 'the important feature in fertilization, in the way that the action potential might be said to be the important feature in nervous reactivity'.

The last theory of fertilization to be discussed here is that of Runnström (1949): as already mentioned, he has proposed that an enzyme-inhibitor complex might be present in the cortex of the unfertilized sea urchin egg and that penetration of the spermatozoon (or parthenogenesis) might remove the inhibitor. We have also seen that the work of Lundblad (1949–1954) and that of Maggio (1957) bring a fair amount of support for the view that proteases are in fact set free at fertilization. Finally, we have drawn the attention on Monroy's (1957) viewpoint: mitochondria would be involved in the first changes following fertilization.

The hypotheses of Runnström (1949) and Monroy (1957) are very satisfactory for the chemical embryologist. We would like, however, to modify somewhat Monroy's hypothesis and raise the question of the possible role of *lysosomes* in fertilization processes. We have already mentioned the existence of these particles, which are difficult to separate from mitochondria by differential centrifugation methods. According to their discoverer, de Duve (1957), they should be considered as small bags, containing a number of hydrolytic enzymes surrounded by a lipoprotein membrane. We think that the lysosomes concept might be extremely valuable in explaining the biochemical changes which occur immediately upon fertilization: the breakdown of cortical lysosomes (which might perhaps be identical with the cortical granules) would occur under the influence of the spermatozoon, since Monroy's (1950) model experiments have shown that sea urchin sperm releases phospholipids from lipoproteins. As a result, the hydrolytic enzymes present in the lysosomes would be set free: such a breakdown of the lysosomes would account for the increased proteolytic activity observed by Lundblad (1949–1954) and Maggio (1957). The results of Maggio (1957) are especially striking in this respect since what has been observed in this case is the liberation of protease previously bound to 'mitochondria'. But, as pointed out just before, it is difficult to separate mitochondria from lysosomes, unless very special care is taken in the isolation procedure. The fact that ATPase, according to Monroy (1957), behaves differently from protease only reinforces our hypothesis, since ATPase belongs much more to the category of mitochondrial enzymes than to that of the lysosomal enzymes. The *in vitro* release of protease by ribonuclease, observed by Lundblad and Hultin (1954), is understandable if the membrane surrounding the lysosomes is, in sea urchin eggs, made of RNA associated to lipoproteins. And it is perhaps a significant fact that the antifertilizin from eggs is also released from small cytoplasmic particles by a ribonuclease treatment (Runnström *et al.*, 1955).

Admittedly, the ideas which have just been expressed are, for the time being, nothing more than a hypothesis which fits a number of facts. It is presented here in the hope that it will be tested experimentally by some of the workers actively engaged in the field of the biochemistry of fertilization. Much remains to be done: one should first demonstrate that, in unfertilized sea urchin eggs, the hydrolytic enzymes usually associated with the lysosomes are really accumulated in sedimentable cytoplasmic granules and that they can be released by the many treatments which break down the lysosomes. These enzymes are acid phosphatase, ribonuclease, deoxyribonuclease and protease. If the hypothesis presented here is correct, fertilization should set free simultaneously all these enzymes. It should be a relatively easy task to test experimentally our suggestion, which has one advantage: according to de Duve (1957), the enzymes present in liver lysosomes are liberated by many physical and chemical agents; this might explain the fact that parthenogenesis can also be induced by a great variety of treatments.

REFERENCES

ABELSON, P. H. (1948): *Biol. Bull.* **95**, 262.
AFZELIUS, B. A. (1956): *Exp. Cell Res.* **10**, 257.

68 THE BIOCHEMISTRY OF DEVELOPMENT

AFZELIUS, B. A. and A. MURRAY. (1957): *Exp. Cell Res.* **12**, 325.
AKATA, K. (1957): *Embryologia* **3**, 267.
ALLEN, R. D. (1957): *J. cell. comp. Physiol.* **49**, 379.
ALLEN, R. D. (1958): In: *The Chemical Basis of Development*, p. 17. Johns Hopkins Press, Baltimore.
ALLEN, R. D. and J. L. GRIFFIN. (1958): *Exp. Cell Res.* **15**, 163.
ALLEN, R. D., B. MARKMAN and E. C. ROWE. (1958): *Exp. Cell Res.* **15**, 346.
BATAILLON, E. (1910): *Arch. Zool. expér. génér.* **56**, 101.
BATAILLON, E. (1912): *Ann. Sc. nat. Zool.* **16**, 249.
BATAILLON, E. (1929a): *Roux' Arch. Entw. Mech.* **115**, 707.
BATAILLON, E. (1929b): *Roux' Arch. Entw. Mech.* **117**, 146.
BOREI, H. (1948): *Biol. Bull.* **95**, 124.
BOREI, H. (1949): *Biol. Bull.* **96**, 117.
BRACHET, J. (1934): *Arch. Biol.* **45**, 611.
BRACHET, J. (1950): *Chemical Embryology*, Interscience Ltd., N.Y.
BROOKS, S. C. and E. L. CHAMBERS. (1948): *Biol. Bull.* **95**, 262.
BROOKS, S. C. and E. L. CHAMBERS. (1954): *Biol. Bull.* **106**, 279.
BURTON, K. (1955): *Biochem. J.* **61**, 473.
CÉAS, M. P., M. A. IMPELLIZERI and A. MONROY. (1955): *Exp. Cell Res.* **9**, 366.
CHAMBERS, E. L. and T. MENDE. (1953a): *Arch. Biochem. Biophys.* **44**, 46.
CHAMBERS, E. L. and T. MENDE. (1953b): *Exp. Cell Res.* **5**, 508.
CHANTRENNE, H. (1956): *Arch. Biochem. Biophys.* **65**, 414.
CLELAND, K. W. (1950): *Proc. Linn. Soc. N.S.W.* **75**, 282, 296.
CLELAND, K. W. and LORD ROTHSCHILD. (1952): *J. exp. Biol.* **29**, 285, 416.
COHEN, A. I. (1954): *Physiol. Zool.* **27**, 128.
COHEN, A. I. (1955): *J. Embryol. exp. Morphol.* **3**, 77.
COHEN, S. (1954): *J. biol. Chem.* **211**, 337.
COLWIN, A. L. and L. H. COLWIN. (1957): In: *The Beginnings of Embryonic Development*, p. 135, A.A.A.S., Publ. No. 48, Washington.
COLWIN, L. H. and A. L. COLWIN. (1956): *Biol. Bull.* **110**, 243.
CONNORS, W. M. and B. T. SCHEER. (1947): *J. cell. comp. Physiol.* **30**, 271.
DALCQ, A. (1928): *Les Bases Physiologiques de la Fécondation*, Presses Univ. de France.
DAN, J. C. (1952): *Biol. Bull.* **103**, 54.
DAN, J. C. (1954): *Biol. Bull.* **107**, 203.
DAN, J. C. (1956): *Internat. Rev. Cytol.* **5**, 365.
DE DUVE, C. (1957): *Sympos. Soc. exp. Biol.* **10**, 50.
ELSON, D., T. GUSTAFSON and E. CHARGAFF. (1954): *J. biol. Chem.* **209**, 485.
GIARDINA, G. and A. MONROY. (1955): *Exp. Cell Res.* **8**, 406.
GIUDICE, G. and A. MONROY. (1958): *Acta Embryol. Morphol. exp.* **2**, 58
GOLDSTEIN, L. (1953): *Biol. Bull.* **105**, 87.
HAGSTRÖM, B. E. (1959): *Exp. Cell Res.* **16**, 165.
HAGSTRÖM, B. E. and B. HAGSTRÖM. (1954a): *Exp. Cell Res.* **6**, 491.
HAGSTRÖM, B. E. and B. HAGSTRÖM. (1954b): *Exp. Cell Res.* **6**, 532.
HAGSTRÖM, B. and J. RUNNSTRÖM. (1959): *Exp. Cell Res.* **16**, 309.
HARDING, C. V. and D. HARDING. (1952): *Arkiv Zool.* **4**, 91.
HARDING, D. (1951): *Nature* **167**, 355.
HEILBRUNN, L. V. (1915): *Biol. Bull.* **29**, 149.
HEILBRUNN, L. V. (1952): *An Outline of General Physiology*, W. B. Saunders, Philadelphia.
HEILBRUNN, L. V. (1956): *The Dynamics of Living Protoplasm*, Academic Press, N.Y.

HERSHEY, A. D. (1953): *J. gen. Physiol.* **37**, 1.
HERSHEY, A. D. (1955): *Carnegie Inst. Washington Year Book* no. 54.
HERSHEY, A. D. and M. CHASE. (1952): *J. gen. Physiol.* **36**, 39.
HIRAMOTO, Y. (1959): *Exp. Cell Res.* **16**, 421.
HORI, R. (1958): *Embryologia* **4**, 79.
HULTIN, T. (1947): *Pubbl. Staz. zool. Napoli* **21**, 153.
HULTIN, T. (1950): *Exp. Cell Res.* **1**, 599.
HULTIN, T. (1953): *Studies on the Structure and Metabolic Background at Fertilization*, Stockholm.
IMMERS, J. (1949): *Arkiv. Zool.* **42 A**, no. 6.
IMMERS, J. (1957): *Exp. Cell Res.* **12**, 145.
ISHIHARA, K. (1956): *J. Fac. Sci. Univ. Tokyo*, Sect. IV, **7**, 355.
ISHIKAWA, K. (1954): *Embryologia* **2**, 57.
JEENER, R. (1959): *Biochim. biophys. Acta* **32**, 106.
KAVANAU, J. L. (1953): *J. exp. Zool.* **122**, 285.
KAVANAU, J. L. (1954a): *Exp. Cell Res.* **6**, 563.
KAVANAU, J. L. (1954b): *Exp. Cell Res.* **7**, 530.
KRANE, S. M. and R. K. CRANE. (1958): *Biol. Bull.* **115**, 355.
LASER, H. and LORD ROTHSCHILD. (1939): *Proc. Roy. Soc.* B**126**, 539.
LEUCHTENBERGER, C. and F. SCHRADER. (1950): *Proc. nat. Acad. Sci. Wash.* **36**, 677.
LILLIE, F. R. (1912): *Science* **36**, 527.
LILLIE, F. R. (1914): *J. exp. Zool.* **16**, 523.
LILLIE, F. R. (1919): *Problems of Fertilization*, Chicago.
LINDAHL, P. E. and H. HOLTER. (1941): *C. R. Trav. Lab. Carlsberg (Sér. chim.)*, **24**, 49.
LINDBERG, O. (1941): *Naturwiss.* **29**, 651.
LINDBERG, O. (1948): *Arkiv Kemi* **26 B**, no. 13.
LINDBERG, O. and L. ERNSTER. (1948): *Biochim. biophys. Acta* **2**, 471.
LOEB, J. (1913): *Artificial Parthenogenesis and Fertilization.* The Univ. of Chicago Press, Chicago, Ill.
LUNDBLAD, G. (1949): *Nature* **163**, 643.
LUNDBLAD, G. (1950): *Exp. Cell Res.* **1**, 264.
LUNDBLAD, G. (1954): *Proteolytic Activity in Sea Urchin Gametes*, Uppsala
LUNDBLAD, G. and E. HULTIN. (1954): *Exp. Cell Res.* **6**, 249.
MAGGIO, R. (1957): *J. cell. comp. Physiol.* **50**, 135.
MAGGIO, R. and A. GHIRETTI. (1958): *Exp. Cell Res.* **15**, 95.
METZ, C. B. (1957): In: *The Beginnings of Embryonic Development*, p. 23, A.A.A.S., Publ. No. 48, Washington.
MINGANTI, A. (1957): *Acta Embryol. Morphol. exp.* **1**, 150.
MIRSKY, A. E. (1936): *Science* **84**, 333.
MITCHISON, J. M. and M. M. SWANN. (1952): *J. exp. Biol.* **29**, 357.
MITCHISON, J. M. and M. M. SWANN. (1955): *J. exp. Biol.* **32**, 734
MONNÉ, L. and S. HÅRDE. (1951): *Arkiv Zool.* **1**, 487.
MONROY, A. (1950): *Exp. Cell Res.* **1**, 92.
MONROY, A. (1953a): *Experientia* **9**, 424.
MONROY, A. (1953b): *Arch. néerl. Zool.* **10**, suppl. 1, 18.
MONROY, A. (1956): *Exp. Cell Res.* **10**, 320.
MONROY, A. (1957): *J. cell. comp. Physiol.* **50**, 73.
MONROY, A. (1957): *Internat. Rev. Cytol.* **6**, 107.
MONROY, A. and A. RUFFO. (1945): *Bull. Soc. ital. Biol. sper.* **20**, 406
MONROY, A. and J. RUNNSTRÖM. (1952): *Exp. Cell Res.* **3**, 10.

MOTOMURA, I. (1941): *Science Reports Tohoku Imperial Univ.* 4th ser. **16**, 345.
NAKANO, E. (1956): *Embryologia* **3**, 139.
NAKANO, E., G. GUIDICE and A. MONROY. (1958): *Experientia* **14**, 11.
NAKANO, E. and A. MONROY. (1958): *Exp. Cell Res.* **14**, 236.
ÖHMAN, L. O. (1945): *Arkiv Zool.* **36 A**, no. 7.
ÖRSTRÖM, A. (1941): *Z. physiol. Chem.* **271**, 1.
ÖRSTRÖM, A. and O. LINDBERG. (1940): *Enzymologia* **8**, 367.
PASQUINELLI, F. (1954): *Pubbl. Staz. zool. Napoli* **25**, 341.
PERLMANN, P. (1954): *Exp. Cell Res.* **6**, 485.
PERLMANN, P. (1956): *Exp. Cell Res.* **10**, 324.
PERLMANN, P. (1957): *Exp. Cell Res.* **13**, 365.
PERLMANN, P. and B. E. HAGSTRÖM. (1957): *Exp. Cell Res.* **12**, 418.
PERLMANN, P. and H. PERLMANN. (1957): *Exp. Cell Res.* **13**, 454, 475.
RAPOPORT, S., E. C. G. HOFFMANN and A. GHIRETTI-MAGALDI. (1958): *Experientia* **14**, 169.
RICOTTA, C. M. (1956): *Naturwiss.* **43**, 258.
ROTHSCHILD, LORD. (1956): *Fertilization*, Methuen and Co., London.
ROTHSCHILD, LORD. (1958a): *Biol. Rev.* **33**, 373.
ROTHSCHILD, LORD. (1958b): *Quart. J. microsc. Sci.* **99**, 1.
ROTHSCHILD, LORD. (1958c): *J. exp. Biol.* **35**, 843.
ROTHSCHILD, LORD and A. TYLER. (1954): *J. exp. Biol.* **31**, 252.
ROTHSCHILD, LORD and A. TYLER. (1958): *Biol. Bull.* **115**, 136.
RUNNSTRÖM, J. (1930): *Protoplasma* **10**, 106.
RUNNSTRÖM, J. (1933): *Biochem. Z.* **258**. 257.
RUNNSTRÖM, J. (1935): *Biol. Bull.* **68**, 327.
RUNNSTRÖM, J. (1949): *Advances in Enzymol.* **9**, 241.
RUNNSTRÖM, J. (1952): *Sympos. Soc. exp. Biol.* **6**, 39.
RUNNSTRÖM, J. (1956): *Pubbl. Staz. zool. Napoli* **28**, 315.
RUNNSTRÖM, J. (1957): *Festschr.* Arthur Stoll, Birkhäuser, Basel.
RUNNSTRÖM, J. (1958): *Exp. Cell Res.*, suppl. **5**. 527.
RUNNSTRÖM, J., B. HAGSTRÖM and H. LÖW. (1955): *Exp Cell Res.* **8**, 235.
RUNNSTRÖM, J., B. HAGSTRÖM and P. PERLMANN. (1959): *The Cell*, Vol. **1**, p. 327, Academic Press, N.Y.
RUNNSTRÖM, J. and J. IMMERS. (1956): *Exp. Cell Res.* **10**, 354.
RUNNSTRÖM, J., L. MONNÉ and L. BROMAN. (1944): *Ark. Zool.* **35 A**, no. 3.
SAMUEL, R. E., S. EPSTEIN and A. TYLER. (1958): *Biol. Bull.* **115**, 153.
SHAVER, J. R. (1953): *J. exp. Zool.* **122**, 169.
SUGIYAMA, M. (1951): *Biol. Bull.* **101**, 235.
TYLER, A. (1940): *Proc. nat. Acad. Sci. Wash.* **26**, 249.
TYLER, A. (1957): In: *The Beginnings of Embryonic Development*, p. 341, A.A.A.S., Publ. No. 48, Washington.
TYLER, A. and J. W. BROOKBANK. (1956): *Proc. nat. Acad. Sci. Wash.* **42**, 304.
TYLER, A. and W. D. HUMASON. (1937): *Biol. Bull.* **73**, 261.
TYLER, A. and A. MONROY. (1956): *Biol. Bull.* **111**, 296.
TYLER, A., A. MONROY, C. Y. KAO and H. GRUNDFEST. (1956): *Biol Bull.* **111**, 153.
VASSEUR, E. (1952): *The Chemistry and Physiology of the Jelly Coat of the Sea Urchin Egg.* Dissertation, Stockholm.
VOLKIN, E. and L. ASTRACHAN. (1956): *Virology* **2**, 149.
WADA, S., J. R. COLLIER, and J. C. DAN. (1956): *Exp. Cell Res.* **10**, 168.
WARBURG, O. (1908): *Z. physiol. Chem.* **57**, 1.
WHITAKER, D. M. (1933): *J. gen. Physiol.* **16**, 497.
ZOTIN, A. I. (1958): *J. Embryol, exp. Morphol.* **4**. 79.

CHAPTER III

Cleavage

CLEAVAGE immediately follows the fusion of the two pronuclei; the precise mode of segmentation is correlated with the amount and the distribution of yolk within the egg. As a rule, an accumulation of yolk platelets hinders the formation of furrows; for this reason, embryologists describe a number of different types of cleavage, which are linked to the localization of protein yolk: equal and total cleavage, unequal (spiral) cleavage, partial cleavage and peripheric cleavage are the main types. Equal and total cleavage occurs, usually, in eggs which are poor in yolk granules; but, as soon as the vegetal pole becomes loaded with yolk (Amphibians and Prochordates, for instance), segregation of micromeres and macromeres takes place at the 8-cell stage. Unequal cleavage is very frequent in Worms and Molluscs: one blastomere (CD) is larger than the other (AB), at the 2-cell stage, because these eggs possess a special plasm which forms the polar lobe and becomes integrated within the CD blastomere. At the second cleavage, a second polar lobe is formed and it is in turn assimilated by the D blastomere; the latter contains the mesoderm and, as we shall see in the next chapter, it has special importance for morphogenesis. Partial cleavage is characteristic of the yolk-laden eggs, such as those of Fishes and Birds; the furrows can no longer penetrate the yolk and the blastula forms only at the animal pole. Finally, peripheric cleavage is characteristic of insect eggs: the yolk mass lies in the centre of the egg, where repeated division of the nuclei takes place until some of them migrate towards the surface of the egg; the clear cytoplasm which surrounds the egg becomes suddenly divided into many cells and a 'periblastula' is formed.

This is, of course, only a very brief account of the different types of cleavages occurring in eggs; more details will be found in all text-books on Embryology.

Whatever the method adopted for cleavage by the eggs, this period of embryonic development is dominated by one single process: *mitosis*. Since mitosis has been discussed recently in detail by the author elsewhere (Brachet, 1957), we shall restrict ourselves to a relatively short discussion and describe this process as it occurs in eggs.

Figure 30 (a, b, c, d, e), which is taken from Brachet (1957), shows the various stages of mitosis in amphibian eggs: in *prophase* (30a), a single

71

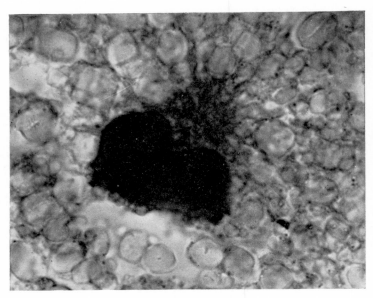

FIG. 30 (a)

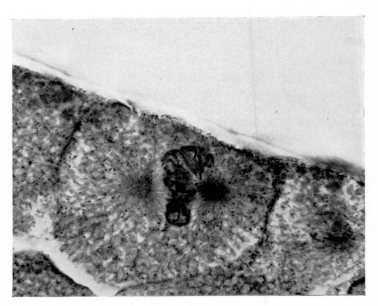

FIG. 30 (b)

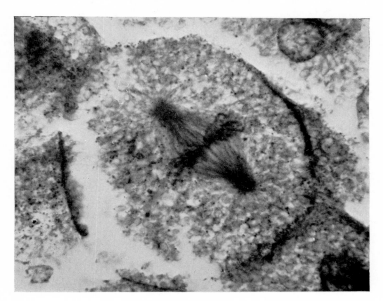

FIG. 30 (c)

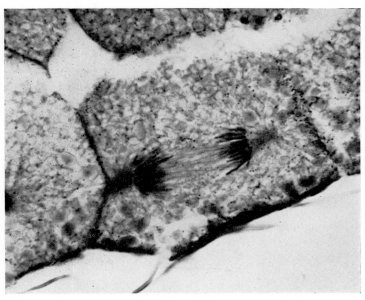

FIG. 30 (d)

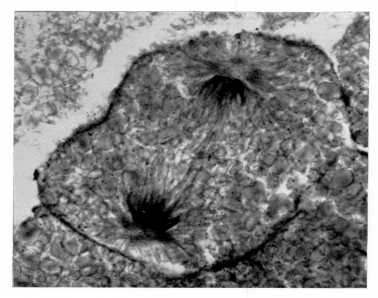

FIG. 30 (*e*)

FIG. 30. Mitosis during cleavage of frog eggs: *a*, prophase; *b*, prometaphase; *c*, metaphase; *d*, anaphase; *e*, early telophase (Brachet, 1957).

centrosome and aster are visible. At *prometaphase* (30b), the centrosome and asters have divided; the nuclear membrane has broken down and the chromosomes already are clearly visible. Figure 30c represents a typical *metaphase:* spindle and asters are well developed and the chromosomes are located at the equatorial plate. They are attached to spindle fibres by the centromeres, which are poor in DNA. At *anaphase* (Fig. 30d), the chromosomes have migrated toward the centrosomes. Finally, Fig. 30e shows an early *telophase:* the chromosomes have come close to the centrosomes and the furrow which will separate the daughter cells has already become visible.

Two remarks should be made about mitosis in cleaving eggs: firstly, there are no nucleoli in the resting nuclei until the blastula stage. It looks as though the egg, while dividing so fast, has not sufficient time to build up nucleoli during the exceedingly short interphases. Secondly, there may be, in cleaving eggs, a certain dissynchronism between nuclear and cytoplasmic divisions: nuclear division takes place so quickly that, in early cleavage stages of amphibian eggs, the nuclei are already in prophase before the furrows are complete. These differences with mitosis in somatic cells are obviously due to the extreme speed at which cell divisions follow each other during egg cleavage, and to the difficulty, for the furrows, to progress through cytoplasm when it is rich in yolk.

After a brief summary of morphological and cytochemical observations made on dividing eggs, the biochemical aspects of mitosis will be considered in more detail.

1. Morphology and cytochemistry of the dividing egg

(a) CHROMOSOMES

Chromosomes, because of their genetical importance, have, of course, been first to attract the interest of cytologists. It is often said that mitosis is nothing but a device for the equal distribution of the genetic material present in chromatin to the daughter cells. While this view is probably correct, there are cases where an egg divides repeatedly in the complete absence of nuclei. Cleavage is thus more than equal distribution of the chromosomes to daughter cells and the 'purpose' of mitosis is defeated in such cases where cleavage occurs in the absence of nuclei.

The most conspicuous and important constituent of the chromosomes is DNA. This substance can easily be detected, with the Feulgen reaction, in cleaving eggs as well as in other cells. The intensity of the Feulgen reaction is often very weak during the brief interphase period; this almost complete failure of the resting nuclei to give, in eggs, the cytochemical DNA reactions is due to dilution of the DNA present in chromatin by the relatively large amount of nuclear sap. There is no reason to believe that DNA is actually broken down during interphase in cleaving eggs any more than in ordinary cells. The problem of DNA synthesis and the mechanism of its replication during the mitotic cycle will be discussed later in this chapter.

Nothing, beyond their existence, is known about the nature of the proteins which are associated with DNA in eggs. It is probable that this DNA, as well as the DNA in other nuclei, is present in the form of a nucleohistone, but even this does not seem to have been experimentally established. A number of other questions are still waiting to be answered: what happens at fertilization to the protamines which were present in the nuclei of certain spermatozoa? Are they broken down and replaced by pre-existing histones? Do they rather undergo changes of increasing complexity and are they transformed into histones by a process which is the reverse of that occurring during spermiogenesis? Are there more complex proteins, enzymes for instance, in the nuclei and chromosomes of dividing eggs? Cytochemical studies of the proteins during cleavage should bring answers to these puzzling questions.

Another constituent of the chromosomes, according to Fujii (1954) and Miura *et al.* (1957), is zinc; as we have seen in Chapter I, this metal is present also in the nucleolus of sea urchin oocytes. It is possible, as suggested by the Japanese workers, that the zinc present in the chromosomes during cleavage of sea urchin eggs originates from the nucleolus of the oocyte. One might expect to find a similar situation in the case of RNA, with respect to the origin of this material in chromosomes. In fact, it has been reported by Brachet (1942), Jacobson and Webb (1952), and many others, that chromosomes usually contain some RNA. This is not the case, however, for cleaving amphibian eggs. We have often observed that, during cleavage, the chromosomes stain bright green with methyl green-pyronine (the so-called Unna mixture). After cleavage, i.e. in blastulae or gastrulae, the chromosomes stain blue or violet. Pretreatment of the sections, at these stages, with ribonuclease brings back a purely green staining of the chromosomes. The conclusion of these still unpublished observations is the following: chromosomes contain no RNA and therefore take up no pyronine during cleavage; however, they have a definite RNA content at later stages. It is interesting to note that the blastula stage is precisely the one when nucleoli again make their appearance. It is therefore a possibility that the chromosomal RNA comes out of the nucleolus after the initial period of cleavage. Mitosis, from the blastula stage on, might thus distribute evenly in the daughter cells not only DNA, but also nucleolar RNA.

Such a possibility might be tested on eggs originating from stocks which have no nucleoli: as recently discovered, a deficiency of the nucleolar organizer in the chromosomes can lead to the production of individuals which have no visible nucleoli in *Xenopus* (Gurdon *et al.*, 1958) and *Chironomus* (Beermann, 1959). It would be very interesting to know more about these 'nucleolusless' mutants from many viewpoints: are there typical abnormalities of morphogenesis, as a result of the absence of nucleoli? Is there an effect of the lack of a nucleolus on RNA and protein metabolism? And, as just discussed, would the chromosomes of a *nucleolusless* embryo contain RNA? For the time being, unfortunately, all that we know is that the absence of a large, visible nucleolus does not lead to a fully lethal condition.

Before leaving the subject of the role of the nucleolus in mitotic processes, a last remark should be made: according to a recent report of Gaulden and Perry (1958), who worked with grasshopper neuroblasts, localized U.V. irradiation of the nucleolus inhibits mitosis. In this material, the nucleolus thus seems to play a role in the initiation of mitosis; at any rate, U.V. irradiation inhibits more effectively the entry into mitosis when the nucleolus rather than the chromatin is irradiated.

(b) THE ACHROMATIC APPARATUS (SPINDLE AND ASTERS)

In cleaving eggs, the achromatic apparatus does not deserve its name at all. Due to a high content of RNA, it stains stronger with basic dyes than the surrounding cytoplasm (Brachet, 1942; Stich, 1954)! During early cleavage, as at the time of maturation (cf. Chapter I), the nuclear sap becomes strongly basophilic when it mixes with the surrounding cytoplasm (Stich, 1954; Brachet, 1954). This curious phenomenon recently has been discovered again, by Fautrez-Firlefyn (1957) in *Artemia* eggs and by Stich and McIntyre (1958) in those of *Cyclops*. These authors found that the beginning of prophase does more than to increase basophilia, i.e. the RNA content: they observed very similar phenomena for polysaccharides and proteins as well. It therefore looks as if mixing of the nuclear sap with the egg cytoplasm really led to a *synthesis* of RNA, proteins and polysaccharides. The nature and the reason for these sudden anabolic processes remain unknown; perhaps autoradiography methods might throw some light on this puzzling problem.

The cytochemical methods thus suggest that the nuclear sap contributes to the formation of the spindle, in agreement with the results of the experiments of Dalcq and Simon (1932) on cleavage after irradiation or trypaflavine treatment of the gametes in the frog. On the other hand, calculations by Mazia (1955) have clearly demonstrated that the whole of the achromatic apparatus cannot originate solely from the two pronuclei: the major part of its mass is of cytoplasmic origin.* But, as pointed out in the first chapter of this book, it is by no means impossible that the spindle and the asters might originate, during early cleavage, from the sap of the broken germinal vesicle. The reason for this supposition is that both the nuclear sap of the oocyte and, as shown by Brachet (1940) and by Kawamura and Dan (1958), the achromatic apparatus during early cleavage give very strong reactions for protein —SH groups after fixation.

But really significant progress in the field has only been made since Mazia and Dan (1952) succeeded in isolating in mass, from cleaving sea urchin eggs, the whole *mitotic apparatus*, i.e. the asters and the spindle, with attached chromosomes (Fig. 31). Chemical analysis of the isolated mitotic apparatus (Mazia and Dan, 1952; Mazia, 1954, 1955, 1956) has shown that it is made of a single protein, homogeneous on electrophoresis and having a molecular weight of about 20,000. This protein exists in association with RNA. Apparently the astral and spindle fibres are made of elongated macromolecular units: their parallel orientation is responsible for the birefringence of the spindle, a phenomenon which has been described by Inoue (1952) and others.

Further experiments by Mazia (1954, 1955, 1956) have shown that reducing agents, such as thioglycollate, produce the breakdown of the long fibres into smaller globular protein units: the latter are connected by —S—S— bonds, while the spindle fibres are held together by bonds,

---

* Using immunological methods, Went (1959) has shown that certain proteins of the unfertilized egg have the same immuno-chemical structure as the protein which forms the spindle.

presumably hydrogen bonds, which are broken by concentrated urea. It is very interesting that Mazia (1955, 1956) succeeded in isolating a mitotic apparatus from sea urchin eggs which had been treated with colchicine (Fig. 32): this well-known poison of the spindle prevents the parallel organization of the fibres and all that can be isolated is an amorphous gel.

The microscopic structure of the isolated mitotic apparatus has been

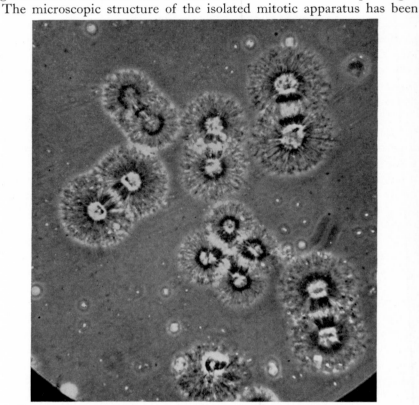

FIG. 31. Isolated mitotic apparatus at metaphase and anaphase. In the centre, tetracentric mitotic apparatus. Phase contrast (courtesy of Prof. D. Mazia).

studied in detail by Dan and Nakajima (1956); but the most important conclusion which can be drawn from their paper is that a mitotic apparatus can be isolated from several different species: the results of Mazia (1954–1956) are valid for these species also and thus his findings have a general significance.

The problem of the role of —S—S— linkages in the organization of the mitotic apparatus has been taken one step further by Mazia (1958) and by Mazia and Zimmerman (1958). They compared the effect of a —SH-containing, strongly reducing substance (β-mercaptoethanol) on cleavage of sea urchin eggs and on the properties of the isolated mitotic apparatus. Here are their main conclusions: cleavage can be blocked reversibly by mercaptoethanol; at a critical concentration of 0·075 M, the divisions are blocked if mercaptoethanol is introduced at any time up to metaphase. If it is introduced shortly after metaphase, cell division proceeds normally, but the next mitosis is blocked. It is an interesting fact that nuclear reproduction and possibly the division of centrioles proceed during the mercaptoethanol block. Finally, it was found that the mitotic

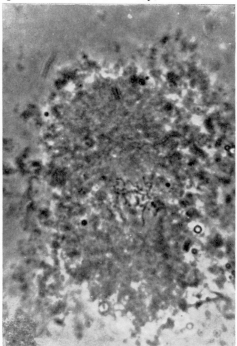

Fig. 32. Mitotic apparatus isolated from colchicine-treated sea urchin eggs (Mazia, 1955) (courtesy of Prof. D. Mazia).

apparatus isolated from the blocked eggs have a highly disorganized structure at the microscopic level; however, this disorganization does not imply an equally drastic disruption of the underlying organization. The authors conclude that mercaptoethanol might produce a 'relaxation' or 'loosening' of structure that can be reversed almost instantaneously.

Before we leave the subject, it should be added that, in amphibian eggs also, mercaptoethanol produces a marked inhibition of mitosis, although it has little toxicity (Brachet, 1959). Its effects on early cleavage would certainly deserve careful cytological and cytochemical studies on a favourable material such as the eggs of the Urodeles.

The observations presented in this section certainly suggest an intervention of —SH groups in mitotic processes; more will be said about this question later in this chapter.

(c) Ultra-structural Changes During Cleavage

Studies with the electron microscope on the ultra-fine structure of eggs during cleavage are not yet very numerous; special mention should be made of the work of Lehmann and Mancuso (1957), of Lehmann (1959) and of Mercer and Wolpert (1958).

Lehmann and Mancuso (1957, 1958) and Lehmann (1959) used improved methods of fixation for the study of astral rays and nuclear membrane in *Tubifex* eggs; according to these workers, the astral centre consists of a dense sponge-like reticulum which contains no mitochondria. The fibrous structure of the asters is clearly visible in their electron micrographs; many microsome-like bodies are embedded in the fibrous axis.* The nuclear membrane is double-layered and is thus similar to all other nuclear membranes.

The work of Mercer and Wolpert (1958) has been concentrated on possible changes occurring in the membrane at the time of the formation of the furrow: they observed, in cleaving sea urchin eggs, the appearance of a new layer below the plasma membrane. This new layer is most strongly developed in the furrow, and it might play a mechanical role in the phenomenon of cleavage.

(d) Short Description of Frequent Mitotic Abnormalities During Egg Cleavage

Cleaving eggs, presumably because of their large yolk content, are especially liable to undergo mitotic abnormalities; the most important of these abnormalities will be described briefly here, because knowledge of their existence helps in understanding better the mechanisms of cleavage.

A first peculiarity of cleaving eggs, as compared to ordinary somatic cells, is the unusual frequency and importance of aster production and reduplication. The appearance of numerous asters (cytasters: Fig. 33) in the cytoplasm of unfertilized, fertilized and cleaving eggs is easily produced by a variety of experimental treatments (narcotics, heat, hypertonic sea water, etc.). Asters, in eggs, can form around almost any cytoplasmic granule. It would be of great interest to study the ultra-structure of such cytasters with the electron microscope, since normal centrosomes have, as shown by de Harven and Bernhard (1956), a very complicated structure. We are completely ignorant of whether the granules, which are found at the centre of the cytasters, have the same elaborate organization.

---

*According to Gross (1959), the spindle contains a large number of ribonucleoprotein particles (ribosomes) devoid of ergastoplasmic membranes.

A few things are known, however, concerning cytaster formation in eggs: as shown by Costello (1940), breakdown of the germinal vesicle is required in order to obtain cytaster formation; the nuclear sap seems very likely to play a role in their production, a conclusion which is in keeping with what has been said above about the probable role of this sap in the formation of the mitotic apparatus. Another remarkable observation is that of Lorch (1952), who found that, if an aster is removed from a cleaving sea urchin egg with a micromanipulator, it can reform—after a long delay— even if the nucleus has also been removed. The purely cytoplasmic origin of asters, in eggs, is thus established beyond doubt.

Another manifestation of the tendency inherent to eggs to form asters

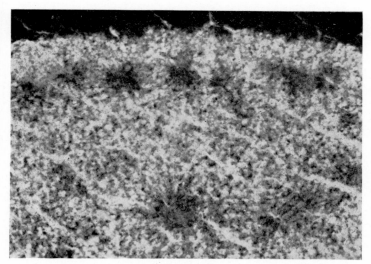

Fɪɢ. 33. Cytasters in large, uncleaved blastomere of an abnormal frog egg (Brachet, 1957).

is the frequent occurrence of *multipolar* mitoses (Fig. 34) in eggs which have been placed under abnormal conditions for some time. The result is, of course, a highly abnormal distribution of the chromosomes in the daughter cells (if the mother cell divides at all), leading to *aneuploidy*; this condition of chromosomal unbalance will, sooner or later, be lethal for the embryo (Fankhauser, 1934).

Sometimes, the cytasters follow each other in a row, as if the asters had been able to divide in an autonomous way in the absence of a spindle; this type of abnormality has been called *catenar* mitosis by Dalcq and Simon (1932).

Still more interesting are the cases in which, as already mentioned, non-nucleated eggs divide repeatedly. Cleavage in the total absence of

G

nuclei has been obtained by Harvey (1933, 1936) in the sea urchin and by Dalcq and Simon (1932), Fankhauser (1934) and Briggs *et al.* (1951) in Amphibians. In the latter case, the sperm was heavily irradiated and, as a result, quickly degenerated, while the maturation spindle was removed by pricking. In E. B. Harvey's (1933, 1936) experiments, the unfertilized sea urchin eggs were separated in two halves (nucleated and non-nucleated) by strong centrifugation in a density gradient; the non-nucleated frag-

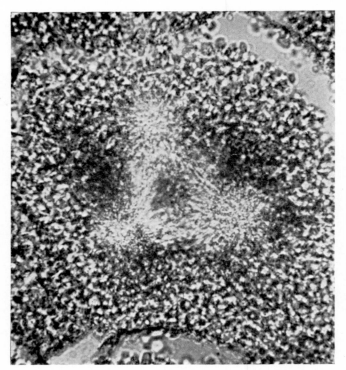

FIG. 34. Tripolar mitosis in an abnormal frog egg (Brachet, 1957).

ments were then treated with parthenogenetic agents and repeated cleavage, due to aster reduplication, was found to take place (Fig. 35). Of course, cleavage in the absence of the nucleus is rather irregular and does not follow closely the pattern of normal cleavage. Nevertheless, there is no doubt that, in eggs, asters have considerable autonomy and can carry on for several 'mitotic' cycles all by themselves. We shall see later (Chapter VI), that development never proceeds further than cleavage in anucleate eggs.

It would be a mistake, however, to believe that the achromatic apparatus (asters and spindle) possesses some sort of special immunity when eggs are placed under unfavourable circumstances. On the contrary, destruction of the achromatic apparatus is very frequently the result of experimental interventions. Colchicine is certainly not specific in this respect and moderate temperature changes (cold and heat shocks) easily produce the disintegration of the spindle (Fankhauser and Godwin, 1948; Brachet,

 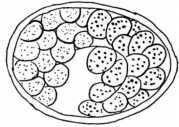

FIG. 35. Thirteen-hour non-nucleated morula and 3-day non-nucleated blastula in the sea urchin (E. B. Harvey, 1936).

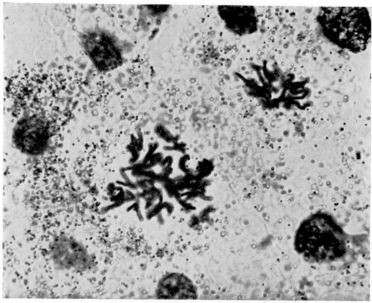

FIG. 36. Polyploidy in an amphibian egg submitted to a heat shock: polyploid (below) and diploid (above, right) equatorial plates (Brachet, 1957).

1949). Another agent which leads to the same results is ribonuclease, whose effects will be discussed in more detail a little later (Brachet and Ledoux, 1955): this enzyme easily penetrates into many cells, including amphibian eggs, where it injures the achromatic apparatus. Whatever the external agent used for the disruption of the spindle, the results are the same: polyploidy (Fig. 36) or aneuploidy are obtained.

It is also possible that asters are completely missing in abnormal eggs: on a normal or barrel-shaped spindle, scattered chromosomes are found. This is the so-called *anastral* mitosis (Fig. 37a, b). In many instances, as in the case shown in Fig. 35, the anastral spindle lies near the cell membrane

FIG. 37 (*a*)

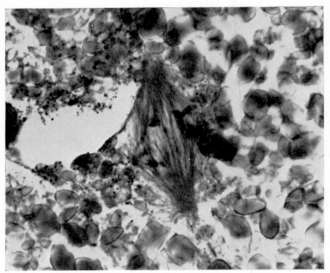

FIG 37 (*b*)

FIG. 37 (*a*) and (*b*). Two cases of anastral mitoses in ribonuclease-treated amphibian eggs (Brachet, 1957).

of the blastomere. There is a close resemblance between such anastral mitoses and the maturation divisions at the end of oogenesis. However, experimentally induced anastral mitosis is, as a rule, not followed by cell division; in fact, chromosomes usually do not migrate toward the poles in such cases.

Amitosis is the fragmentation of a resting nucleus; it is usually thought to be merely a degenerative process. One cannot help being struck, however, by the large number of binucleate or multinucleate cells which

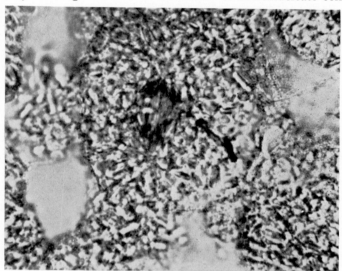

Fig. 38. Elimination of injured chromosomes (right) into the cytoplasm of a frog inter-species hybrid (Brachet, 1954).

can be observed in amphibian eggs. But the precise mechanism of the multiplication of nuclei in a single blastomere remains unknown.

Chromosomal abnormalities can be found in cleaving eggs as well as in other cells: radiations (Dalcq and Simon, 1932) or nitrogen mustard (Brachet, 1954) easily induce chromosomal breakage, or elimination of the injured chromosomes into the cytoplasm. Hybridization or ultra-violet radiation of sperm also often results in the expulsion into the cytoplasm of a 'pycnotic' mass, made of all the foreign or irradiated chromosomes (Fig. 38). In fact, *pycnosis* (shrinking of the nucleus into a single spherical mass) and *karyorrhexis* (breakdown of the dying nucleus into a number of spherical bodies inside the nuclear membrane: Fig. 39) are so prevalent in developing eggs that it has often been suggested (see Glücksmann, 1951, for a review) that these are normal processes in morphogenesis. Breakdown of certain cells may release substances necessary for the development of the others.

Finally, the obvious difficulty experienced by the cleaving eggs in producing furrows normally, because of the large excess of yolk, makes suppression of the formation of the cleavage furrows easily obtainable: inhibition of plasmodieresis (i.e. cytoplasmic division) without inhibition of karyodieresis (i.e. nuclear division) occurs frequently after treatment with narcotics, phenylurethane for instance. Treatment of frog eggs, at the 2-cell stage, with phenylurethane completely blocks cleavage; each of the two blastomeres, however, contains many nuclei (Brachet, 1934).

This short description of the main mitotic abnormalities which can be

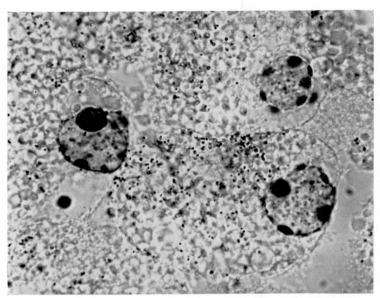

FIG. 39. Karyorrhexis in injured amphibian egg (Brachet, 1957).

found in cleaving eggs, after treatment with a variety of agents, will suffice to show the very great sensitivity of the egg at that stage: normal cleavage is not always an easy task for the dividing egg.

2. Biochemistry of cleavage

Under this heading, two important biochemical aspects of mitosis in eggs will be considered: the production of the energy required for cleavage and the mechanism of DNA synthesis.

(a) ENERGY REQUIREMENTS

It is a well-known fact that, in general, mitosis is impossible in the absence of oxygen (cf. Brachet, 1950, for a review of the older literature): this is the case, for instance, in sea urchin (Runnström, 1930) and *Ascaris*

(Bataillon, 1910) eggs. There are, however, important exceptions: frog eggs (Brachet, 1934) and trout eggs (Devillers, 1953) reach the blastula stage in complete anaerobiosis. Similar results are obtained when cleaving eggs are treated with poisons of cytochrome oxidase, cyanide for instance: eggs of different species show great variations in their susceptibility to specific inhibitors of cellular oxidations.

The situation becomes clearer when inhibitors of phosphorylations, dinitrophenol for instance, are studied. It is well established that dinitrophenol *uncouples* phosphorylations from oxidations; as a result, oxygen consumption proceeds normally or even increases, while synthesis of the energy-rich phosphate bonds of ATP becomes impossible. Since biological endergonic processes, protein synthesis for instance, cannot draw directly the energy they require from oxidations but only from ATP, it is to be expected that inhibitors of ATP synthesis will soon lead to the arrest of mitotic activity. Experiments have largely confirmed this expectation and egg cleavage has repeatedly been found to be much more susceptible to an uncoupling agent, such as dinitrophenol, than to inhibitors of cellular oxidations like KCN. For instance, frog eggs, which can divide in anaerobiosis or cyanide, as already mentioned, rapidly stop developing in dinitrophenol (Brachet, 1954); they behave toward this poison exactly like the sea urchin eggs, although the latter are exceedingly sensitive towards lack of oxygen or poisons of the cytochrome system (Clowes and Krahl, 1936).

More recent biochemical work (Barth and Jaeger, 1947; Brachet, 1955) has demonstrated that, as one would expect, lack of oxygen leads to a marked decrease in the ATP content of frog eggs. However, mitosis stops long before the ATP store is exhausted. Furthermore, there seems to be a critical ATP concentration below which mitotic activity comes to a standstill in these eggs.

More interesting, because of the more direct approach adopted, is the work of Barnett (1953) which, in view of its importance, requires independent confirmation. He first found that division, in sea urchin eggs, is blocked by malonate, which is a competitive inhibitor of the important succinic dehydrogenase of the tricarboxylic acid cycle, and that malonate inhibition can be reversed by fumarate and succinate. But the really fundamental point, in Barnett's (1953) work, is that ATP can reverse inhibition of division by malonate, cyanide, anaerobiosis and even dinitrophenol. If this is true, it would provide unequivocal proof of the necessity of ATP for cell division.

Several workers have studied the effects of ATP alone on cell division in sea urchin eggs: for instance, Runnström and Kriszat (1950) found that ATP exerts a favourable influence on cleavage in batches of eggs which show relatively poor development. In a more recent study, Wolpert (1958) comes to the conclusion that ATP exerts an inhibitory effect on cell division in sea urchin eggs. He believes that ATP directly participates in cell division and that it acts on the cell cortex. This is a very likely suggestion for, as will be seen later, there are certain analogies between furrow formation and muscle contraction: ATP might produce a 'contraction' of the egg cortex, which might prevent further division.

Another important piece of research, in a closely related field, is that of Swann (1953, 1954, extensive review of the whole problem of control of cell division in 1957). He first studied the effects of carbon monoxide, a specific cytochrome oxidase inhibitor, on cleavage of sea urchin eggs. The experiments clearly showed that the inhibitor, if applied before a certain critical point in the cycle (30–35 minutes after fertilization), causes a delay in division equal to the length of the inhibitions. If the inhibitor is applied after this critical point, it has no effect on the division, but delays the next one for a time equal to the length of time of the inhibitions. Swann's (1953) interpretation of his own results is that 'the energy required for division itself (as opposed to the various processes that must precede it) is built up in advance in chemical form—the "energy reservoir".'

The nature of this 'energy reservoir' remains uncertain. Experiments on the action of ether on cell division have shown that this substance can block cleavage without affecting the rate of filling of the reservoir (Swann, 1954). Swann (1957) was unable to find direct evidence that the energy reservoir is a phosphorylated compound, ATP for instance; but he found indications favouring the view that it might be a thiol-ester or some other activated acyl compound. Further work obviously is required for the elucidation of the chemical nature of the energy reservoir; the results of these investigations will be awaited with interest and impatience, since they might throw very important light on the nature of the energy supply required for division.

In view of Swann's (1953, 1954, 1957) work, one would expect to find cyclical variations during mitosis in cleaving eggs. This question has been studied by Zeuthen (1946, 1950, 1953, 1955) on frog and sea urchin eggs with very delicate methods (description of earlier work, which has now lost much of its interest, in Brachet, 1950). The general conclusion is that, in spite of contradictory results obtained by Scholander et al. (1952, 1958), mitosis is, in general (but not always) accompanied by small variations in the oxygen uptake of the eggs (Fig. 40). There are also cyclic variations in the oxygen consumption of colchicine-treated sea urchin eggs during the first cleavages (Fig. 41). On close analysis, it is difficult to avoid the conclusion drawn by Holter and Zeuthen (1957): the respiratory rate often increases during interphase and reaches its maximum at prophase; it is lowest at telophase. In other words, oxidations are higher when the

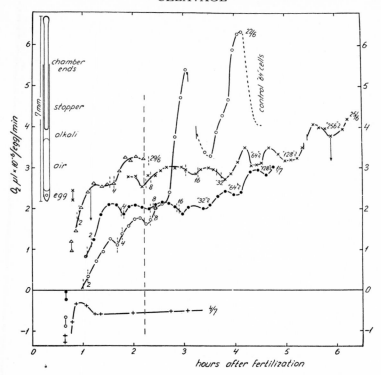

FIG. 40. Four experiments on single sea urchin eggs, with one control experiment (4/7). Left: schematic view of the diver in these experiments (Zeuthen, 1955).

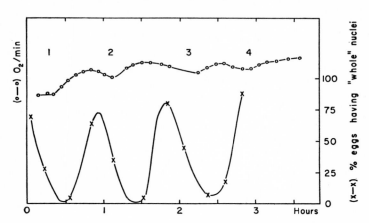

FIG. 41. Oxygen consumption of sea urchin eggs treated with colchicine: rhythmic respiration (upper curve) and rhythmic dissolution and reappearance of nuclei (lower curve) (Zeuthen, 1951).

nuclei are surrounded by the nuclear membrane than when they are 'open'. Although the differences in oxygen uptake are very small and not absolutely constant, they probably are real; in any event, the view that the resting nucleus is in a metabolically more active state than the dividing one is in agreement with several other experimental data (see Brachet, 1957, for a discussion of this point).

(b) DNA Synthesis During Cleavage

If synthetic processes are highest when the nucleus is in interphase (the classical term of 'resting' nucleus would then be highly misleading!), one would expect the synthesis of the chromosomes components to occur during this period: this is true for the most important constituent of chromatin, DNA, and it is likely that the proteins which are associated with it are also synthesized during interphase (Bloch and Godman, 1955). However, there are no rules without exceptions and cleaving eggs may be one of these exceptions. According to Pasteels and Lison (1951), Fautrez and Fautrez-Firlefyn (1953), Roels (1954) and Bergerard (1955), DNA synthesis already takes place in anaphase in *Sabellaria* and *Artemia* eggs. These observations are not too surprising: as pointed out before, eggs divide as fast as they can during cleavage and it is not astonishing that they synthesize DNA earlier than most other cells. In fact, there is no

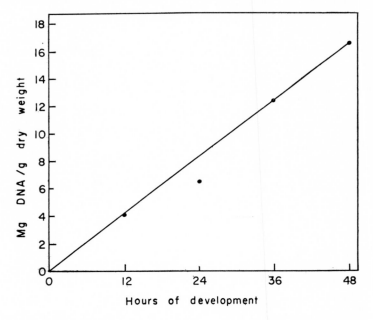

Fig. 42. DNA synthesis in developing sea urchin eggs (Brachet, 1933).

reason why DNA synthesis should occur at the same stage of the mitotic cycle in *all* cells, as pointed out rightly by Dalcq and Pasteels (1955).

In view of the now well-demonstrated genetical importance of DNA, the mechanism of its synthesis during embryonic development has become a major problem. The existence of such a synthesis in sea urchin eggs was first demonstrated, more than 25 years ago, by a combination of cytochemical and analytical methods (Brachet, 1933; Fig. 42). The methods of analysis in those days were, however, still rather crude and the DNA content during early cleavage—which remains a controversial problem—could not be accurately measured. There is, nevertheless, no doubt that a DNA synthesis occurs during the development of all the organisms which have been studied so far and all the available evidence indicates that it is a universal phenomenon.

The difficult question to answer is the following: what is the origin and what are the precursors of the DNA which is synthesized during embryogenesis? A first suggestion, which seems rather improbable now, was made by the author some 25 years ago (Brachet, 1933): synthesis of nuclear DNA occurs at the expense of cytoplasmic RNA. Estimations of the DNA and RNA content of developing sea urchin eggs indicated that the DNA synthesis is balanced by a drop in RNA content; but analytical methods were necessarily unsatisfactory in those days where the very existence of RNA in animal cells was unknown. The orthodox (and entirely wrong) view was then that DNA is an 'animal' nucleic acid and RNA a 'plant' nucleic acid. Furthermore, it was not realized that the jelly coat which, as we have seen, is rich in carbohydrates could interfere with ribose estimations. The most accurate and recent work on the subject is that of Elson *et al.* (1954). As shown in Fig. 43, the RNA content undergoes a short and still unexplained drop just after fertilization (cf. Chapter II), followed by a rise during cleavage and a second rise just prior to gastrulation; this second increase might be linked with the onset of new protein synthesis.

It is obvious, from even casual examination of Fig. 43, that the whole of the synthesized DNA cannot originate from RNA. Isotope experiments by Villee *et al.* (1949), Abrams (1951) and Scarano and Kalckar (1953) have confirmed this conclusion. As shown in Fig. 44, the specific radio-activity of DNA increases faster than that of RNA during development of sea urchin eggs.

These isotope experiments are, however, open to a number of questions: for instance, Abrams (1951) found that 70 to 80 per cent of the DNA synthesized by the eggs comes from an unknown and unlabelled precursor, which might or might not be RNA. Furthermore, little care seems to have been taken, in all these experiments, in order to check bacterial contamination, which can become very important if some of the eggs undergo cytolysis. Incorporation of the nucleic acid precursors might be much more rapid in contaminating micro-organisms than in the eggs themselves. Finally, as pointed out by Villee *et al.* (1949), the possibility that DNA

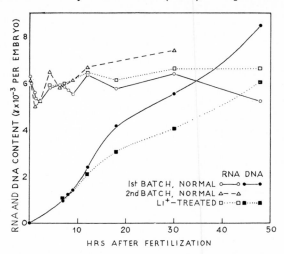

FIG. 43. DNA and RNA synthesis in normal and lithium-treated sea urchin embryos (Elson *et al.*, 1956).

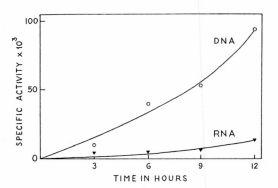

FIG. 44. Incorporation of ^{32}P into DNA and RNA in developing sea urchin eggs (after Villee *et al.*, 1949).

arises from a small, but metabolically very active, fraction of the total RNA cannot be ruled out.

All of this work should therefore be repeated under aseptic conditions or in the presence of antibiotics which do not interfere with the egg's development. But the really crucial experiment so far has never been done: one should try to label RNA with a very specific precursor, during oogenesis;

the radioactive eggs should then be fertilized and the radioactivity of the isolated DNA determined at all stages of development. Preliminary experiments were carried out in the author's laboratory with orotic acid as a precursor; they failed to give any clearcut results, because the radioactivity of the unfertilized eggs was extremely weak. Labelled nucleosides, uridine for instance, might be better incorporated and the so far unsuccessful attempts deserve repetition. That the experiment is feasible is indicated by a recent paper of Giudice (1958) who succeeded in labelling unfertilized sea urchin eggs by injecting ^{32}P in the female; he found, at the blastula stage, a decrease in the specific activity of the total homogenate and an increase in the mitochondrial fraction. But it is not impossible that the latter was contaminated with nuclei; in any event, no conclusion can be drawn from the experiments of Giudice (1958) for our present purpose until the distribution of ^{32}P in the various phosphorus-containing constituents of the egg is studied.

The reason why we think that these experiments should be done is that recent biochemical literature is bringing forward more and more evidence for the view that, in systems other than sea urchin eggs, ribonucleotides can be converted into the corresponding deoxyribonucleotides. For instance, Astrachan and Volkin (1958), Wacker *et al.* (1959) and Loeb and Cohen (1959) have published data which suggest that, in bacteria, an intact transfer of ribonucleotides to deoxyribonucleotides occurs. According to recent work of McNutt (1958) on *Neurospora*, the deoxyribose of DNA comes from the ribose of nucleosides such as adenosine and cytidine. Still more interesting for the chemical embryologist is the work of Reichard (1958, 1959), because he has been working with chick embryos. His experiments show that pyrimidine ribonucleotides can give rise to pyrimidine deoxyribonucleotides in this material. Finally, recent work on the structure of RNA indicates that it is much more similar to that of DNA than was believed a few years ago (Cohn, 1956; Zubay, 1958).

In conclusion, although it remains likely that RNA can only contribute to a small extent to DNA synthesis in developing eggs, the question is still in a fluid state. Experiments such as those of Reichard (1958) should be extended to more favourable embryological material, sea urchin eggs for instance. It certainly would be important to know whether enzymatic systems for the conversion of ribose compounds into deoxyribose compounds already exist in early embryonic stages. Until such experiments, as well as further studies with isotopes, are performed, the question of a possible RNA into DNA conversion remains unsolved. The fact that, as recently as 1957, Pelc has come to the conclusion that a RNA into DNA conversion is the most probable and simple explanation for his autoradiography studies on spermatogenesis clearly shows that the problem still deserves close scrutiny.

If we eliminate RNA as the major precursor of DNA in developing eggs, where can the latter originate? We are here met with two possibilities: nuclear DNA might simply come from a store of cytoplasmic DNA, which has been built up during oogenesis; or, alternatively, there might be a total and autonomous synthesis of DNA at the expense of such simple precursors as purine and pyrimidine bases, nucleosides and nucleotides. These two possibilities will now be discussed.

The idea that nuclear DNA originates from a reserve of cytoplasmic DNA is a revival of the old 'migration' theory of E. Godlewski (1918). He

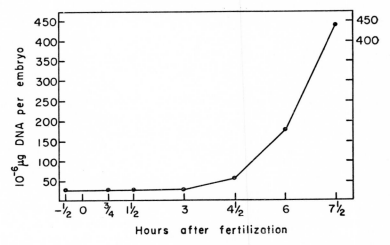

FIG. 45. DNA synthesis in sea urchin eggs during development (Hoff-Jørgensen, 1954).

believed that the 'nuclear substances' present in the germinal vesicle are given to the cytoplasm at maturation and that they are progressively taken back by the nuclei during cleavage. The migration theory cannot, despite the recent evidence in favour of a cytoplasmic DNA store, which will soon be discussed, be retained as such. We have already seen, in Chapter I, that the germinal vesicle, in general, does not contain more than the expected amount of DNA (i.e. four times the DNA content of a spermatozoon).

Recent biochemical studies, especially those of Hoff-Jørgensen (1954), strongly suggest that many eggs contain a large cytoplasmic DNA reserve: the method used by Hoff-Jørgensen (1954) is a microbiological one, based on the fact that deoxyribonucleotides are required for growth in a certain strain of *Thermobacterium acidophilus*. Hoff-Jørgensen's (1954) method certainly is the most specific technique now available for DNA estimation. However, it is difficult to decide whether the method is absolutely specific in the case of eggs, which contain very little DNA as compared to the enormous mass of reserve materials. With this reservation in mind about the *absolute* specificity of the microbiological assay method, we shall now consider the results obtained with the eggs of several species.

Beginning with sea urchin eggs, it can be said that they contain only a rather small reserve of DNA (Hoff-Jørgensen, 1954; Elson *et al.*, 1954; Agrell and Persson, 1956a). As shown in Fig. 45, the DNA content of the cleaving eggs does not increase measurably during the first 3 hours of development: at this time, the eggs have reached the 16-cell stage. According to the more recent study of Agrell and Persson (1956a), there are appreciable

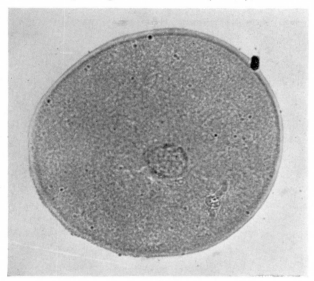

Fig. 46. Thin layer of Feulgen-positive material under nuclear membrane of unfertilized sea urchin egg (Brachet and Ficq, 1956).

differences according to the species of sea urchin which is under study: DNA synthesis begins, according to these workers, when synchronization of the mitoses during cleavage is lost; this corresponds to stage 32 or 400 blastomeres, depending on the species.

The situation, in the case of sea urchin eggs, is, however, considerably complicated by the results of Marshak and Marshak (1954, 1955a, b), who used a different technique for DNA-analysis (isotope dilution method). They came to the very unexpected conclusion that, if the presence of contaminating ovarian cells and polar bodies is taken into account, unfertilized sea urchin eggs contain no DNA at all and that, therefore, DNA cannot play any important genetic role. Marshak and Marshak (1955b) found further support for this revolutionary view in the fact that they could not detect any DNA with the Feulgen reaction in the nucleus of unfertilized sea urchin eggs. These negative results, which have been confirmed by Immers (1957), are probably due to faulty technique. Using better fixation and Feulgen staining techniques, Burgos (1955), Brachet and Ficq (1956) and Agrell (1958a, b) found that, in sea urchin eggs, a thin layer of DNA-containing granules is always present close under the nuclear membrane, in the female pronucleus (Fig. 46).

There is no doubt that Marshak and Marshak (1954, 1955) have gone too far in their conclusions and that their data are not sufficient to deny the otherwise well-established genetic role of DNA. On the other hand, their work has been very useful in drawing attention to the fact that unfertilized eggs can easily be contaminated with polar bodies, follicle cells and small fragments of ovaries. The values obtained by Hoff-Jørgensen (1954), Elson et al. (1954), Agrell and Persson (1956) for the DNA content of unfertilized sea urchin eggs must thus be considered, even if the method used is absolutely specific, as *maximal*. The very existence of a DNA reserve, which is only sufficient to reach the 16- or 32-cell stage, then becomes rather doubtful. In any event, such a reserve is insufficient to explain Abrams' (1951) results showing that 60–70 per cent of the DNA of the embryos comes from an unlabelled and unknown precursor. The result of this analysis of present experimental data indicates that, if sea urchin eggs contain a DNA reserve, it is an extremely small one, insufficient to allow prolonged nuclear DNA synthesis during cleavage.

The situation is very complex also in the case of frog eggs (Hoff-Jørgensen and Zeuthen, 1952; Hoff-Jørgensen, 1954): they contain, according to the Danish authors, a DNA reserve which is large enough for the production of about 5000 cells. DNA is present in the cytoplasm of the frog eggs, as shown by experiments in which the germinal vesicle of oocytes has been removed without reducing appreciably their DNA content. As a result of this large DNA cytoplasmic reserve in the unfertilized egg, there is no DNA synthesis until the late blastula stage, where DNA rapidly increases (Fig. 47). More recently, the question of cytoplasmic DNA in frog eggs has been re-examined by Finamore and Volkin (1958), who injected ^{32}P into females of *Rana catesbeiana* and studied the nucleotide composition of nuclear and cytoplasmic DNA's and RNA's, as well as their specific activities. The main conclusion is that, in the oocytes (which were studied before and after removal of the germinal vesicle), cytoplasmic DNA has twice the radioactivity of nuclear DNA, while cytoplasmic RNA is about three times less radioactive than is nuclear RNA. No significant differences in nucleotide composition could be found between ovarian or liver DNA's and RNA's. Finally, Bieber et al. (1959) have followed pentose, deoxypentose and DNA (the latter with the microbiological method) during oogenesis in the frog; their main conclusion is in general agreement with those of Hoff-Jørgensen and Zuethen (1952): mature oocytes contain enough DNA for the production of 4000 to 25,000 diploid cells, according to their physiological conditions.

However, it is difficult to draw definite conclusions from these results, because too much depends on the specificity of the methods used: exact estimation of traces of DNA in the presence of enormous quantities of yolk remains an almost impossible task. As one might expect, the more specific the method used, the smaller the amount of DNA found in frog eggs: for instance, Sze (1953), who estimated DNA phosphorus, and the

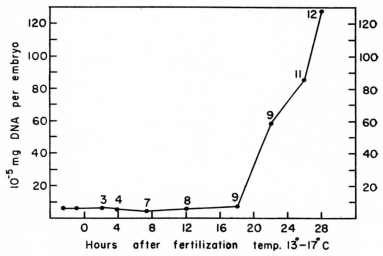

FIG. 47. DNA synthesis in developing frog eggs (Hoff-Jørgensen, 1954).

author (1954), who used a colorimetric method for deoxyribose, found much larger amounts of DNA in unfertilized frog eggs than did Hoff-Jørgensen (1954) with his more specific microbiological technique. Finamore and Volkin (1958) have tried to use as good a method as possible: but ^{32}P is a very dangerous precursor to use in oocytes which contain enormous amounts of phosphoproteins and phospholipids. Their results must be viewed with caution until the experiments are repeated with a more specific precursor for DNA, thymidine for instance. It should be added that still unpublished autoradiography experiments by A. Ficq have, so far, completely failed to demonstrate any uptake of thymidine in amphibian oocytes: both the lampbrush chromosomes and the cytoplasm remained completely unlabelled. The only ovarian cells to show strong incorporation of thymidine in their nuclei were follicle cells; although Finamore and Volkin (1958) have tried to remove follicle cells from the oocytes in their experiments, one may consider whether this has been

H

entirely successful until the cytological proof, which is still lacking, is presented. This last criticism is, however, not valid for the most recent experiments of Bieber *et al.* (1959), since part of their work was done on oocytes which had accumulated in the peritoneal cavity after ligation of the oviducts and stimulation of ovulation by injection of pituitary extracts. One wonders, however, why these authors have not studied a simpler and more physiological system, i.e. unfertilized eggs.

In hen eggs, which are of course richer in yolk and where the analytical

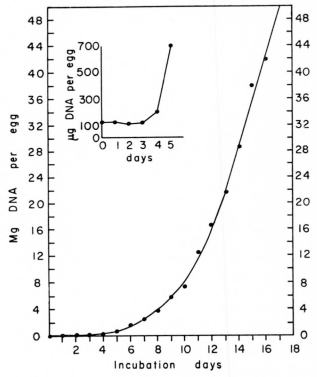

FIG. 48. DNA synthesis in chick embryo (Hoff-Jørgensen, 1954).

difficulties are therefore still greater, the 'DNA reserve' is still much larger (Hoff-Jørgensen, 1954; Solomon, 1957a): no DNA would be synthesized until the fourth day of development, when the embryo contains as much as 5×10^7 cells (Fig. 48). Such a conclusion is somewhat difficult to accept for embryologists, since primary morphogenesis is well over by that time: morphogenesis, of course, is impossible in the absence of cell divisions, which imply DNA synthesis. Furthermore, it is known from the work of Spratt (1949) that the chick blastoderm can grow and differentiate *in vitro* (thus in the absence of all yolk reserves) to a considerable extent.

The evidence for the existence of a cytoplasmic DNA reserve seems to be better in the case of insect eggs: both in *Drosophila* (Nigon and Daillie, 1958) and in *Gryllus* (Durand, 1955, 1958), relatively large amounts of DNA have been demonstrated in unfertilized eggs. The evidence presented by Durand (1955, 1958) seems to the present writer particularly convincing. He found, in a very carefully performed thymine isotope dilution experience, that the egg of *Gryllus* contains 1600 times more DNA than the spermatozoon. Furthermore, his last paper (1958) demonstrates that thymidine is incorporated in the cytoplasm of the growing oocyte and that a pretreatment with deoxyribonuclease abolishes the radioactivity. But, as already pointed out in Chapter I, insect eggs might well be a special case because of the frequent incorporation of DNA-rich follicle cells into the growing oocytes.

In view of the genetic importance of DNA, the question of the existence of cytoplasmic DNA deserves much more than casual interest. It is likely that geneticists, embryologists and biochemists will reserve judgement until DNA is isolated, in purified form, from unfertilized eggs, which cannot possibly be contaminated by nuclei from other cells.

But even if complete proof of the existence of cytoplasmic DNA is provided, other questions still remain to be answered: is cytoplasmic DNA the precursor of the DNA present in the cleaving nuclei? Or, alternately, are the cleaving eggs capable of synthesizing DNA at the expense of a pool of simpler precursors?

No clearcut answer can, for the time being, be given to these questions. There is no doubt, however, that eggs, already in the period of cleavage, are able to utilize precursors of small molecular weight for DNA synthesis. For instance, Solomon (1957b, c) has shown that both DNA and RNA can be synthesized by young explanted chick embryos. The rate of synthesis, when the embryos are cultivated on a simple synthetic medium is, however, slower than when they are left *in situ*, and can thus utilize the reserve materials accumulated in the yolk. It has also been established that simple precursors, such as CO_2, glycine or adenine, can be used for DNA synthesis in sea urchin, amphibian and young chicken embryos (Brachet and Ledoux, 1955; Grant, 1955, 1958; Tencer, 1958, Harding and Hughes, 1958). According to a personal communication of Dr. B. C. Moore, thymidine, which had been introduced in mature oocytes by injection into a female frog, is incorporated into the nuclei and the chromosomes, if the eggs were allowed to be fertilized and to undergo cleavage.

In conclusion, there is no doubt that eggs, even during early cleavage, can utilize small precursors such as CO_2, ^{32}P, glycine, adenine or thymidine for DNA synthesis. But such a capacity for autonomous and total DNA synthesis does not mean that other mechanisms, such as utilization of cytoplasmic DNA or breakdown products of RNA, do not also take place. Only new experiments, designed to test the relative importance of total synthesis, partial synthesis and utilization of a pre-existing store of cytoplasmic DNA, will give an answer to these old questions.

The fact that, according to Levenbook *et al.* (1958), unfertilized *Drosophila* eggs contain a great variety of free purines, pyrimidines, ribosides and deoxyribosides suggests that DNA synthesis occurs at the expense of this pool of soluble, low molecular weight substances. But, as we have seen, insect eggs might be a special case and similar work on other species is highly desirable. All that we know is that large amounts of free purines, especially hypoxanthine, are present in frog eggs (Steinert, 1952) and sea urchin eggs (Hultin, 1953); we also know that injected labelled hypoxanthine is efficiently utilized for nucleic acid synthesis in amphibian eggs (Steinert, 1955). These observations suggest that there might be nothing peculiar about DNA synthesis in eggs. This synthesis might take place at the expense of nucleoside phosphates and be mediated by an enzyme similar to that discovered in other cells by Kornberg *et al.* (1956). It certainly would be interesting to follow the activity of Kornberg *et al.*'s (1956) enzyme throughout embryonic development.

Finally, one would especially like to know whether the mechanism for DNA and gene reduplication proposed by Watson and Crick (1953) is operative in eggs, at the chromosomal level. The well-known double-strand model proposed by Watson and Crick (1953) gives an elegant answer to the hitherto formidable problem of chromosome and gene reduplication: the DNA molecule is supposed to be made of two polynucleotide chains, which are complementary regarding their base composition (adenine in one chain corresponding to thymine in the other, and guanine in one chain to cytosine in the other); all one has to postulate is the that two strands can separate from each other at the time of cell division; by a template mechanism, each of these strands could reproduce its counterpart.

This very attractive hypothesis of Watson and Crick (1953) is steadily gaining weight and there is little doubt that it comes very near to the truth. What remains, however, to be seen is whether it is still valid at the chromosomal level. Present evidence, in this respect, remains controversial. While Mazia and Plaut (1955) obtained, with autoradiography methods, results which are not easily explained by the Watson–Crick (1953) theory, Taylor *et al.* (1957) and Taylor (1958), using a similar technique, made observations which are in essential agreement with this theory. The work of Taylor *et al.* (1957) involved a colchicine treatment, which has been the object of recent criticisms by La Cour and Pelc (1958).

Since the problem is obviously not yet solved, it might be worth while to point out the obvious advantages of cleaving eggs as experimental material: autoradiography studies of cell division in eggs which contain one labelled pronucleus might provide very interesting evidence for or against the Watson–Crick (1953) theory.

(c) LINKS BETWEEN DNA SYNTHESIS AND ENERGY PRODUCTION

It has been reported by the author (Brachet, 1938) that a good correlation between oxygen consumption and DNA synthesis is found when normal and parthenogenetic embryos of *Chaetopterus* are compared. Parthenogenesis, in *Chaetopterus*, can be obtained by a treatment of the unfertilized eggs with 5 per cent isotonic KCl in sea water; the result is

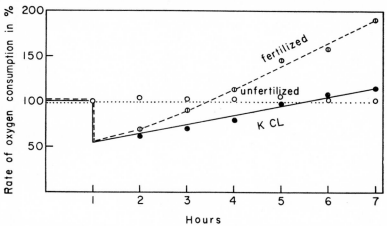

FIG. 49. Increase in oxygen consumption is slower in eggs differentiating without cleavage (KCl) than in fertilized controls; the same is true for DNA synthesis (Brachet, 1938).

the remarkable phenomenon described by F. R. Lillie (1902) as 'differentiation without cleavage': after the eggs have completed maturation, they start undergoing a series of monaster cycles. As a result, there is a considerable increase in the size of the nucleus and in the number of the chromosomes. Finally, the big single nucleus breaks down and processes comparable to gastrulation occur; in best cases, unicellular ciliated eggs, resembling trochophores in certain respects, can even be obtained.

As shown in Fig. 49, the embryos which undergo differentiation without cleavage have a slower increase in oxygen consumption than normal controls; chemical estimations of the DNA content showed that the DNA synthesized in the 8 hours during differentiation without cleavage amounts to only 30 per cent of the quantity produced in the fertilized eggs during the same period.

In similar work, done on different material, Comita and Whiteley (1953) obtained comparable results and were the first to suggest the existence of a correlation between DNA synthesis and respiratory metabolism. In a comparative study of DNA synthesis and oxygen consumption of diploid, haploid and early lethal frog embryos, a satisfactory correlation between the two phenomena was also found (Brachet, 1954). It might be added that isolated polar lobes of fertilized invertebrate eggs, which have no nucleus and therefore synthesize no DNA, have a constant respiratory level, while isolated blastomeres from the same eggs, which undergo repeated cleavage, show a definite increase in respiration (Berg and Kutsky, 1951).

Similar ideas to those of Comita and Whiteley (1953) have been presented, quite independently, by Zeuthen (1953), who pointed out that the increase in oxygen consumption, which he found to occur during interphase in cleaving sea urchin eggs, might be linked to concomitant DNA synthesis.

These observations all suggest the interesting possibility that DNA synthesis and energy production are closely linked phenomena; further studies, in which attempts to dissociate the two phenomena are made, are of course required before a definite conclusion can be drawn.

3. The importance of nucleic acids and proteins in cleavage

Although very many—if not all—of the chemical constituents of the cell may play a role in mitosis, we shall restrict ourselves to a short analysis of those which seem to be the most important because they enter into the composition of the mitotic apparatus: these are DNA, RNA and proteins, especially the sulphur-containing proteins.

(a) DNA

Enough already has been said concerning DNA synthesis during cleavage that any addition would be repetitious. One might perhaps mention, however, that cleaving eggs, as all actively dividing cells, are very sensitive to the many physical and chemical agents which affect the structural integrity and the synthesis of DNA, and which thus induce mutations (X-rays, U.V.-radiation, nitrogen mustards, heat shocks, etc.).

(b) RNA

The most direct evidence we have for the view that RNA plays a direct role in egg cleavage comes from experiments in which ribonuclease (RNase) was introduced into amphibian eggs (Thomas et al., 1946; Ledoux et al., 1954; Brachet and Ledoux, 1955). When they are in the morula stage, simple immersion of the eggs in a RNase-containing solution (0·5–1 mg/ml) is enough to produce a very rapid inhibition of cleavage. As shown in Fig. 50, mitotic activity is completely blocked in the blastomeres which form the outer layer: the nuclei, which are usually arrested in interphase, swell considerably in this region. When the enzyme has penetrated at the time the blastomere is actually dividing, the mitotic apparatus quickly disintegrates: the asters and the spindle fade away. When the injury is not too severe, as is the case for blastomeres which lie deeper inside the morula, distortion of the spindle and pluricentric mitoses are found: as a result, such cytological abnormalities as polyploidy, aneuploidy, chromosome elimination or amitotic breakdown of the nuclei are observed. Cytological and cytochemical studies show that the main action of ribonuclease is probably not on DNA synthesis, but on cytoplasmic processes in which RNA is involved at early prophase. According to all probabilities, it is the duplication of the centrosomes or the formation of

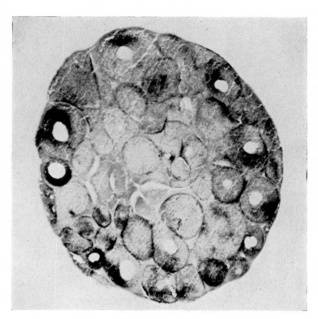

FIG. 50. Swollen interphase nuclei in ribonuclease-treated amphibian morula (Brachet and Ledoux, 1955).

the asters which is first hit when amphibian morulae are treated with RNase. It certainly would be interesting to know whether similar observations could be made with eggs of other species; one also would like to have experimental proof, by spectrophotometric measurements of the DNA content of individual nuclei, that RNase does not interfere with DNA synthesis in eggs as well as in other cells (Chèvremont et al., 1956). For if so, the experiments would suggest that the 'trigger' for cell division, during cleavage, is not DNA synthesis, but some cytoplasmic event for which the integrity of RNA is required.

It is a possibility that other substances which inhibit cleavage also act on RNA or its synthesis: this might be the case for substances like oestradiol, testosterone and stilboestrol, which stop cleavage in sea urchin, amphibian and hen eggs (Agrell, 1954, 1955; Agrell and Persson, 1956b; Rickenbacher, 1956; Colombo, 1956). According to the cytochemical studies of Rickenbacher (1956), who worked with chick embryos, stilboestrol exerts a definite inhibitory action on RNA synthesis. One would, of course, like to see such a conclusion substantiated by more quantitative work: chemical estimations of the RNA content, as well as studies on the incorporation of labelled precursors. Autoradiography might, once more, prove to be a useful tool, since it might perhaps allow a comparison between the metabolic activity of the RNA present in the mitotic apparatus with that of the rest of the RNA.

(c) —SH-containing Compounds

L. Rapkine presented, in 1931, the very attractive hypothesis that a *reversible denaturation of proteins* might be a fundamental process in mitosis. Such a denaturation would be accompanied by an increase in —SH groups bound to proteins and would precede cell division. In Rapkine's (1931) hypothesis, soluble —S-S— compounds (oxidized glutathione, for instance) would oxidize the free —SH groups of the proteins and vice versa: there would thus be cyclic changes in the acid soluble —SH groups during mitosis, correlated with complementary and opposite changes in the —SH content of the egg proteins.

Such an hypothesis of reversible denaturation of proteins explains a number of well-known facts about cell division: for instance, increase in viscosity at the time of aster gelation might be due to denaturation and partial insolubilization of the proteins which form the mitotic apparatus. Since denaturation of a globular protein involves a change towards a more fibrous state, the existence of astral and spindle fibres is easy to understand if one assumes that the proteins of the mitotic apparatus are in a reversibly denatured state. The reversibility of the denaturation process also easily explains the disappearance of the mitotic apparatus at telophase and the migration of the chromosomes towards the poles: folding of the proteins, which were in the denatured fibrous state during metaphase, could, at anaphase and telophase, pull the chromosomes from the equator towards the asters.

Furthermore, Rapkine (1931, 1936) was the first to point out that there must be a link between carbohydrate metabolism and mitosis, because glycolysis is very sensitive to specific poisons of —SH groups. He particularly insisted on the necessity of —SH groups for normal functioning of such important enzymes as glyceraldehyde phosphate dehydrogenase and succinic dehydrogenase; there is no doubt now that carbohydrate metabolism is important for cell division and we have already seen that, according to Barnett (1953), malonate (which is a specific competitive inhibitor of succinic dehydrogenase) is a powerful inhibitor of cleavage in sea urchin eggs. The fact that malonate inhibition can be lifted by the addition of succinate and fumarate—which are the normal substrates for succinic dehydrogenase—gives very good proof for a direct intervention of the enzyme in cleavage.

The experimental evidence brought forward by Rapkine (1931, 1936) has followed two different lines: first, he found, in 1931, cyclical changes in the content of free —SH groups during cleavage of sea urchins; second, he demonstrated (1936) that treatment of dividing cells with —SH inhibitors such as $HgCl_2$ or monoiodacetic acid inhibits mitosis; the inhibition, in the case of sublimate, can be reversed by the addition of an —SH-containing substance (cysteine, for instance), but not by simple washing (Fig. 51).

We shall now consider the present, still controversial, status of the

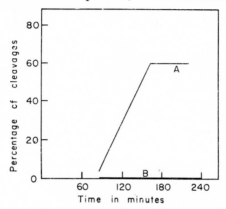

FIG. 51: Cleavage of sea urchin eggs treated with $HgCl_2$ after fertilization; (A) sea water + cysteine; (B) pure sea water (Rapkine, 1931)

evidence for and against Rapkine's theory. We have already seen that recent cytochemical work by Kawamura and Dan (1958) has shown that, in sea urchin eggs as well as in amphibian eggs (Brachet, 1940), the mitotic apparatus gives strong —SH reactions after fixation. But, since fixation produces protein denaturation and even coagulation, these experiments tell us nothing about the presence of free —SH groups in the *living* sea urchin eggs. The work of Kawamura and Dan (1958) certainly deserves to be repeated on material fixed in a gentler way—freeze-drying or freeze-substitution particularly.

Coming now to the question of possible changes in the soluble —SH groups (reduced glutathione, for instance) during the mitotic cycle, no precise answer can be given for the time being. While Rapkine's results have been largely corroborated by Stern (1958), who worked on the anthers of *Lilium* and *Trillium* and found a rise in soluble —SH groups before mitosis, followed by a decrease during division itself, recent work by

Neufeld and Mazia (1958) shows that, in contradiction to Rapkine's (1931) experimental data, there are no appreciable changes in soluble —SH during the cleavage cycle in sea urchin eggs.

A very recent paper by Sakai and Dan (1959) helps considerably in solving this contradiction: they found, in agreement with Rapkine (1936), cyclical changes in the —SH content of trichloracetic acid extracts of cleaving sea urchin eggs; but these changes are not due to either reduced or oxidized glutathione, which remain constant during cleavage: what is fluctuating, according to the Japanese authors, is a protein-bound form of —SH.

If we now consider the problem of the inhibition of cleavage by —SH reagents, there is no doubt that Rapkine's (1931, 1936) findings on the effects of sublimate and monoiodacetic acid have been completely confirmed by many workers: for instance, we found (Brachet, 1944) that specific —SH inhibitors, such as monoiodacetamide and chloropicrine, inhibit cleavage and destroy the mitotic apparatus in amphibian eggs. Another —SH reagent, chloroacetophenone, leads to the formation of giant, heteroploid nuclei, according to Beatty (1951). There is no doubt that, in this case again, the main action of the inhibitor is on the spindle. Another specific inhibitor of —SH groups, p-chloromercuribenzoic acid has been studied in detail by L. J. Barth (1956), who again worked with amphibian eggs: she obtained specific inhibition of cleavage at the animal pole and found that the addition of —SH-containing substances, thioglycollate or cysteine for instance, reverses the effect of the inhibitors. In sea urchin eggs also, p-chloromercuribenzoic acid inhibits mitosis (Wilson and Heilbrunn, 1957) and destroys gel structure. Finally, we have already seen earlier in this chapter that the —SH-containing substance, β-mercaptoethanol, inhibits mitosis (Mazia, 1958; Brachet and Delange-Cornil, 1959). Since cleavage is stopped by both mercaptoethanol—which keeps the —SH protein groups in the reduced form—and by —SH inhibitors such as sublimate, p-chloromercuribenzoic acid, iodacetamide, chloropicrine, etc.—which effectively block the oxidation of —SH groups —there is little doubt that, as Rapkine (1931) has so clearly foreseen, reversible oxidation of —SH protein groups is an essential process during mitosis.

Reversible denaturation of proteins has also been advocated to explain the contraction of muscle; although, as pointed out by Mazia (1956), analogies between muscle contraction and cell division should not be pushed too far, it is a striking fact that ATP is required for both processes.* We have already mentioned the work of Barnett (1953) and of Brachet (1954), indicating that normal ATP production is required for cleavage in

---

* In fact, Holtzer et al. (1959) were unable to detect any myosin in the mitotic apparatus by cytochemical methods.

both sea urchin and amphibian eggs; according to a more recent analysis of the question by Marsland (1956) and Zimmerman *et al.* (1957), cleavage, in sea urchin eggs, results from the contraction of the plasmagel; the energy required for such a contraction results from the hydrolytic break-down of ATP. These observations lead us to the last problem to be discussed here: the mechanisms of furrow formation.

4. The formation of the furrow during cleavage

In this discussion, we shall follow a recent and excellent review by Swann and Mitchison (1958) on the mechanisms of furrow formation during egg cleavage. According to these authors, who have greatly contributed experimentally to the question, no less than six different theories have been proposed in order to explain cleavage in animal cells. All but one (the so-called 'amoeboid movement theory') of these theories are based on studies of cleavage in eggs, especially sea urchin eggs.

Two of these theories, the 'astral growth theory' and the 'spindle elongation theory' depend on enlargement of the mitotic apparatus. In the astral growth theory, asters force the cell to elongate as they increase in size and draw the cell surface round themselves, thus forming the cleavage furrow. In the spindle elongation theory, it is supposed that aster rays attach themselves to the cell surface; as a result of an elongation of the spindle, the equatorial surface is pulled inwards in order to make the furrow.

These two theories are dismissed by Swann and Mitchison (1958) on the ground that it is now well established that cells will cleave in the absence of the mitotic apparatus, provided that the early anaphase stage has been reached. There is no doubt that sea urchin eggs have been found capable of cleavage after removal of the asters with a micropipette (Hiramoto, 1956) or after their destruction by stirring with a microneedle (Chambers, 1938; Mitchison, 1953). But it is not certain that the situation is exactly the same in larger eggs, such as those of Amphibians: as mentioned earlier, phenyl-urethane inhibits furrow formation without affecting nuclear division (Brachet, 1934). This narcotic has no effect on the mitotic apparatus itself, but it completely inhibits the gelation of the cytoplasm which surrounds the asters. The suppression of periasterial gelation, in amphibian eggs, is sufficient to suppress cleavage.

The other theories discussed by Swann and Mitchison (1958) consider that cleavage results from activity on the part of the cell surface. In the 'cortical gel contraction theory', it is assumed that an equatorial band of jellied cortex contracts and divides the cell in two. The main objection to this rather popular theory, which is still accepted by Hiramoto (1958), is that the constriction undergone by the ring is tremendous, being greater than the shortening of a contracting muscle.

The favourite theory of Swann and Mitchison (1958) is of course their own: it is the 'expanding membrane theory' which postulates an active expansion at the poles of the cell, which would spread towards the equator and push the furrow inwards.

The 'growth theory' implies the formation of an entirely new cell wall in the furrow region: it certainly corresponds to something real in amphibian eggs (Schechtman, 1937; Selman and Waddington, 1955) where cell division is linked to localized cell growth. But it is very doubtful that the theory is valid for sea urchin eggs as well, since the furrow region does not increase in area in this case.

Finally the 'amoeboid movement theory' depends on the formation of pseudopodia at either pole of the dividing cell, with amoeboid movement in opposite directions and, finally, cell division as a result. As pointed out by Swann and Mitchison (1958), this theory becomes very similar to that of the 'expanding membrane hypothesis', if polar expansion be equated to polar pseudopodia formation.

Swann and Mitchison (1958) conclude their analysis in an attempt to outline a general theory of cleavage; the assumption should be made that 'daughter chromosome groups initiate molecular changes in the cell surface, leading to active expansion (as a result of disorientation) and growth (by intake)'. The relative importance of the two processes varies in different cells, and there is no doubt that the authors are right when they point out that mechanisms for furrow formation might be very different in amphibian and sea urchin eggs.

What seems to be more doubtful is the importance ascribed to chromosomes by Swann and Mitchison (1958) in their general theory. As we have seen, repeated cleavage is possible in the total absence of nuclei and it is impossible, in such cases, to imagine that active expansion and growth can be initiated by the chromosomes.

It is probable that the real situation is, in fact, extremely complex: it should not be forgotten, for instance, that, according to Pasteels and Mulnard (1957), Pasteels (1959) and Rebhun (1958), metachromatic granules or vacuoles, which perhaps are similar to lysosomes or Golgi elements, migrate into the asters during several cleavages in sea urchin eggs. This is probably more than a coincidence since, as shown recently by Marsland and Auclair (1958), external pressure applied on sea urchin eggs induces cleavages as soon as these metachromatic vacuoles break down.

Once again, more work is needed to solve present difficulties; but, one should not forget, in attempting to present a theory of furrow formation, the fact that ATP certainly plays a role in the process (Marsland, 1956; Wolpert, 1958). In view of the prominent part played by ATP in muscle contraction and the fact that the plasmagel, in many cells, has contractile properties, one cannot eliminate the possibility that plasmagel contraction might co-operate with membrane expansion and growth in order to insure egg cleavage.

REFERENCES

ABRAMS, R. (1951): *Exp. Cell Res.* **2**, 235.
AGRELL, I. (1954): *Nature* **173**, 172.
AGRELL, I. (1955): *C. R. Soc. Biol.* **149**, 1322, 1754.
AGRELL, I. and H. PERSSON. (1956a): *Nature* **178**, 1398.
AGRELL, I. and H. PERSSON. (1956b): *Biochim. biophys. Acta* **20**, 543.
AGRELL, I. (1958a): *Ark. Zool.* **11**, 29.
AGRELL, I. (1958b): *Ark Zool.* **12**, 7.
ASTRACHAN, L. and E. VOLKIN. (1958): *Biochim. biophys. Acta* **29**, 536.
BARNETT, B. C. (1953): *Biol. Bull.* **104**, 263.
BARTH, L. G. and L. J. JAEGER. (1947): *Physiol. Zool.* **20**, 135.
BARTH, L. J. (1956): *J. Embryol. exp. Morphol.* **4**, 73.
BATAILLON, E. (1910): *Roux' Arch. Entw. Mech.* **30**, 24.
BEATTY, R. A. (1951): *Proc. Roy. Soc.* B**138**, 575.
BEERMAN, W. (1959): In : *Biological Organisation*, Pergamon Press (in press).
BERGERARD, J. (1955): *C. R. Acad. Sci. Paris* **240**, 564.
BIEBER, S., J. A. SPENCE and G. H. HITCHINGS. (1959): *Exp. Cell Res.* **16**, 202.
BLOCH, D. P. and G. C. GODMAN. (1955): *J. biophys. biochem. Cytol.* **1**, 17.
BRACHET, J. (1933): *Arch. Biol.* **44**, 519.
BRACHET, J. (1934): *Arch. Biol.* **45**, 611.
BRACHET, J. (1938): *Biol. Bull.* **74**, 93.
BRACHET, J. (1940): *Arch. Biol.* **51**, 151.
BRACHET, J. (1942): *Arch. Biol.* **53**, 207.
BRACHET, J. (1944): *Embryologie chimique*. Desoer, Liège and Masson, Paris.
BRACHET, J. (1949): *Pubbl. Staz. zool. Napoli* **21**, 77.
BRACHET, J. (1954): *Arch. Biol.* **65**, 1.
BRACHET, J. (1957): *Biochemical Cytology*. Academic Press, N.Y.
BRACHET, J. and M. DELANGE-CORNIL. (1959): *Developmental Biology*, **1**, 19.
BRACHET, J. and A. FICQ. (1956): *Arch. Biol.* **67**, 431.
BRACHET, J. and L. LEDOUX. (1955): *Exp. Cell Res.*, suppl. **3**, 27.
BRIGGS R., E. H. GREEN and T. J. KING. (1951): *J. exp. Zool.* **116**, 455.
BURGOS, M. H. (1955): *Exp. Cell Res.* **9**, 360.
CHAMBERS, R. (1938): *J. cell. comp. Physiol.* **12**, 149.
CHÈVREMONT, M., S. CHÈVREMONT-COMHAIRE and H. FIRKET. (1956): *Arch. Biol.*
    67, 635.
CLOWES, G. H. A. and M. E. KRAHL. (1936): *J. gen. Physiol.* **20**, 145.
COHN, W. E. (1956): *Currents in Biochemical Research*, D. E. GREEN, ed., p. 460,
    Interscience Ltd., N.Y.
COLOMBO, G. (1956): *Caryologia* **9**, 56.
COMITA, J. J. and A. H. WHITELEY. (1953): *Biol. Bull.* **105**, 412.
COSTELLO, D. P. (1940): *J. Morphol.* **66**, 99.
DALCQ, A. and J. PASTEELS. (1955): *Exp. Cell Res.*, suppl. **3**, 72.
DALCQ, A. and S. SIMON. (1932): *Protoplasma* **14**, 497.
DAN, K. and T. NAKAJIMA. (1956): *Embryologia* **3**, 187.
DE HARVEN, E. and W. BERNHARD. (1956): *Z. Zellforschg.* **45**, 378.
DEVILLERS, CH. (1953).: *C. R. Acad. Sci. Paris* **237**, 1561.
DURAND, M. C. (1955): *C. R. Acad. Sci. Paris* **241**, 1340.
DURAND, M. C. (1958): *Exp. Cell Res.* **29**, 246
ELSON, D., T. GUSTAFSON and E. CHARGAFF. (1954): *J. biol. Chem.* **209**, 285.
FANKHAUSER, G. (1934): *J. exp. Zool.* **67**, 349.
FANKHAUSER, G. and D. GODWIN. (1948): *Proc. nat. Acad. Sci., Wash.* **34**, 544.

FAUTREZ, J. and N. FAUTREZ-FIRLEFYN. (1953): *Nature* **172**, 119.
FAUTREZ-FIRLEFYN, N. (1957): *Arch. Biol.* **68**, 249.
FINAMORE, J. and E. VOLKIN. (1958): *Exp. Cell Res.* **15**, 405.
FUJII, T. (1954): *Nature* **174**, 1108.
GAULDEN, N. E. and R. P. PERRY. (1958): *Proc. nat. Acad. Sci., Wash.* **44**, 553.
GIUDICE, G. (1958): *Acta Embryol. Morphol. exp.* **2**, 88.
GLÜCKSMANN, A. (1951): *Biol. Rev.* **26**, 59.
GODLEWSKI, E. (1918): *Roux' Arch. Entw. Mech.* **44**, 499.
GRANT, P. (1955): *Biol. Bull.* **199**, 543.
GRANT, P. (1958): *J. Cell comp. Physiol.* **52**, 227, 249.
GROSS, P. R. (1959): *Fed. Proc.* **18**, 60.
GURDON, J. B., T. R. ELSDALE and M. FISCHBERG. (1958): *Nature* **182**, 64
HARDING, C. V. and W. L. HUGHES. (1958): *Biol. Bull.* **115**, 372.
HARVEY, E. B. (1933): *Biol. Bull.* **64**, 125.
HARVEY, E. B. (1936): *Biol. Bull.* **71**, 101.
HIRAMOTO, Y. (1956): *Exp. Cell Res.* **11**, 630.
HIRAMOTO, Y. (1958): *J. exp. Biol.* **35**, 407.
HOFF-JØRGENSEN, E. (1954): *Colston Papers* **7**, 79.
HOFF-JØRGENSEN, E. and E. ZEUTHEN. (1952): *Nature* **169**, 245.
HOLTER, H. and E. ZEUTHEN. (1957): *Pubbl. Staz. zool. Napoli* **29**, 585.
HOLTZER, H., J. ABBOTT and M. W. CAVANAUGH (1959): *Exp. Cell Res.* **16**, 595.
HULTIN, T. (1953): *Arkiv Kemi* **6**, 195.
IMMERS, J. (1957): *Exp. Cell Res.* **12**, 145.
INOUÉ, S. (1952): *Exp. Cell Res.*, suppl. **2**, 305.
JACOBSON, W. and M. WEBB. (1952): *Exp. Cell Res.* **3**, 163.
KAWAMURA, N. and K. DAN. (1958): *J. biophys. biochem. Cytol.* **4**, 615.
KORNBERG, A. *et al.* (1956): *Biochim. biophys. Acta* **21**, 197.
LA COUR, L. F. and S. R. PELC. (1958): *Nature* **182**, 506.
LEDOUX, L., J. LE CLERC and J. BRACHET. (1955): *Exp. Cell Res.* **9**, 338.
LEHMANN, F. E. (1959): *Exp. Cell Res.*, suppl. **6**, 1.
LEHMANN, F. E. and V. MANCUSO. (1957): *Exp. Cell Res.* **13**, 161.
LEHMANN, F. E. and V. MANCUSO. (1958): *Rev. Suisse Zool.* **65**, 360.
LEVENBOOK, L., E. C. TRAVAGLINI and J. SCHULTZ. (1958): *Exp. Cell Res.* **15**, 43.
LILLIE, F. R. (1902): *Roux' Arch. Entw. Mech.* **14**, 477.
LOEB, M. R. and S. S. COHEN. (1959): *J. biol. Chem.* **234**, 360.
LORCH, I. J. (1952): *Quart. J. microsc. Sci.* **93**, 475.
MARSHAK, A. and C. MARSHAK. (1954): *Nature* **174**, 919.
MARSHAK, A. and C. MARSHAK. (1955a): *J. biophys. biochem. Cytol.* **1**, 167.
MARSHAK, A. and C. MARSHAK. (1955b): *Exp. Cell Res.* **8**, 126.
MARSLAND, D. (1956): *Pubbl. Staz. zool. Napoli* **28**, 184.
MARSLAND, D. and W. AUCLAIR. (1958): *Biol. Bull.* **115**, 356.
MAZIA, D. (1954): *Proc. nat. Acad. Sci., Wash.* **40**, 521.
MAZIA, D. (1955): *Sympos. Soc. exp. Biol.* **9**, 335.
MAZIA, D. (1956): *Advanc. biol. med. Physics* **4**, 70.
MAZIA, D. (1958): *Exp. Cell Res.* **14**, 484.
MAZIA, D. and K. DAN. (1952): *Proc. nat. Acad. Sci., Wash.* **38**, 826
MAZIA, D. and W. S. PLAUT. (1955): *Biol. Bull.* **100**, 335.
MAZIA, D. and A. M. ZIMMERMAN. (1958): *Exp. Cell Res.* **15**, 138.
MCNUTT JR., W. S. (1958): *J. biol. Chem.* **233**, 189, 193.
MERCER, E. H. and L. WOLPERT. (1958): *Exp. Cell Res.* **14**, 629.
MITCHISON, J. M. (1953): *J. exp. Biol.* **30**, 515.
MIURA, Y., T. FUJII and T. MIZUNO. (1957): *C. R. Soc. Biol.* **151**. 1460.

CLEAVAGE

NEUFELD, E. J. and D. MAZIA. (1957): *Exp. Cell Res.* **13**, 622.
NIGON, V. and J. DAILLIE. (1958): *Biochim. biophys. Acta* **15**, 257
PASTEELS, J. J. (1959) : *Arch. Biol.* **69**, 591.
PASTEELS, J. and L. LISON. (1951): *Nature* **167**, 984.
PASTEELS, J. and J. MULNARD. (1957): *Arch. Biol.* **68**, 115
PELC, S. R. (1957): *Exp. Cell Res.* **12**, 320.
RAPKINE, L. (1931): *Ann. Physiol.* **7**, 382.
RAPKINE, L. (1936): *J. Chim. phys.* **33**, 492.
REBHUN, L. (1958): *Biol. Bull.* **115**, 235.
REICHARD, P. (1958): *Biochim. biophys. Acta* **27**, 344.
REICHARD, P. (1959): *J. biol. Chem.* **234**, 1244.
RICKENBACHER, J. (1956): *Z. Zellforschg.* **45**, 339.
ROELS, H. (1954): *Nature* **173**, 1039.
RUNNSTRÖM, J. (1930): *Protoplasma* **10**, 106.
RUNNSTRÖM, J. and G. KRISZAT. (1950): *Exp. Cell Res.* **1**, 497.
SAKAI, H. and K. DAN. (1959): *Exp. Cell Res.* **16**, 24.
SCARANO, E. and H. M. KALCKAR. (1953): *Pubbl. Staz. zool. Napoli* **24**, 188.
SCHECHTMAN, A. M. (1937): *Science* **85**, 222.
SCHOLANDER, P. F. *et al.* (1952): *Biol. Bull.* **102**, 185.
SCHOLANDER, P. F., H. LEIVESTED and G. SUNDNES. (1958): *Biol. Bull.* **115**, 505.
SELMAN, G. G. and C. H. WADDINGTON. (1955): *J. exp. Biol.* **32**, 700.
SOLOMON, J. B. (1957a): *Biochim. biophys. Acta* **23**, 211.
SOLOMON, J. B. (1957b): *Biochim. biophys. Acta* **24**, 584.
SOLOMON, J. B. (1957c): *Biochim. biophys. Acta* **25**, 69.
STEINERT, M. (1952): *Bull. Soc. Chim. Biol.* **34**, 923.
STEINERT, M. (1955): *Biochim. biophys. Acta* **18**, 511.
STERN, H. (1958): *J. biophys. biochem. Cytol.* **4**, 157.
STICH, H. (1954): *Chromosoma* **6**, 199.
STICH, H. and J. MCINTYRE. (1958): *Exp. Cell Res.* **14**, 635.
SWANN, M. M. (1953): *Quart. J. microsc. Sci.* **94**, 369.
SWANN, M. M. (1954): *Exp. Cell Res.* **7**, 505.
SWANN, M. M. (1957): *Cancer Res.* **17**, 727.
SWANN, M. M. and J. M. MITCHISON. (1958): *Biol. Rev.* **33**, 103.
TAYLOR J. H. (1958): *Exp. Cell Res.* **15**, 350.
TAYLOR, J. H. *et al.* (1957): *Proc. nat. Acad. Sci., Wash.* **43**, 122.
TENCER, R. (1958): *J. Embryol. exp. Morphol.* **6**, 117.
THOMAS, A. J., J. ROSTAND, J. GRÉGOIRE. (1946): *C. R. Acad. Sci., Paris* **222**, 1139.
VILLEE, C. A., M. LOWENS, M. GORDON, E. LEONARD and A. RICH. (1949): *J. cell. comp. Physiol.* **33**, 93.
WACKER, A., S. KIRSCHFELD and L. TRÄGER. (1959): *Z. Naturforsch.* **14b**, 145.
WATSON, J. D. and H. F. CRICK. (1953): *Nature* **171**, 737, 964.
WENT, H. A. (1959): *J. biophys. biochem. Cytol.* **5**, 353.
WILSON, W. L. and L. V. HEILBRUNN. (1957): *Exp. Cell Res.* **13**, 234.
WOLPERT, L. (1958): *Nature* **181**, 716.
ZEUTHEN, E. (1946): *C. R. Trav. Lab. Carlsberg, Sér. Chim.* **25**, 33.
ZEUTHEN, E. (1950): *Biol. Bull.* **98**, 144, 150.
ZEUTHEN, E. (1935): *Arch. néerl. Zool.*, suppl. **1**, 31.
ZEUTHEN, E. (1955): *Biol. Bull.* **108**, 366.
ZIMMERMAN, A. M., J. V. LANDAU and D. MARSLAND. (1957): *J. cell. comp. Physiol* **49**, 395.
ZUBAY, G. (1958): *Nature* **182**, 1290

CHAPTER IV

Chemical Embryology of Invertebrate Eggs

THE experimental embryology of invertebrate eggs has long been dominated by the dogma that there are two, entirely different, types of eggs: those which are made of a *mosaic* of different plasms, corresponding to different 'germinal localizations' and those which are capable of *regulation*. In the latter, in sea urchin eggs for instance, each blastomere at the 2-cell stage gives a complete, but dwarf, pluteus larva: regulation is a regeneration of the missing part, but which occurs at an early stage, before its differentiation into typical tissues or organs (Driesch, 1891). On the other hand, removal of part of the egg results, in many Invertebrates, in the formation of abnormal larvae, in which certain organs are missing or underdeveloped: in such cases (for instance, the egg of the Mollusc *Dentalium* studied by E. B. Wilson in 1904), the egg is apparently a mosaic of territories, each of which will form a definite region of the larva. These territories have been called germinal localizations by the pioneers of experimental embryology.

More recent analysis (cf. Dalcq, 1941, 1957a) has shown that mosaic and regulative eggs should not be opposed to each other in a too categorical way: regulation is an attribute of all eggs, but its quantitative importance is very variable. There is complete regulation in sea urchin eggs at the 2- or 4-cell stage; but the capacity for regulation decreases afterwards, as shown by the famous experiments of Hörstadius (1939) which demonstrated that cells isolated from either the animal or the vegetal pole can no longer give a normal pluteus larva. On the other hand, even in the mosaic eggs of Worms, Molluscs and Ascidians, a certain amount of regulation can be detected in isolated parts. Dalcq (1957a) is undoubtedly right when he insists on the fact that the apparently opposite results obtained, after separation of the two first blastomeres in different species, have no great theoretical significance. Regulation is found, in such experiments, in the eggs of *Amphioxus* and Urodeles, but not in those of Tunicates or Anurans; nevertheless, there is no doubt that developmental processes are essentially the same in *Amphioxus* and Tunicates, as well as in Urodeles and Anurans.

The recent development of cytochemical methods has prompted a number of leading experimental embryologists (Dalcq, Lehmann, Raven, Reverberi and many others) to study the distribution of the substances that

112

can be detected with these methods in both 'mosaic' and 'regulative' eggs. Unequal distribution of chemical substances in different 'plasms', which have different localization and morphogenetic significance, has been recently described in both mosaic and regulative eggs; curiously enough, these substances are almost always linked to mitochondria. For the time being, chemical embryology of invertebrate eggs is thus essentially a study of the distribution of mitochondria and the enzymes they contain. Similar studies have already been done long before we knew that mitochondria contain, in a specific way, important respiratory enzymes (cytochrome oxidase and succinic dehydrogenase, especially). For instance, the distribution of mitochondria, with classical staining methods, has been studied long ago by Meves (1913), Duesberg (1926) and Conklin (1931) in ascidian eggs; the granules they studied have probably no great morphogenetic importance, since they can be displaced by centrifugation without serious interference with morphogenesis (Conklin, 1931). More interesting results have since been obtained by the detection of respiratory enzymes with the indophenoloxidase reaction (Nadi reaction) or Janus Green staining. One can hardly escape the conclusion that invertebrate eggs, those of Ascidians for instance, contain two kinds of 'mitochondria': osmiophilic granules, which have apparently little or no morphogenetic significance, and 'true' mitochondria, which play a leading role in oxidative phosphorylations, i.e. in energy production; the latter seem to be important for normal development (Reverberi, 1957). It is obvious for anyone who has looked at living invertebrate eggs under the microscope that they are filled with many granules, which resemble each other very much in size and shape. Unless cytochemical tests or electron microscopy are applied to these eggs, it is impossible to decide whether one is dealing with mitochondria or other indifferent granules. A good deal of confusion has arisen from this difficulty; there is no doubt that this confusion will ultimately be resolved by more extensive use of the electron microscope.

The story which will now be told is thus a story of mitochondrial segregation during embryonic development; although it will lead to the conclusion that such a segregation of mitochondria is an important factor in morphogenesis for Invertebrates, it might be dangerous to conclude that it is the only one. More work should be done on localization of other cell organelles in normal and centrifuged eggs before one can conclude that morphogenesis, in Invertebrates, is essentially regulated by unequal distribution of the mitochondria.

The limited scope of the present book does not allow a full treatment of the chemical embryology of invertebrate eggs and all we shall do is to examine a few typical examples. A much more detailed analysis of the eggs of the Molluscs will be found in a recent book by Raven (1958), who has so much contributed himself to the experimental and cytochemical study of

I

development in *Limnaea*. Important reviews have recently been published by Reverberi (1957 a) on the ascidian eggs, Lehmann (1956) on those of *Tubifex*, Shaver (1957) and Ranzi (1957 a, b) on those of the sea urchins.

1. Ctenophores

While the eggs of the Hydroid *Amphisbetia operculata* show an unusually high capacity of regulation even in the blastula stage (Teissier, 1931), morphogenetic plasms or substances are apparently present in those of Ctenophores, such as *Eucharis* or *Beroë*. In the latter, Spek (1926) described a cortical plasm which displays a green fluorescence and seems to

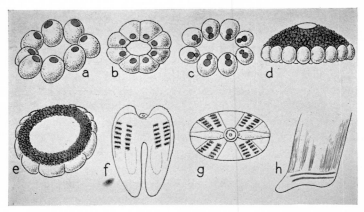

Fig. 52. Distribution of mitochondria (Janus Green staining) in *Beroë* embryos. *a*: beginning of fourth cleavage; *b*: 16-cell stage; *c*: 24-cell stage; *d, e*: epibolic gastrulae; *f, g*: larvae, side and upper view; *h*: comb plate, isolated from an adult animal (after Reverberi, 1957b).

play a role in morphogenesis (formation of the comb plates). In the closely related species *Eucharis*, peroxidases have the same localization as this green pigment, at least in the larval stage (Reverberi and Pitotti, 1940). More recent work by Reverberi (1957 b) has shown that, in *Beroë*, the cortical plasm containing the green pigment of Spek (1926) is largely formed of mitochondria: typical mitochondrial enzymes such as cytochrome oxidase and succinic dehydrogenase can be detected cytochemically in this part of the egg. During cleavage, as shown in Fig. 52, there is an unequal distribution of the mitochondria in the various blastomeres; these cell organelles are segregated very early in the stem cells of the ciliary plates, where they might provide energy for differentiation of these plates and later for the movements of the cilia.

2. Worms

By far the most important work, in the case of Worms, is that which has been done on *Tubifex*. Experimental studies by Penners (1938), who destroyed various blastomeres with U.V. rays, has shown the great importance, for morphogenesis, of the ectodermic and mesodermic 'somatoblasts" which respectively form the ectoderm and the mesoderm of the germ band. Cytochemical (1941) and electron microscopal (1956, 1958) observation, by F. E. Lehmann have considerably contributed towards an understanding of the biochemical mechanisms underlying morphogenesis in *Tubifex*.

Here are the main results obtained by Lehmann (1956, 1958) and his co-workers (Lehmann and Mancuso, 1957, Weber, 1956, 1958): indophenoloxidase (i.e. cytochrome oxidase, according to all probabilities) is diffuse in unfertilized eggs; after maturation, this enzyme, which is associated with the mitochondria, becomes accumulated in the polar plasm, which has great morphogenetic importance, as shown by centrifugation experiments. In later stages, the cytochrome oxidase-containing granules (mitochondria) accumulate in the C-D blastomere, and then in the micromeres and the D blastomere (Fig. 53). During further cleavage, the all-important 2d and 4d blastomeres (which will give rise to the ectoderm and the mesoderm of the germ band) are particularly rich in material which yields a positive indophenoloxidase reaction.

Quantitative studies of Weber (1958) have largely confirmed the cytochemical observations made on *Tubifex* embryos: he found that the cells which give a positive indophenoloxidase reaction (somatoblasts) contain three times more cytochrome oxidase than the macromeres. The latter, on the other hand, contain much more cathepsin than the ectoblastic and mesoblastic somatoblasts. It should be noted that the difference between the animal and the vegetal halves of the embryo is of a *quantitative* nature only. Weber (1958) also found that the oxygen consumption of the embryos increases 20 times during development, without any appreciable increase of the cytochrome oxidase content; we shall see later that similar observations have been made in the case of frog eggs.

The results of the electron microscope studies of Lehmann (1957, 1958) and Lehmann and Mancuso (1957) are summarized in the following table, in which the most important blastomeres (2d, 4d and 4D) are described from the viewpoint of the relative development of endoplasmic reticulum (ergastoplasm), mitochondria, yolk platelets and lipid droplets:

	2d	4d	4D
Ergastoplasm	+++	+++	+
Mitochondria	++	++++	++
Yolk	+	++	+++
Lipids	+	++++	+

It will be noticed that the 4d blastomere, which gives rise to the mesoderm of the embryo and which, according to the work of Penners (1938) has the greatest morphogenetic importance, is especially rich in mito-chondria and ergastoplasm. It is thus to be expected that both energy production and protein synthesis (which are the functions, respectively, of mitochondria and ergastoplasm) are particularly intense in this region of the morula. It should, however, be pointed out that there is no *specific*

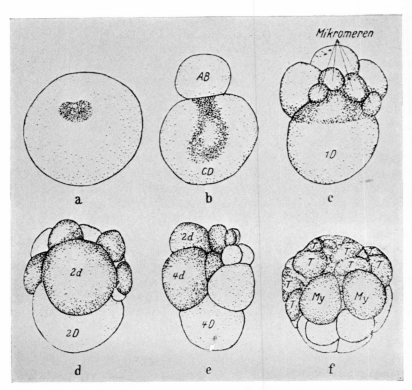

Fig. 53. Distribution of mitochondria (indophenoloxidase) during development of *Tubifex* eggs. *a*: stage 1, with polar plasm; *b*: stage 2, with accumulation of mitochondria in the CD blastomere; *c*: formation of 4 indophenoloxidase-containing micromeres and a large mass of polar plasm in 1D; *d*: formation of the first (ectodermic) somatoblasts 2d; *e*: formation of the second (mesodermic) somatoblasts 4d; *f*: for-mation of telectoblasts (T) and myoblasts (My) (Lehmann, 1956).

constituent of a given blastomere: as pointed out by Lehmann (1958), the differences between the various blastomeres are essentially *quantitative* in nature: it is the balance between the different egg constituents which varies from a given blastomere to another and it is presumably this balance which is important for further morphogenetic processes.

The work of Lehmann (1958) and his co-workers has certainly not yet solved the riddles of morphogenesis in *Tubifex*; nevertheless, their studies are extremely important because they point towards the right direction: correct answers will only be given by studies in which electron microscopy, cytochemistry and quantitative microtechniques are combined.

3. Molluscs

(a) *Limnaea* EGGS

It suffices to have a glance at Raven's (1958) book to see that it is completely impossible to condense in a few pages the wealth of material that he has presented on morphogenesis in Molluscs: in this remarkable book, Raven has gone much further than mere description and has produced a very complete study of cytochemistry and causal analysis in mollusc eggs. In the cytochemical realm, the distribution of glycogen, mucopolysaccharides, DNA, RNA, —SH groups, oxidative enzymes, vitamin C, etc. are studied in great detail, at all stages of development. Here are, in a very summarized form, Raven's (1958) conclusions: in Molluscs, as elsewhere, oogenesis is a period of active synthesis, in which nurse cells participate in a direct way. The nucleolus seems to be an especially important centre for these synthetic processes; but the nucleolus itself remains under the control of the genes present in the germinal vesicle. The various substances present in the oocyte are rather uniformly distributed and one must therefore look to the cortex as the seat of polarity and dorsoventrality. In Raven's (1958) opinion, the cortical field could be built up during oogenesis under the influence of the nurse cells.

Development is the result of interactions between nucleus, cytoplasm and cortex: chemical reactions start, leading to the production of new substances, and previously inhibited enzymes become activated. Simultaneously, nuclear genes begin to play a role in development and to interact with cytoplasmic substances. More will be said, later in this book, about nucleocytoplasmic interactions during embryonic development. But the picture given by Raven (1958), as he has pointed out himself, is a valid one for any group of the animal kingdom.

After this very brief summary of Raven's (1958) conclusions about morphogenesis in Molluscs, a little more will be said about two species in which quantitative methods have been used to an appreciable extent, *Mytilus* and *Ilyanassa*.

(b) *Mytilus* EGGS

Cytochemical methods are, without any doubt, extremely valuable, since they are the only ones which can detect biochemical constituents at the microscopical level; however, they are open to a number of questions regarding specificity and possibility of diffusion artifacts. Therefore, the biochemically minded embryologist feels the need for independent control with really quantitative methods. For this reason, the work of Berg and his colleagues, on Mollusc, Ascidian and Echinoderm eggs deserves special mention here.

We owe to Berg and his group two interesting studies about the biochemistry of the eggs of *Mytilus edulis*, which undergo a typical unequal cleavage: a large polar lobe forms at the vegetal pole of the fertilized egg and is later incorporated in the CD blastomere. As in the *Dentalium* egg studied long ago by E. B. Wilson (1904), the polar lobe plays an important role in morphogenesis, in particular in the formation of the apical tuft of the larva.

Using an ingenious method for the separation on a large scale of isolated blastomeres (based on the presence of lysine in sperm extracts), Berg and Kutsky (1951) were able to follow the oxygen consumption of isolated blastomeres and of isolated polar lobes. Figures 54, 55 and 56 are graphs

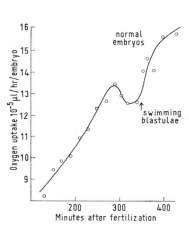

FIG. 54. Oxygen consumption rate of normal *Mytilus* embryos (Berg and Kutsky, 1951).

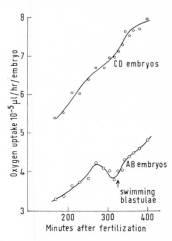

FIG. 55. Oxygen consumption rate of AB and CD embryos (Berg and Kutsky, 1951).

showing respectively the oxygen consumption of normal embryos, AB blastomeres, CD blastomeres and isolated polar lobes. The CD blastomere has a 13 per cent lower oxygen uptake than the AB blastomere; this lower respiratory rate is due to the presence of polar lobe cytoplasm, which has unusually low oxidations. It is interesting to note that, while the respiration of both the isolated AB and CD blastomeres steadily increases with time, that of isolated polar lobes remains essentially constant. This difference, as pointed out in the preceding chapter, might possibly be due to the fact that no DNA is synthesized in these anucleate fragments.

In a more recent study, Berg and Prescott (1958) reported that the uptake of radioactive phosphate into the AB and CD blastomeres is correlated with the surface area; on the other hand, isolated polar lobes or D blastomeres exhibit a lower accumulation rate than AB or C blastomeres. Phosphate uptake and oxygen consumption thus run parallel in the case of isolated *Mytilus* blastomeres.

The reduced uptake of phosphate in isolated polar lobes cannot, according to Berg and Prescott (1958), be due to the absence of a nucleus: similar results have been obtained in anucleate fragments of amoebea (Mazia and Hirshfield, 1950; Brachet, 1955); but in this case, in contrast to what happens in isolated polar lobes, there is a rapid and continuous decrease in phosphate uptake (Brachet, 1955). The difference between AB and CD blastomeres can obviously not be due to the absence of the nucleus. For this reason, it is more likely that the surface of the polar lobe cytoplasm is responsible, more than the absence of the nucleus, for their low phosphate uptake (Berg and Prescott, 1958).

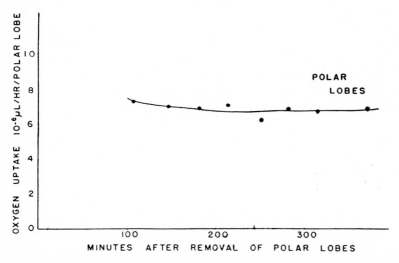

Fig. 56. Oxygen consumption rate of isolated polar lobes (Berg and Kutsky, 1951).

In view of the particularly low permeability to phosphate of isolated polar lobes, experiments on their incorporation of methionine, glycine and adenine have rather doubtful meaning (Abd-el-Wahab and Pantelouris, 1957): it was found, with autoradiography, that incorporation of these precursors markedly and quickly decreases after isolation in polar lobes. But, as in too many autoradiography experiments, nothing is known about permeability of isolated polar lobes to the various precursors: it might be that, as in the case of phosphate, permeability is so much lower than in the blastomeres that it becomes a limiting factor in the incorporation processes. It therefore is difficult to accept without reserve the contention of Abd-el-Wahab and Pantelouris (1957) that the effects they observed are due to the absence of the nucleus.

Finally, the work of Pasteels and Mulnard (1958) should be mentioned: they studied the formation and distribution of the granules which are stained metachromatically by toluidine blue *in vivo* in oyster eggs. They found that small α-granules enlarge into larger metachromatic vacuoles (β-granules), which contain acid phosphatase and mucopolysaccharides. A majority of β-granules, which probably have nothing to do with mitochondria and are perhaps related to lysosomes, goes into the polar lobe and later into the CD blastomere during cleavage.

It is rather unfortunate that if more is known about respiration and phosphate uptake in the eggs of *Mytilus* than in those of many other species, no study of mitochondrial distribution, using the methods of Reverberi (1957), has been made so far in oyster eggs. The situation, for the time being, remains unclear. There is no doubt that the polar lobe, in mollusc eggs, has real morphogenetic significance, since its removal leads to developmental abnormalities. Furthermore, artificially induced equal cleavage in mosaic eggs (by U.V. radiation or centrifugation) often results in the formation of double embryos; equal repartition of the polar lobe material into the AB and CD blastomeres has thus the production of Siamese twins as a consequence. On the other hand, the metabolic activities of the polar lobe are definitely lower than elsewhere; it is, at first sight, difficult to understand this observation, if mitochondria do control both energy production and morphogenesis. But, as we shall see in the case of Ascidians, there is no reason to believe that the rate of respiration is limited by the number of mitochondria, at least in early cleavage stages.

(c) *Ilyanassa* AND *Dentalium* EGGS

The role of the polar lobes in the development of *Ilyanassa* eggs has been extensively studied by Clement (1952, 1956): he has demonstrated well, for instance, that the formation of foot, eye and shell depends on the presence of either the polar lobe or the D blastomere. In a continuation of these studies, Clement and Lehmann (1956) have studied the distribution of mitochondria and lipid droplets in cleaving *Ilyanassa* eggs (Fig. 57): they found that, at the beginning of cleavage, the regional distribution of both is almost the same. It is especially interesting to note, in connexion with what has first been said about the eggs of *Mytilus*, that the polar lobe of *Ilyanassa* is especially *poor* in these inclusions. It is also worth mentioning that, according to Collier (1957), the enzyme dipeptidase has an even distribution in *Ilyanassa* eggs: there is no segregation according to potentialities of this ubiquitous enzyme during cleavage. The same situation exists for

RNA, according to the same author (Collier, 1958). The case of *Ilyanassa* is important because it clearly shows that mitochondria do not necessarily accumulate in a region (i.e. the polar lobe) which has great morphogenetic importance; it also shows that one enzyme at least, which is presumably present in the clear cytoplasm (hyaloplasm), retains an even distribution despite the complexities of unequal and spiral cleavage.

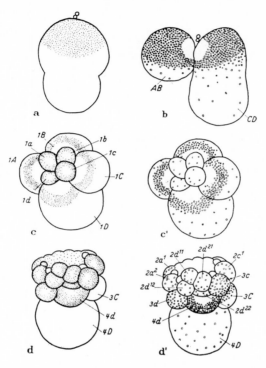

FIG. 57. Distribution of mitochondria and lipid droplets during development of the egg of *Ilyanassa*: left, mitochondria; right, lipid droplets. *a*: beginning of first cleavage; *b*: stage 2; *c*, *c*¹: formation of the first micromeres quartet; *d*, *d*¹: distribution after formation of the mesentoblast 4D (Clement and Lehmann, 1956).

Finally, a few words remain to be said about a recent cytochemical study of the old favourite material for embryological studies on Molluscs: the eggs of *Dentalium*, which have been famous since E. B. Wilson's experiments in 1904. The distribution of mitochondria has been followed in this material by Reverberi (1958), who used once more indophenoloxidase reaction and Janus Green staining for their detection. The conclusions of this study are very different from those which have been drawn for the egg of *Ilyanassa* by Clement and Lehmann (1956): in *Dentalium* (Fig. 58), mitochondria are accumulated in the polar lobe, and later in blastomeres D1, 2d, 3d and 4d. According to Reverberi (1958), the polar lobe insures the transfer of mitochondria, as well as of the β-granules of Pasteels and

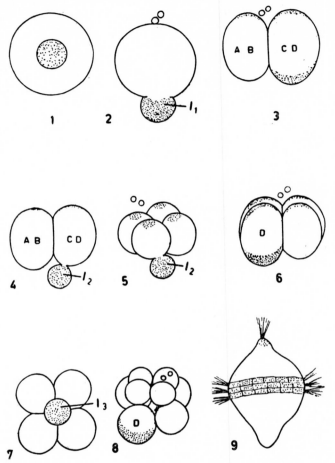

Fig. 58. Distribution of mitochondria in eggs of *Dentalium*. *1*: undivided egg; *2*: formation of the polar lobe (1_1); *3*: 2-cell stage; *4*: formation of the second polar lobe (1_2); *5*: 3-cell stage with second polar lobe (1_2); *6*: 4-cell stage; *7*: 4-cell stage with third polar lobe (1_3); *8*: 8-cell stage; *9*: larva (Reverberi, 1958).

Mulnard (1958), to the mesodermal organs. There is another accumulation of mitochondria at the animal pole: they will ultimately pass into the 'trochal' cells, which will later form the cilia of the larva.

As can be seen from this brief summary of the existing literature, the situation remains far from clear and much more work will be required before a more accurate, if not unified, picture emerges. Real understanding of morphogenesis will not be achieved until, as already pointed out, the problem is attacked simultaneously by all available methods: results given by cytochemical tests such as the indophenoloxidase reaction and Janus Green staining should be substantiated by electron microscopy as well as quantitative estimations of mitochondrial enzymes (cytochrome oxidase and succinic dehydrogenase). When this first descriptive (both morphologically and biochemically) phase of the work is over, the same methods should be applied to eggs which have been submitted to experimental classical procedures such as centrifugation, removal of polar lobes, separation of blastomeres. The task which lies ahead in this field remains a considerable one. Fortunately, much more has already been achieved along that line with two other types of invertebrate eggs, those of the Ascidians and the sea urchins.

4. Ascidian eggs

Experimental embryology of ascidian eggs owes a lot to Conklin (1931), Dalcq (1938) and Reverberi and Minganti (1947, 1951): their work shows that, even in the unfertilized egg, a tendency for dorsoventral organization is already present (Dalcq, 1938). In the fertilized egg, plasms are recognizable by pigmentation differences in certain favourable species, *Styela* for instance (Conklin, 1931). The analysis by Reverberi and Minganti of the 8-cell stage is a very thorough one. The conclusion of their experiments is by no means an oversimplified one: they think that vegetative anterior blastomeres stimulate nervous system (especially brain and sensory organs) formation, while vegetative posterior blastomeres are inhibitory for the development of neural tissue. Finally, the animal anterior blastomeres apparently have an intrinsic tendency towards formation of medulla. This brief summary shows that the situation is a complex one: there is no clear-cut induction of nervous system by chorda in Prochordates as in the case of Chordates. In fact, Prochordates, from the standpoint of experimental embryology, stand intermediate between Invertebrates and Vertebrates.

The complexities of morphogenesis in Ascidians, as well as the existence of the various 'plasms' described by Conklin (1931) in fertilized eggs, have quickly attracted the interest of cytochemists: the first—and still important—work in this field is that of E. Ries (1937, 1939) who followed the distribution of 'phenolases' in ascidian eggs. In fact, Ries (1937, 1939) studied with cytochemical methods, the distribution of peroxidase and indophenoloxidase. It was not known, at the time, that indophenoloxidase is identical with cytochrome oxidase and that the latter is a typical mitochrondrial enzyme. Ries (1937) erroneously believed that the enzymes he studied were diffusely distributed in the hyaloplasm and not localized in mitochondria.

The studies of Ries (1937, 1939) lead, however, to important results: as shown in Fig. 59, positive reactions for peroxidase and indophenol (cytochrome) oxidase are only found in the posterior blastomeres at the 4-cell and morula stages. The region which contains the respiratory enzymes will ultimately differentiate into the muscles of the tadpoles;

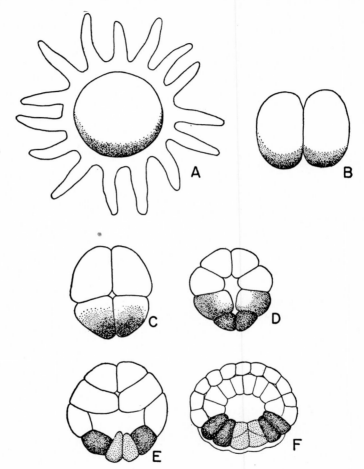

Fig. 59. Distribution of oxidative enzymes in ascidian eggs (Ries, 1937).

elegant centrifugation experiments of Ries (1937, 1939) have shown that displacement of these enzymes produces larvae which are very deficient in musculature. It will be seen in Fig. 60 that there is a very good correlation between the localization of peroxidase and cytochrome oxidase on one hand, and differentiation of muscle cells on the other.

The conclusions of Ries (1937, 1939), which have been essentially confirmed by Reverberi and Pitotti (1940), did not remain unchallenged for long: already in 1944, Holter and Zeuthen measured, with the Cartesian diver ultramicromethod, the oxygen consumption of anterior and posterior blastomeres at the 4-cell stage; they found no appreciable difference (within an experimental error of 20 per cent) between the two types of blasto-meres, although only the posterior ones give positive reactions for respiratory enzymes. Since the anterior blastomeres apparently lack the respiratory enzymes and, nevertheless, respire at almost the same rate as the posterior ones, the author (1944) drew the conclusion that the staining reactions used by Ries (1937, 1939) and by Reverberi and Pitotti (1940) are probably unspecific.

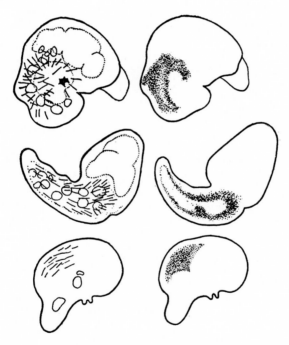

FIG. 60. Localization of muscles (left) and oxidative enzymes (right) in centrifuged ascidian eggs (Ries, 1939)

But more recent, quantitative work by Berg (1956, 1957) has clearly shown that this view was too pessimistic and that Ries' (1937, 1939) results are essentially correct: as in Holter and Zeuthen's (1944) experiments, he separated anterior and posterior blastomeres at the 4-cell stage; he then analysed them for a number of enzymes and got the following results: the average cytochrome oxidase activity of the posterior blastomeres is 2·7 times that of anterior blastomeres, a result which confirms a localization of mitochondrial enzymes in the posterior blastomeres. A conclusion can be drawn from this first result of Berg (1956): since posterior blastomeres contain more cytochrome oxidase and, nevertheless, have no higher respiration than the anterior ones, oxygen consumption, in ascidian eggs, is not limited by cytochrome oxidase content and—presumably—by the number of mitochondria. A further conclusion is that, although the anterior blastomeres are, according to Ries (1937), devoid of oxidative enzymes, they contain, however, measurable amounts of cytochrome oxidase. As is often the case, cytochemical techniques tend to overemphasize differences and quantitative methods are required to reach a more correct appraisal of the real situation.

In his second paper, Berg (1957) studied the distribution of succinic dehydrogenase, adenosinetriphosphatase, acid and alkaline phosphatases, and RNA in anterior and posterior blastomeres of the 4-cell stage of *Ciona*. He found succinic dehydrogenase, adenosinetriphosphatase and RNA to be accumulated in posterior cells, whereas acid phosphatase activity is higher in anterior blastomeres. Berg's (1957) results suggest that a segregation occurs during early cleavage of ascidian eggs between true mitochondria (which accumulate in the posterior blastomeres) and cell particles which are rich in acid phosphatase; the latter are probably identical with the metachromatic staining granules described by Dalcq (1957b) in the eggs of other Ascidians and which might be related to the lysosomes.

Berg's (1956, 1957) results will now be compared with those obtained by Reverberi (1956, 1957a, c, d) and his school: as usual, the Italian authors have relied on cytochemical methods for the detection of mitochondria, especially on indophenoloxidase reaction and vital staining with Janus Green.

Figure 61 summarizes the results obtained with Janus Green staining of the mitochondria in developing eggs of *Phallusia*: the mitochondria, which are evenly distributed in the unfertilized egg (Fig. 61a), migrate towards the vegetal pole after fertilization (Fig. 61b), where they form a mass of intersecting filaments (Fig. 61c). After the transient formation of a mitochondria-containing lobe at the vegetal pole (Fig. 61d), transverse mitochondrial strips are equally divided by the first furrow of segmentation (Fig. 61e). In later cleavages (Fig. 61f, g), the mass of the mitochondria is segregated in the two posterior blastomeres and, at the 8-cell stage, in the two vegetal posterior blastomeres. The next figures (Fig. 61h–l) show that the distribution of the Janus Green-staining mitochondria becomes more and more restricted during further cleavage; in the tadpole, only the muscle cells are stained. It is clear, from this description and a comparison of Figs. 59 and 61, that the distribution of mitochondria and that of the phenolases studied by Ries (1937, 1939) are essentially the same.

La Spina (1958), a co-worker of Reverberi, has recently reinvestigated the effects of centrifugation on mitochondrial distribution in Ascidians: he found that displacement of the mitochondria does not necessarily produce developmental abnormalities. In fact, a majority of the larvae developed

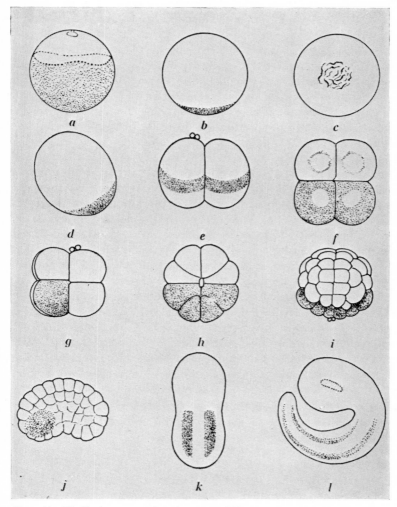

FIG. 61. *Phallusia* eggs and embryos at different stages of development, after staining of the unfertilized egg with Janus Green (Reverberi, 1957a).

normally in La Spina's (1958) experiments; 'chaotic' larvae were obtained from eggs which had cleaved abnormally, while slight abnormalities could be explained by the assumption that mitochondria play a role in muscle formation.

It is worth mentioning that another student of Reverberi, Durante (1957), has extended this work to a study of the localization of cholin-esterase in ascidian eggs; using a cytochemical method, Durante (1957) could show that this enzyme is present only in the posterior blastomeres at the 4-cell stage. Later, cholinesterase is found, in a specific way, in muscle cells. One would, of course, have rather expected an association of cholinesterase with the nervous system and thus, at earlier stages, with the anterior blastomeres. These experiments of Durante (1957) certainly deserve more study, since the specificity of the cytochemical method used is open to discussion: one would like to know, for instance, whether, in homogenates of ascidian eggs, cholinesterase is associated with the mitochondrial fraction. Direct estimation, by chemical methods, of the cholinesterase content of anterior and posterior blastomeres would also be of interest.

In more recent studies, Reverberi (1957a, c, d) and De Vincentiis (1956) have studied the effects on morphogenesis of various inhibitors of mito-chrondrial enzymes (sodium azide, malonate, selenite, anaerobiosis): the main result is that they produce a marked inhibition of the differentiation of muscle cells, leading to abnormalities in the tails of the tadpoles (Fig. 62). The 'heads' of the tadpoles obtained after treatment of developing eggs with inhibitors of the respiratory enzymes remain essentially normal: they form normal brain, sensorial organs and palps. These experiments strongly suggest that normal activity of cytochrome oxidase and succinic dehydrogenase is required for normal development of muscles in ascidian eggs. Taken together with the cytochemical evidence presented above and the quantitative results of Berg (1956, 1957), the studies made with enzyme inhibitors provide a nearly complete demonstration that mito-chrondria play a very fundamental part in muscle differentiation in ascidian embryos. This demonstration would be absolutely complete if one could substantitate it with electron microscope observations. One would very much like to know whether mitochondria, in ascidian eggs, greatly differ in number or in structural complexity (or in both) according to their localization in the various embryonic stages.

5. Sea urchin eggs

(a) EXPERIMENTAL EMBRYOLOGY AND ULTRA-STRUCTURE

The experimental embryology of sea urchin eggs remains dominated by the works of Driesch (1891) and Hörstadius (1939, 1949); while Driesch (1891) discovered regulation in separated blastomeres at the 2-cell stage, Hörstadius (1939, 1949) demonstrated that cells isolated from either the animal or the vegetal pole at the 64-cell stage have very different potenti-alities. Animal blastomeres can only form a ciliated blastula, while vegetal blastomeres give very abnormal larvae, characterized by a great excess of endoderm as compared to the ectoderm. The result of such a vegetalization is often (but not always) the production of exo-gastrulae. Furthermore, Hörstadius (1939, 1949) was able to combine cells obtained from the

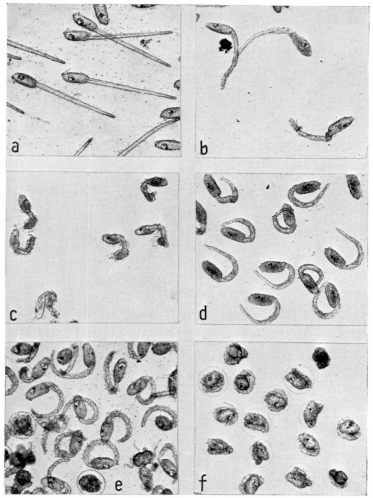

FIG. 62. Tadpoles with abnormal tails after treatment of the eggs at the 2-cell stage with inhibitors of respiratory metabolism. a: controls; b: Na azide 10^{-3} M; c: Na azide 2.10^{-3} M; d: Na malonate 5.10^{-2} M; e: Na selenite 10^{-3} M; f: Na azide 10^{-3} M + Na selenite 10^{-3} M. (Reverberi, 1957a) (courtesy of Prof. G. Reverberi).

animal and vegetal halves of the morula and to arrive at very clear conclusions. In order to improve the development of an isolated animal half,

K

vegetal material should be added, and the more vegetal this material is, the more efficiently it counteracts animalization. The sea urchin egg is thus the site of two opposite, hostile gradients: an animal-vegetal one and a second one, which decreases from the vegetal to the animal pole (Fig. 63); the latter counteracts the first one.

An important fact for chemical embryologists, who seldom have at their disposal methods sensitive enough to analyse the biochemical properties of cells which have been manually separated under the microscope, is that animalization and vegetalization can be obtained by treating *whole* eggs with chemical agents: as shown by Herbst (1892), lithiumions exert a strong vegetalizing influence, while other agents (Na thiocyanate or iodide, for instance) induce the animal type of development. Figure 64 shows how strikingly similar are vegetal halves and lithium-treated whole eggs, as well as animal halves and whole eggs treated by an animalizing agent before fertilization (Hörstadius, 1949).

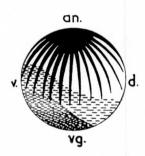

FIG. 63. Diagram to illustrate the morphogenetic organization of the fertilized sea urchin egg. The gradients decreasing from the animal pole (*an.*) towards the vegetable pole (*vg.*) are shown in black. The opposing gradient is shown by horizontal broken lines. It has been assumed that the 'vegetalizing' tendency lies slightly to one side of the *an.–vg.* axis, so that it exerts more influence on the side which becomes ventral (Dalcq, 1957a).

Finally, we owe to Hörstadius (see Hörstadius, 1949) an elegant experimental demonstration that, under the influence of lithium, the most vegetal material of the animal half becomes as vegetal as any micromeres.

The impressive effects of lithium on morphogenesis in sea urchin eggs has led to a great number of biochemical studies, which will be discussed a little later. What should, however, be pointed out is that more and more vegetalizing and animalizing agents have been found in recent years: one should therefore not expect substances like lithium or thiocyanate to act in a very specific way. They probably modify complex metabolic steps or pathways, which are of importance for embryonic differentiation; but similar or identical changes can be obtained with many other agents. For instance, Hörstadius (1953a) obtained vegetalization of sea urchin eggs by dinitrophenol (a typical inhibitor of oxidative phosphorylations) and animalization by the proteolytic enzymes trypsin and fucin. Other animalizing agents are DNA extracted from sea urchin sperm, as well as abnormal derivatives of cytidine (glucopyranosyl-cytosine, xylopyranosyl-cytosine and arabinopyranosyl-cytosine) (Hörstadius, 1954b); zinc

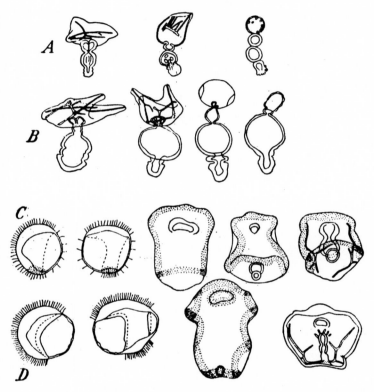

Fig. 64. A, B. embryos of vegetal type (exogastrulæ). (A) obtained by reducing the animal material, (B) by lithium ion treatment. (C, D) embryos of animal type, (C) obtained by cutting down the vegetal material, (D) by animalizing treatment before fertilization (Hörstadius, 1949).

(Lallier, 1955a) and many dyes (Lallier, 1955b) also produce animalization. A number of amino acids have been found, by Gustafson and Hörstadius (1957), to have variable or no effects on animal–vegetal determination; but L-glutamine and L-lysine have an animalizing effect.

In view of the unspecificity of the reactions (animalization or vegetalization) elicited in sea urchin eggs by a variety of chemically unrelated compounds, it is becoming more and more unlikely that studies such as those just summarized will give a definite clue to those interested in the biochemical aspects of the problem.

Long studies will thus be required before a common denominator will be found and we discover why substances as different as thiocyanate, DNA, iodide, zinc, glutamine, etc., have the same effect on morphogenesis. In recent years, however, a more hopeful line of investigation has opened with the discovery that certain substances can *reverse* the morphogenetic effects elicited by others: for instance, 2-thiomethyl-5-cytosine counteracts the vegetalizing action of lithium (Gustafson and Hörstadius, 1956). More recently, Backström (1958) has made the interesting observation that glutathione can inhibit the animalizing effects exerted by thiomalic acid and thiomethyl-cytosine: these results suggest that the animalizing action of these two substances might be due to a competition with glutathione. This hypothesis certainly deserves further study.

This very brief outline of the experimental embryology of sea urchin eggs would be incomplete if a few words were not said about the fine structure of these eggs: without going back to the studies made on the sea urchin oocyte (see Chapter I), the recent work of Pasteels *et al.* (1958, 1959a, b) on normal and centrifuged fertilized eggs should be recalled here. Electron microscope studies show that these eggs contain very numerous 'annulated lamellae', resembling in structure the nuclear membrane. These lamellae lie free in the cytoplasm and they represent a special form of the ergastoplasm. The latter, which can be observed in the hyaline layer after centrifugation, is atypical: it is very rich in Palade's granules and has a vesicular structure. In centrifuged eggs, part of the RNA is found in this ergastoplasmic layer; but, curiously enough, another part of the RNA is displaced toward the centrifugal pole, together with the mitochondria, after centrifugation. Acid phosphatase and mucopolysaccharides, which are associated with granules staining metachromatically *in vivo*, are accumulated in a zone which contains many Golgi elements. Finally, Pasteels *et al.* (1958) have made curious and interesting observations about the frequent accumulation of mitochondria around the lipid droplets (Fig. 65). It is of course impossible to decide, on purely morphological grounds, whether such an association of mitochondria with lipids corresponds to synthesis or utilization of fatty material.

After these preliminary remarks about the experimental embryology and the ultra-structure of sea urchin eggs, we can now go into their chemical embryology.

(b) CHEMICAL EMBRYOLOGY

Figures 66 and 67 represent the curves obtained by Lindahl (1939) for the oxygen consumption of normal and lithium-treated eggs. Figure 66 shows typical curves for normal eggs during the first day of development. In Fig. 67, lithium-treated eggs are compared to controls, in experiments of shorter duration. It will be seen that the curve of Fig. 66 is S-shaped, up to

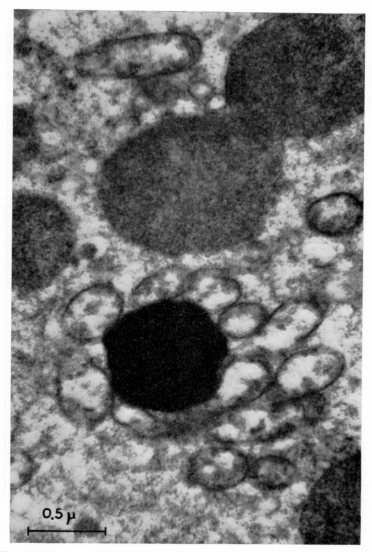

FIG. 65. Electron micrograph showing the accumulation of mitochondria around a lipid droplet of a fertilized sea urchin egg (Pasteels *et al.*, 1958).

hatching. A sharp rise in the respiratory rate is characteristic of gastrulation; it is followed by a plateau during the differentiation of the gastrula

into the pluteus larva. Lithium, as shown in Fig. 67, has no effect on the
initial respiratory rate, but it slows down considerably the normal increase
in respiration which is characteristic of cleavage. It is not known unfortunately whether this inhibition of the 'growing' part of respiration is simply
due to retardation of cleavage or to more remote causes.

It has been suggested by Lindahl (1936), on the ground of interesting,
but unfortunately indirect, experiments, that metabolism might be
qualitatively different at the two poles of sea urchin eggs. Carbohydrate
metabolism would be most active at the animal pole and would be inhibited
by lithium, while protein metabolism would predominate at the vegetal
pole. More than twenty years after Lindahl (1936) proposed his hypothesis,

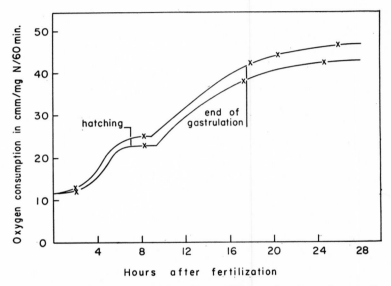

FIG. 66. Oxygen consumption of two different batches of normally
developing sea urchin eggs (Lindahl, 1939).

our ignorance on the subject remains practically complete. All that we
know for certain is that, as shown by Lindahl himself in collaboration with
Holter (Lindahl and Holter, 1940), there is no difference in the oxygen
consumption between cells coming from the animal or the vegetal half.
Furthermore, Lindahl and Holter (1940) observed that lithium exerts the
same inhibitory effect (30 per cent) on either animal or vegetal cells: there
is no specific inhibition of respiration in the animal half, as one might have
expected if lithium had blocked, in a specific way, carbohydrate metabolism
in this part of the egg. Of course, these observations are not sufficient to
discard Lindahl's (1936) hypothesis, although they make it rather unlikely; unfortunately, nobody has so far succeeded in measuring the

respiratory quotient of animal and vegetal halves of sea urchin eggs; such measurements would provide better information for or against the view that metabolism is qualitatively different at the two poles of the egg.

A recent paper by Berg (1958b) shows that there is a revival of interest for such problems. He compared the cytochrome oxidase activity of animal and vegetal cells of the 16-cell stage of *Dendraster* and found no significant difference.

If one brings together the results of Lindahl and Holter (1940) and those of Berg (1958b), one comes naturally to the conclusion that differences between animal and vegetal cells in sea urchins have nothing to do with a respiratory or mitochondrial gradient. But there is conflicting evidence, coming out of recent work by Gustafson (1954) and by Hörstadius (1952, 1955), which should be examined before any conclusion can be drawn: it throws some light on the mechanism of vegetalization although, as we shall see, the whole situation still remains obscure.

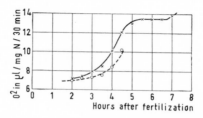

FIG. 67. Respiratory rate of normal (————) and lithium-treated (– – –) sea urchin eggs (Lindahl, 1939).

Gustafson has published, in 1954, an interesting review on enzyme synthesis during development, in which he has summarized a number of his own results. The basic idea is that the changes in respiratory rate observed by Lindahl (1939; cf. Fig. 66) during development of sea urchin eggs are correlated with an increase in number and activity of mitochondria. The first line of evidence for this view is based on experiments by Gustafson and Hasselberg (1951), who studied the activity of a number of enzymes during development of normal and lithium-treated sea urchin eggs. They found, in a rather impressive way, that the enzyme complement of these eggs can be subdivided into two different classes. Certain enzymes, such as pyrophosphatase, hexametaphosphatase, acid phosphatase, adenosinedeaminase, phenylsulphatase and some of the proteinases have a fairly constant activity throughout development. Fig. 68 represents a typical example for such enzymes, the case of phosphomonoesterase. But still more important is the fact that the enzymatic activity, in all of these cases, is essentially the same in normal and lithium-treated eggs.

The situation is entirely different with the second class of enzymes,

which includes succinic and malic dehydrogenases, adenosinetriphosphatase, cathepsin II and glutaminase I. They all show a very marked
increase in activity at the time of gastrulation, just when respiration also
rises quickly according to Lindahl (1939). As shown in Fig. 69, treatment
of the eggs with lithium chloride markedly inhibits the rise in activity of
this second class of enzymes. Since all of them are known to be localized
in the mitochondria in other material, e.g. rat liver, the obvious conclusion
was immediately drawn by Gustafson and Hasselberg (1951): differentiation is characterized by the development of mitochondrial enzymes, and
their development is inhibited by lithium.

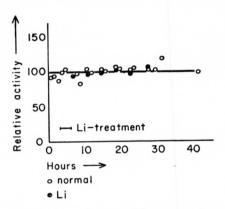

FIG. 68. Phosphomonoesterase in sea urchin eggs: no increase in activity
and no effect of lithium (Gustafson and Hasselberg, 1951).

In view of the importance of such a conclusion, a critical appraisal of
Gustafson and Hasselberg's (1951) work becomes necessary: there is no
doubt that the results they obtained are very striking and that they are
certainly meaningful. However, one cannot help but regret that the
mitochondrial localization of the enzymes belonging to the second group
has not been verified in homogenates of sea urchin eggs. An enzyme might
be linked to mitochondria in rat liver, but not in these eggs. It might also
be that synthesis of some enzymes has nothing to do with their intracellular
localization and that lithium is inhibitory only because it retards development: such a possibility cannot be dismissed without experimental proof,
since it is now known, from the work of Hultin (1957), that synthesis of
proteins and RNA (or, more accurately, incorporation of amino acids into
proteins and of purines into RNA) markedly increases at gastrulation. In
other cells (again, nothing definite is known about sea urchin eggs), such
incorporation phenomena are much more extensive in the ergastoplasm
than in the mitochondria. It might thus be that the development of the
latter is no more important than that of the ergastoplasm.

Furthermore, results obtained by Deutsch and Gustafson (1952) remain another matter of concern. They studied cytochrome oxidase, which is a typical mitochondrial enzyme, and found that its activity increases after fertilization and, unexpectedly, decreases at the blastula stage. The explanation given by the authors for this surprising result is that mitochondrial permeability might change during development. It is a possible explanation, but it does not easily carry conviction in the absence of direct experimental proof.

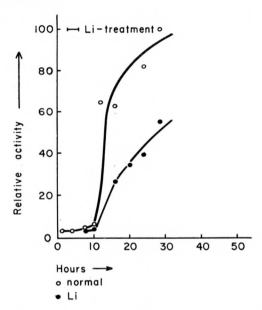

FIG. 69. Cathepsin II in sea urchin eggs: the enzymatic activity increases during development and is markedly inhibited by lithium (Gustafson and Hasselberg, 1951).

In view of these uncertainties, Gustafson and Lenicque (1952, 1955) have attacked the problem from another angle and have tried to follow directly the changes in the number and distribution of mitochondria during sea urchin development. For this purpose, they made counts of mitochondria, in various stages and in different parts of the egg, using phase contrast microscopy and vital staining with Nile Blue sulphate. Unfortunately, Nile Blue sulphate is much less specific for mitochondria than Janus Green, which gives very poor results with sea urchin eggs. Gustafson and Lenicque (1952) have concluded from these observations that mitochondrial distribution is uniform in the blastula. After hatching, at the so-called mesenchyme blastula stage where mesoblastic cells migrate into the

blastocele, an animal–vegetal gradient in the distribution of the mitochondria becomes visible. The increase in number of mitochondria, at that
stage, was found to be much greater in the animal half than in the vegetal
region. More complex changes have been found by Gustafson and Lenicque (1952) at later stages of development.

In their 1955 paper, the same authors have attempted to follow the
increase in the mitochondrial population during cleavage. They found that
the number of particles which stain with Nile Blue sulphate increases
following an S-shaped curve (Fig. 70). Their curve shows close resemblance to that obtained by Lindahl (1939; Fig. 66) for the increase of
oxygen consumption during development of sea urchin eggs.

All these observations obviously suggest that mitochondria are of great
importance for morphogenesis in Echinoderms. Further and strong
support for the same view has been obtained by Lenicque et al. (1953),
when they found that the mitochondrial pattern of an isolated animal half
is very similar to that of a whole egg treated with an animalizing agent;
similarly, the mitochondrial pattern of a vegetal half is very much like that
found in eggs treated with lithium in order to obtain vegetalization.

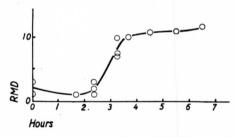

FIG. 70. Change in the relative number of Nile Blue sulphate-stainable
granules during cleavage of the sea urchin egg. RMD: relative density
of the particulate population (Gustafson and Lenicque, 1955).

There is no doubt that the observations of Gustafson and his colleagues
reveal differences in microscopically visible granules in sea urchin eggs.
But it is not certain that all of these granules are true mitochondria, as
shown in recent work by Shaver (1955, 1957). He points out that there
are marked changes in number and, possibly, *kinds* of mitochondria
during sea urchin egg development. Furthermore, Shaver (1955, 1957)
found an increase in numbers of the particles, followed by a sharp decrease
in the immediately following stages. What is still more important is that
Shaver (1955, 1957) has failed to find a gradient distribution of mitochondria in the mesenchyme blastula and in the gastrula of the two
species of sea urchin he studied. His results are thus at variance with those
of Gustafson and Lenicque (1952). Shaver's (1957) conclusion is that his

results do not support hypotheses of differentiation based on such a gradient distribution pattern of mitochondrial particles.

There is no doubt that it is impossible to reconcile the results of Shaver (1955, 1957) with those of Gustafson and Lenicque (1952). If the discrepancy were simply due to differences in the various species which have been studied, then the observations of Gustafson and Lenicque would have no general value and would, therefore, lose much of their interest. There is no doubt that the methods used so far for the detection of 'mitochondria' in sea urchin eggs lack specificity. Nile Blue sulphate might well stain, besides true mitochondria, other cytoplasmic granules, for instance the metachromatic α-granules of Pasteels and Mulnard (1957) and Pasteels *et al.* (1959) and even fat droplets. Only the development of better cytochemical techniques for the detection of mitochondria in developing sea urchin eggs and the extensive use of electron microscopy will solve the still obscure problem of the role of these particles in sea urchin morphogenesis.

Very interesting work by Hörstadius (1952, 1955) on reduction gradients in sea urchin eggs brings, however, strong support for the view that mitochondria play indeed an important and direct role in the development of sea urchin eggs: in confirmation of earlier work by Child (1936) and Ranzi (1939), Hörstadius (1952) found, with Janus Green, that mesenchyme blastulae and early gastrulae are the site of a stronger vegetal (acropetal) and a weaker animal (basipetal) reduction gradient (Fig. 71). These findings are obviously in accordance with those of Gustafson and Lenicque (1952), since mitochondria contain important reducing enzymes, succinic dehydrogenase for instance.

But the most important observations made by Hörstadius (1952) deal with reduction gradients in isolated animal and vegetal halves. Isolated vegetal halves show only the vegetal (acropetal) reduction gradient, while, in isolated animal halves, on the contrary, only the animal (basipetal) gradient can be seen. (Figs. 72, 73). Furthermore, implantation of micromeres (which are the most vegetal cells of the morula) in the animal part of whole eggs induces a new reduction centre (Fig. 74).* Implantation of four micromeres into an isolated animal half induces a new vegetal (acropetal) reduction gradient and restricts the animal one. The reduction gradient pattern, in this case, becomes similar to that of a normal egg (Fig. 71). We know, from Hörstadius' (1939, 1949) previous work, that such a combination of isolated animal half and micromeres leads to the formation of a normal pluteus.

These observations clearly show that reduction gradients bear great similarities with the morphogenetic gradients previously demonstrated

* Micromeres are also the site, according to Agrell (1958), of a particularly active RNA metabolism.

by Hörstadius (1939, 1949) in sea urchin eggs. As pointed out by Hörstadius (1952), his results are not in contradiction to those of Lindahl and Holter (1940) who, as mentioned before, found no difference in oxygen

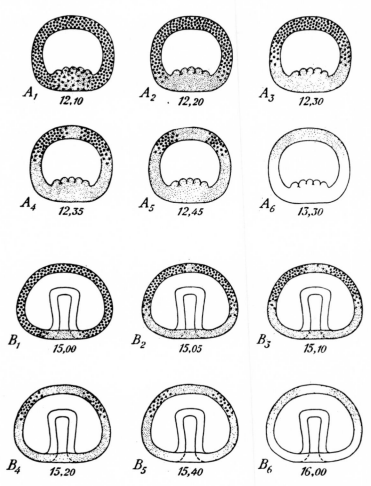

Fig. 71. Change of colour of Janus Green showing reduction gradients in a late blastula (A_1–A_6) and a gastrula (B_1–B_6). Large dots, blue; small dots, red; no dots, the colour has faded. Figures indicate time of observations. In B_1–B_6 the colour was observed only in the ectoderm (Hörstadius, 1952).

consumption between isolated animal and vegetal halves. The apparent contradiction is easily explained by the fact that the vegetal halves, which should show a higher oxygen consumption than the animal ones, exert an inhibitory influence on the latter. When they are liberated from this inhibitory influence, the animal halves show an increase in reduction; their respiration would then become identical with that of vegetal halves.

In a later paper, Hörstadius (1955) extended these very interesting

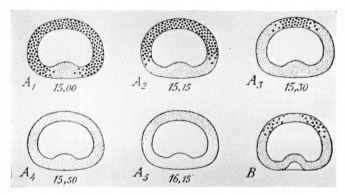

FIG. 72. Isolated vegetal halves (Hörstadius, 1952).

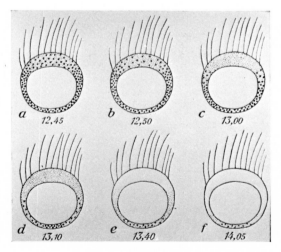

FIG. 73. Isolated animal halves (Hörstadius, 1952).

studies to the case of eggs animalized by trypsin and vegetalized by lithium. As expected, the changes were similar to those found in isolated animal and vegetal halves, except that the reduction in animalized eggs starts earlier than in both normal and vegetalized eggs; the reason for this very early start of reduction in animalized eggs remains unknown. But the main point, i.e. that animalized eggs show a single reduction gradient, in contrast to whole eggs which are the site of two opposite gradients, has been confirmed by Lallier (1956), who used zinc as an animalizing agent. This confirmation is important because it shows that it is animalization —and not just trypsin—which produces by itself the changes observed by Hörstadius (1955) in animalized sea urchin eggs.

The experiments of Hörstadius (1955) are in keeping with Lindahl's (1936) view that the vegetalizing action of lithium might be linked to an

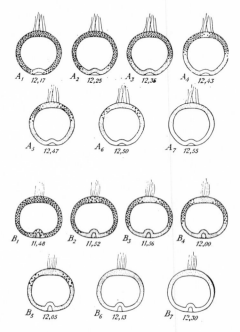

FIG. 74. Implantation of micromeres into an animal half (two cases). A vegetal reduction gradient has been induced and the animal reduction gradient is checked (cf. Figs. 72, 73). The reduction pattern is similar to that of whole eggs (Fig. 71) (Hörstadius, 1952).

inhibition of the respiratory metabolism (possibly carbohydrate metabolism) at the animal pole. Extensive studies of Ranzi and his students, summarized by Ranzi (1957a, b), have shown that the situation might be more complicated than that: while lithium, as Ranzi already showed in 1939, modifies the oxidation–reduction potential of the egg (in decreasing the regions of the egg which have a low potential), it also exerts a strong effect on the egg proteins. According to Ranzi (1957a, b), animalizing substances act in producing a demolition (partial breakdown) of pre-existing proteic structures. The action of vegetalizing substances, such as lithium, is a 'resistance to demolition'. In other words, in Ranzi's (1957a, b) conception, animalization and vegetalization would originate 'from the enlargement or inhibition of the areas in which a process of protein demolition, necessary for new protein synthesis, is acting'. The regions overdeveloped by the action of animalizing agents and inhibited by vegetalizing agents show a higher oxido–reduction potential; this might, according to Ranzi (1957a), indicate a more active protein breakdown. In order to link his own findings with the results of the Swedish workers, Ranzi (1957a) arrives at the following hypothesis: fertilization would activate enzymes at the animal pole; production of metabolites, under the influence of the activated enzymes, would lead to the development of the animal pole, while the failure to form these metabolites would stabilize the vegetal pole.

Although perhaps not directly related to the present problem, mention should be made of a recent paper by Kane and Hersh (1959): using precipitation by traces of calcium and ultracentrifugation as their tools, they made the curious observation that sea urchin eggs contain only two major proteins. One of them precipitates in gel form on the addition of Ca^{++} ions; it is a highly asymmetrical molecule (asymmetry of 15:1), with a molecular weight of $3,5.10^5$. In view of the importance of fibrous proteins, according to Ranzi (1957a, b), it would be interesting to study the effects of lithium, both *in vivo* and *in vitro*, on the protein obtained by Kane and Hersh (1959). It would also be important to know more about its chemical composition, in particular the presence or absence of —SH groups: according to a recent study by Backström (1959), the total —SH content of sea urchin eggs homogenates decreases during differentiation, especially in vegetalized embryos. It certainly would be a considerable progress if, as seems probable, links could be established between apparently unrelated findings such as those of Hörstadius (1952, 1955), Ranzi (1957a,b), Kane and Hersh (1959) and Backström (1959).

It is clear, from this brief review of metabolism and determination in invertebrate eggs, that we are still very far from a satisfactory understanding of their development. Nevertheless, great progress has recently been made in this field. There is little doubt that mitochondria play a role in the development of mosaic as well as in that of regulative eggs. Much progress is to be expected in the future from an attack of the problem with a wider array of methods: vital staining, cytochemistry, microchemical analysis, electron microscopy, etc. But these methods should also be combined with those of experimental embryology: centrifugation, isolation of cells or blastomeres. Such a concerted experimental study of invertebrate eggs should throw new light on the still obscure problem of regulation, which remains a major one for the embryologist.

REFERENCES

ABD-EL-WAHAB, A. and E. M. PANTELOURIS. (1957): *Exp. Cell Res.* **13**, 78.
AGRELL, (1958): *Ark. Zool., ser.* **2**, No. 26.
BACKSTRÖM, S. (1958): *Exp. Cell Res.* **14**, 426.
BACKSTRÖM, S. (1959): *Exp. Cell Res.* **16**, 184.
BERG, W. E. (1956): *Biol. Bull.* **110**, 1.
BERG, W. E. (1957): *Biol. Bull.* **113**, 365.
BERG, W. E. (1958): *Exp. Cell Res.* **14**, 398.
BERG, W. E. and P. B. KUTSKY. (1951): *Biol. Bull.* **101**, 47.
BERG, W. E. and D. M. PRESCOTT. (1958): *Exp. Cell Res.* **14**, 402.
BRACHET, J. (1944): *Embryologie chimique.* Desoer, Liège and Masson, Paris.
BRACHET, J. (1955): *Biochim. biophys. Acta* **18**, 247.
CHILD, C. M. (1936): *Roux' Arch. Entwicklungsmech.* **135**, 426.
CLEMENT, A. C. (1952): *J. exp. Zool.* **121**, 593.
CLEMENT, A. C. (1956): *Biol. Bull.* **69**, 403.
CLEMENT, A. C. and F. E. LEHMANN. (1956): *Naturwiss.* **43**, 478.
COLLIER, J. R. (1957): *Embryologia* **3**, 243.
COLLIER, J. R. (1958): *Biol. Bull.* **115**, 348.
CONKLIN, E. G. (1931): *J. exp. Zool.* **60**, 1.
DALCQ, A. (1938): *Arch. Biol.* **49**, 397.
DALCQ, A. (1941): *L'œuf et son Dynamisme organisateur.* Albin Michel. Paris
DALCQ, A. (1957a): *Introduction to General Embryology.* Oxford Univ. Press.
DALCQ, A. (1957b): *Bull. Soc. Zool. Fr.* **82**, 296.
DEUTSCH, H. F. and T. GUSTAFSON. (1952): *Ark. Kemi.* **4**, 221.
DE VINCENTIIS, M. (1956): *Experientia* **12**, 381.
DRIESCH, H. (1891): *Zeitschr. Zool.* **53**.
DUESBERG, J. (1926): *Arch. Biol.* **36**, 489.
DURANTE, M. (1957): *Acta Embryol. Morphol. exp.* **1**, 131.
GUSTAFSON, T. (1954): *Internat. Rev. Cytol.* **3**, 277.
GUSTAFSON, T. and I. HASSELBERG. (1951): *Exp. Cell Res.* **2**, 642.
GUSTAFSON, T. and S. HÖRSTADIUS. (1956): *Zool. Anz.* **156**, 102.
GUSTAFSON, T. and S. HÖRSTADIUS. (1957): *Pubbl. Staz. zool. Napoli* **29**, 407
GUSTAFSON, T. and P. LENICQUE. (1952): *Exp. Cell Res.* **3**, 251.
GUSTAFSON, T. and P. LENICQUE. (1955): *Exp. Cell Res.* **8**, 114.
HERBST, C. (1892): *Z. wiss. Zool.* **55**, 446.
HOLTER, H. and E. ZEUTHEN. (1944): *C. R. Trav. Labor. Carlsberg, sér. chim.* **25**, 33.
HÖRSTADIUS, S. (1939): *Biol. Rev.* **18**, 132.
HÖRSTADIUS, S. (1949): *Pubbl. Staz. zool. Napoli,* Vol. **21**, suppl., 131.
HÖRSTADIUS, S. (1952): *J. exp. Zool.* **120**, 421.
HÖRSTADIUS, S. (1953a): *J. Embryol. exp. Morphol.* **1**, 327.
HÖRSTADIUS, S. (1953b): *J. Embryol. exp. Morphol.* **1**, 261.
HÖRSTADIUS, S. (1955): *J. exp. Zool.* **129**, 249.
HULTIN, T. (1957): *Exp. Cell Res.* **12**, 518.
KANE, R. E. and R. T. HERSH. (1959): *Exp. Cell Res.* **16**, 59.
LALLIER, R. (1955a): *Arch. Biol.* **66**, 705.
LALLIER, R. (1955b): *Exp. Cell Res.* **9**, 232.
LALLIER, R. (1956): *Arch. Biol.* **67**, 475.
LA SPINA, R. (1958): *Acta Embryol. Morphol. exp.* **2**, 66.

LEHMANN, F. E. (1941): *Naturwiss.* **29**, 101.
LEHMANN, F. E. (1956): *Naturwiss.* **43**, 289.
LEHMANN, F. E. (1958): In : *The Chemical Basis of Development* **1**, 73. Johns Hopkins Press, Baltimore.
LEHMANN, F. E. and V. MANCUSO. (1957): *Arch. Julius-Klaus Stiftung f. Vererbungsforsch.* **32**, 482.
LENICQUE, P., S. HÖRSTADIUS and T. GUSTAFSON. (1953): *Exp. Cell Res.* **5**, 400.
LINDAHL, P. E. (1936): *Acta Zool.* **17**, 179.
LINDAHL, P. E. (1939): *Z. vergl. Physiol.* **27**, 136, 234.
LINDAHL, P. E. and H. HOLTER. (1940): *C. R. Trav. Labor. Carlsberg, sér. chim.* **23**, 249, 257.
MAZIA, D. and H. I. HIRSHFIELD. (1950): *Science* **112**, 297.
MEVES, F. (1913): *Arch. mikrosk. Anat.* **82**, 215.
PASTEELS, J. J., P. CASTIAUX and G. VANDERMEERSCHE. (1958): *J. biophys. biochem. Cytol.* **4**, 575.
PASTEELS, J. J., P. CASTIAUX and G. VANDERMEERSCHE. *Arch. Biol.* **69**, 627.
PASTEELS, J. J. and J. MULNARD. (1957): *Arch. Biol.* **68**, 115.
PENNERS, A. (1938): *Z. wiss. Zool.* **150**, 305.
RANZI, S. (1939): *Arch. Zool. ital.* **26**, 427.
RANZI, S. (1957a): In : *The Beginnings of Embryonic Development*, p. 291, A.A.A.S., Publ. No. 48, Washington.
RANZI, S. (1957b): *Année biologique* **33**, 522.
RAVEN, C. P. (1958): *Morphogenesis.* Pergamon Press. London.
REVERBERI, G. (1956): *Experientia* **12**, 55.
REVERBERI, G. (1957a): In : *The Beginnings of Embryonic Development*, p. 319, A.A.A.S., Publ. No. 48. Washington.
REVERBERI, G. (1957b): *Acta Embryol. Morphol. exp.* **1**, 134.
REVERBERI, G. (1957c): *Acta Embryol. Morphol. exp.* **1**, 12.
REVERBERI, G. (1957d): *Pubbl. Staz. zool. Napoli* **28**, 187.
REVERBERI, G. (1958): *Acta Embryol. Morphol. exp.* **2**, 79.
REVERBERI, G. and A. MINGANTI. (1947): *Pubbl. Staz. zool. Napoli* **21**, 1.
REVERBERI, G. and A. MINGANTI. (1951): *Acta biotheoretica* **9**, 127.
REVERBERI, G. and M. PITOTTI. (1940): *Pubbl. Staz. zool. Napoli* **18**, 250.
RIES, E. (1937): *Pubbl. Staz. zool. Napoli* **21**, 1.
RIES, E. (1939): *Arch. exp. Zellforschg.* **23**, 95.
SHAVER, J. R. (1955): *Experientia* **11**, 351.
SHAVER, J. R. (1957): In : *The Beginnings of Embryonic Development*, p. 263 A.A.A.S., Publ. No. 48, Washington.
SPEK, J. (1926): *Roux' Arch. Entw. Mech.* **107**, 54.
TEISSIER, G. (1931): *Ann. Sci. nat. Zool.* **14**, 5.
WEBER, R. (1956): *Rev. suisse Zool.* **63**, 277.
WEBER, R. (1958): *Roux' Arch. Entw. Mech.* **150**, 542.
WILSON, E. B. (1904): *J. exp. Zool.* **1**, 197.

L

CHAPTER V

Chemical Embryology of Vertebrate Eggs

AMPHIBIAN eggs have always been a favourite material for experimental embryologists. Today much more knowledge is available concerning the Chemical Embryology of Amphibians than of other Vertebrates. For this reason, the present chapter will deal almost exclusively with amphibian eggs, despite the obvious interest of recent studies on Fishes, Birds and Mammals.

The whole field of vertebrate experimental embryology is of course dominated by the problems raised by the inductive activities of the organizer centre. Figures 75 and 76 (*a*, *b*) will remind the reader of the map of the various presumptive regions in the young gastrula and of the changes which occur in these regions during gastrulation. The fundamental experiments of Spemann (1938) have shown that, in the young gastrula, presumptive ectoderm (ectoblast) and presumptive neural system (neuroblast) have not yet undergone determination: they can be exchanged without any effect on the morphology of the embryo at later stages. Neural or ectodermic differentiation depends entirely on the geographical localization of the cells in the embryo. Spemann's work has further demonstrated that the material which forms the dorsal lip of the blastoporus and which will later differentiate into chorda (chordoblast), exerts a decisive influence on the fate of the neighbouring cells. Under its organizing influence, the overlying cells will differentiate into nervous system. Furthermore, this 'organizer' also acts on the neighbouring mesoblast and entoblast. This will induce the formation of somites and pronephros in the former, of an enteron in the latter. Grafting of an additional organizer in the ventral mesoblast or in the blastocele thus results in the induction of a *complete* secondary embryo, not only in the formation of an additional nervous system (Fig. 77).

A word should also be said about the famous explantation experiments of Holtfreter (1931), which have provided the clearest demonstration of neural induction. Ectoblast or neuroblast, if they are isolated from a young gastrula and are cultivated in saline, never give rise to more than abnormal epidermis. If the same fragments are cultivated in the same medium but in contact with a piece of chordoblast, they *both* produce nervous system. An important word of caution is, however, required in

146

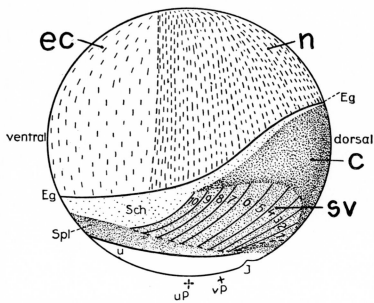

FIG. 75. Map of presumptive regions in the early gastrula. *N*: neuro-blast, *EC*: ectoblast, *Eg*: limit of invagination, *C*: chordoblast, *SV*: somites, *Spl*: lateral plate, *Sch*: tail-bud material (from Spemann, 1938).

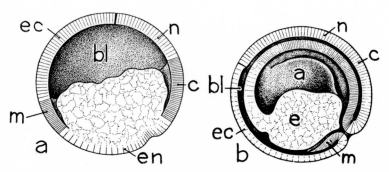

FIG. 76. Schematic description of gastrulation in Amphibians: *a*: early gastrula; *b*: early neurula; *c*: chordoblast; *n*: neuroblast; *ec*: ectoblast; *m*: mesoblast (ventral), *en*: entoblast; *bl*: blastocele: *a*: archenteron (from Spemann, 1938).

the case of these experiments: ectoblast and neuroblast can, in the *absence* of the organizer, differentiate *spontaneously* in neural tissue if the medium in which they are placed has an abnormal pH or lacks calcium ions (Holtfreter, 1947a). Ignorance of this essential point has long hindered progress in our knowledge of the biochemical mechanisms of induction, as we shall soon see. Finally, it should not be forgotten that morphogenesis in vertebrate eggs is not solely controlled by the inducing action of the dorsally situated organizer in the gastrula. As shown by Dalcq and Pasteels (1938), and as confirmed more recently by Paterson (1957), the initial animal–vegetal polarity is also very important in the development of amphibian eggs. Modifications of the animal–vegetal gradient by such

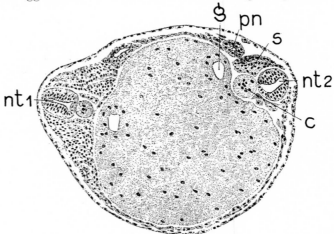

Fig. 77. A typical induction: *nt* 1: primary neural tube; *nt* 2: secondary (induced) neural tube; *c*: chorda originating from the grafted organizer; *S*: secondary (induced) somite; *pn*: secondary (induced) pronephros; *g*: secondary (induced) intestinal lumen (from Spemann, 1939).

experimental interventions as centrifugation (Pasteels, 1940), turning the egg upside down (Pasteels, 1938), removal of blastomeres (Paterson, 1957), etc. has far-reaching consequences on morphogenesis, such as production of microcephalic embryos or of twins, for instance.

After this too brief summary of the experimental embryology of amphibian eggs, we shall attempt to study their biochemistry: energy production, chemical nature of the inducing substance, RNA and protein metabolism, size of the inducing agent will be our main topics.

1. Energy production in vertebrate eggs

(a) Effects of Anaerobiosis and Metabolic Inhibitors on Development

It has been known, for a long time (see Brachet, 1944, for a review of the literature), that fertilized amphibian eggs can undergo repeated cleavage in the absence of oxygen or in the presence of metabolic inhibitors such as KCN or N_3Na. At later stages, the embryos become progressively more and more sensitive to anaerobic conditions and respiratory poisons. Thus increased sensitivity is presumably linked to the progressive increase in oxygen uptake which is characteristic of embryonic development in amphibian eggs (Brachet, 1934; Fig. 78).

We have already seen, in Chapter III, that cell division is, as a rule, more dependent upon phosphorylation than on respiration itself. This situation is also true in the case of amphibian eggs, in which dinitrophenol quickly inhibits cleavage, blocking mitoses in interphase (Brachet, 1954a).

It is interesting to note that high oxygen pressures exert the same general effect as anaerobiosis on cleavage and gastrulation of frog eggs (Nelsen, 1947; Malamed, 1957, 1958). Cleavage may proceed normally while gastrulation is blocked. The exact meaning of these observations is still far from clear; but it is difficult to avoid Malamed's (1957, 1958) conclusion that a new metabolic system sets in at gastrulation. We shall soon see that this conclusion is in accordance with many previously known facts.

Finally, one should mention that, according to Devillers (1953) and Devillers *et al.* (1957a), the effects exerted by anaerobiosis and cyanide on trout eggs are essentially similar to those which have just been described for amphibian eggs.

(b) OXYGEN CONSUMPTION

Figure 78 represents a typical curve for the oxygen consumption of developing frog eggs: it will be seen that the increase in oxygen uptake is tremendous during development, especially when neuralization and differentiation occur. As shown by the author (Brachet, 1934), a ten-fold increase in the oxygen consumption of frog eggs is possible without any measurable increase in the cytochrome oxidase activity, a fact which has been repeatedly confirmed since (cf. Petrucci, 1957, 1959). In Anurans, the cytochrome oxidase content is thus not the limiting factor of the respiratory rate, until hatching at any rate.

In Urodeles, *Ambystoma* for instance, a synthesis of cytochrome oxidase has been observed by Boell (1948); but it starts at a rather late stage and it is unlikely that there is any fundamental difference between Anurans and Urodeles in this respect. In fact, Boell and Weber (1955) were able to demonstrate an increase in cytochrome oxidase during late (after hatching) stages of development in frog embryos.

It should be added that it has repeatedly been shown (cf. Brachet, 1944 for the older literature and Selman, 1958 for a recent paper) that the energy required for morphogenetic movements, the closure of the neural folds for instance, represents an exceedingly small fraction only of the energy produced by the respiration of the embryo.

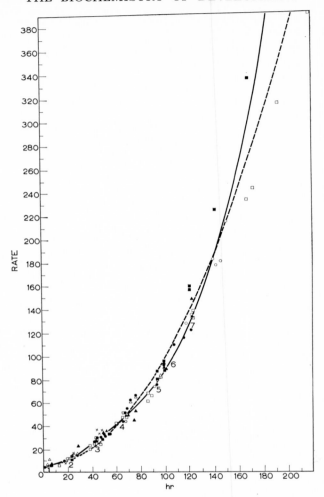

FIG. 78. A typical curve for the oxygen consumption of frog eggs (rate per 100 eggs per hour during development). The abscissae represent hours after fertilization (from M. Atlas, *Physiol. Zool.* **11**, 278, 1938).

(c) LOCAL DIFFERENCES IN OXYGEN CONSUMPTION

There have been many studies on the oxygen consumption of various regions of the amphibian embryo, especially at the gastrula stage; they have generally confirmed and extended the author's early finding (1935) that the respiration is higher in the dorsal lip of the blastoporus than in comparable ventral regions. The latest, and probably the more accurate, of these studies is that of Sze (1953), who cut the gastrula into several parts, as indicated in Fig. 79, and used the Cartesian diver as a very sensitive measuring technique. The result is that the oxygen consumption, on a dry weight basis, varies in the different regions of Fig. 79 in the following order: $2 \geqslant 3 \geqslant 1 > 4 > D > V$. This means that the gastrula is the site of a *double respiratory gradient*: an animal–vegetal one, corresponding to the initial polarity of the egg, and a dorso-ventral one. These two gradients will be found, time and again, for other biochemical activities of the gastrula.

Of great interest also are experiments of Barth and Sze (1951), who compared the oxygen consumption of ectoblast and organizer fragments when they either lie side by side or are in contact. Induction occurs only in the second case and it is accompanied by an increased rate of oxidations. In other words, neuralization of an ectoblastic fragment stimulates its oxygen consumption.

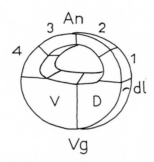

FIG. 79. Dissection of a young gastrula in various parts before measuring the oxygen consumption of the different regions (Sze, 1953).

Recent experiments by Flickinger and Blount (1958), who used a polarographic method which enabled them to measure the respiration of the various parts of the egg *in situ* (i.e. without having to cut it into pieces, with regulation as a possible dangerous complication), have essentially confirmed the existence of the respiratory gradients observed by previous workers.

It is not known for certain whether differences in the oxygen uptake between the dorsal and ventral halves already exist in the just fertilized egg: recent experiments by Løvtrup and Pigon (1958) suggest, without carrying however complete conviction, that local anaerobic conditions can produce an inversion of the dorso-ventral axis of the still uncleaved egg. The question certainly deserves further studies with more efficient methods in order to ensure anaerobiosis.

In any event, the recent measurements of Flickinger and Blount (1958) are in good agreement with much older work, which also was performed *in situ*: we refer to the studies of Fischer and Hartwig (1936), Piepho (1938) and Child (1948), who followed the reduction, under anaerobic conditions, of the dyes present in vitally stained embryos. As shown in Fig. 80, a dorso-ventral reduction gradient is clearly visible at the gastrula stage; the existence of an animal–vegetal reduction gradient also is made clear by the fact that reduction is slowest at the vegetal pole. In neurulae, the medullary plate is the first to become colourless in anaerobiosis and a cephalo-caudal decreasing gradient can be observed in this region of the embryo.

Similar work has been done by Spratt (1955, 1958) on young chick embryos: he found much greater reducing activity in the 'node centre' of the primitive streak, which is the equivalent, in all respects, to the blastoporal lip of amphibian eggs. The node centre, which has reducing properties, also exhibits greater cytochrome oxidase activity than the rest of the blastoderm.

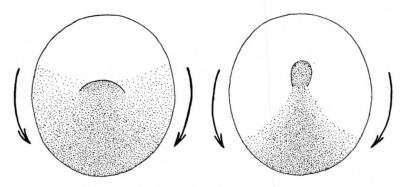

Fig. 80. Dorso-ventral reduction gradients in young and late gastrulae
(Piepho, 1938).

(d) Qualitative Metabolic Changes During Development:
Respiratory Quotient and Carbohydrate Metabolism

While, as we have seen, the oxygen consumption increases smoothly during development, a sharp change in the value of the respiratory quotient (R.Q. $= CO_2/O_2$) often occurs at gastrulation (Brachet, 1934; Barth and Barth, 1954). In *Rana temporaria*, for instance, the R.Q., which is as low as 0·65 during cleavage, jumps to values close to unity at gastrulation (Brachet, 1934); similar changes, but of a smaller magnitude, also occur in *Rana pipiens* (Barth and Barth, 1954).

The reason for this marked and sudden change, which is in agreement with the already mentioned conclusions of Malamed (1957, 1958), is, almost certainly, an increase in the utilization of carbohydrates (see O'Connor, 1957, for a detailed and recent review of the question) when gastrulation movements begin. This interpretation of the R.Q. changes is substantiated by observations made on whole eggs as well as on isolated pieces of amphibian gastrulae. In frog eggs, the glycogen content shows no measurable decrease during cleavage; but glycogenolysis becomes demonstrable as soon as gastrulation begins (Brachet and Needham, 1935; Gregg, 1948). However, it is only fair to say that, in a more recent study made on two other species of Anurans, Urbani (1957a) found a definite decrease in the content of total carbohydrates in the cleaving egg. Unfortunately, he did not measure glycogen changes in his material. Total carbohydrate measurement, in amphibian eggs, is always open to some question because of the high content in carbohydrates of the jelly and of the vitelline membrane in this material.

Work done on fragments isolated from gastrulae confirms the view that changes in R.Q. and carbohydrate utilization really occur when the amphibian egg reaches the gastrula stage. Using different techniques, Brachet (1939) and Boell et al. (1939) found a higher R.Q. in the dorsal half of the gastrula than in the ventral one. As shown in Fig. 81, Boell et al. (1939) found a much faster increase of the R.Q. in the organizer (dorsal lip) than in ventral ectoblast. Analyses of the glycogen content in different parts of the egg during gastrulation have shown also that carbohydrate metabolism begins earlier and is stronger in the dorsal lip than in ventral parts (Heatley, 1935; Heatley and Lindahl, 1937; Jaeger, 1945). It seems that one can safely accept Jaeger's (1945) conclusion: a high carbohydrate metabolism is required for the morphogenetic movements of gastrulation.

The little we know about the biochemical mechanisms of carbohydrate metabolism in amphibian eggs suggests that there is nothing mysterious about them: while A. I. Cohen (1954) found an essentially glycolytic system in *Rana pipiens* embryos, studies on $^{14}CO_2$ incorporation by S. Cohen (1954) have led to the conclusion that the Krebs tricarboxylic cycle is operative in the same material.

There is very good and direct evidence for the view that carbohydrate metabolism is also of the utmost importance for morphogenesis in chick (Spratt, 1955, 1958a, b) and trout (Devillers et al., 1957b) embryos. When blastoderms are explanted in saline, they soon stop developing and undergo cytolysis. But, if glucose is added, a considerable degree of differentiation can occur in the explants. As shown in Fig. 82, which summarizes Spratt's very interesting results on the nutritional requirements of the isolated node area in chick embryos, a number of sugars and products of intermediary carbohydrate metabolism (but not all) can replace glucose to a large extent in supporting development.

Spratt (1955, 1958a, b) also obtained interesting differential effects with metabolic inhibitors, such as iodoacetate, malonate, cyanide and anaero-biosis, which suppress development of the brain without having any effect upon the formation of the heart. He finally found (1958a, b) the curious fact that contact of the blastoderms with living (but not killed) slices of a 14-day embryo heart or liver stops all axial organ-forming activities of the node area.

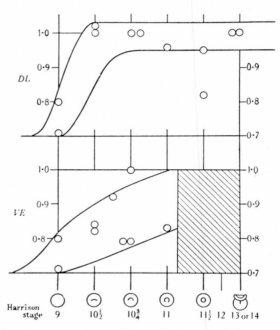

FIG. 81. Respiratory quotients of isolated pieces of *Ambystoma* gastrulae plotted against morphological age according to the progress of gastru-lation. *DL*: dorsal lip; *VE*: ventral ectoderm (Boell *et al.*, 1939).

More details of recent work on the relative utilization of carbohydrates, fats and proteins during amphibian eggs development will be found by the interested reader in recent papers by Løvtrup (1953), Urbani (1955, 1957b) and Løvtrup and Werdinius (1957).

(e) EXPERIMENTS ON THE INCORPORATION OF $^{14}CO_2$

As already mentioned earlier, S. Cohen (1954) found that frog eggs actively incorporate $^{14}CO_2$, via the Krebs tricarboxylic acid cycle. Ultimately, the labelled CO_2 becomes incorporated into the proteins and nucleic acids fractions. The rate of incorporation, into these acid-insoluble components, increases considerably during gastrulation.

Similar work has been done independently by Flickinger (1954) and has led to the same conclusions; but Flickinger (1954) made additional studies, which have great interest for embryologists. He compared the incorporation of $^{14}CO_2$ into nucleic acids and proteins in various parts of gastrulae, which had been dissected much in the same way as Sze (1953) performed his sectioning in studies on the oxygen consumption of gastrula fragments. Like Sze (1953), he found that there are definite gradient patterns in the incorporation mechanisms: incorporation of $^{14}CO_2$ into nucleoproteins proceeds according to a double gradient, an animal–vegetal and a dorso-ventral one.

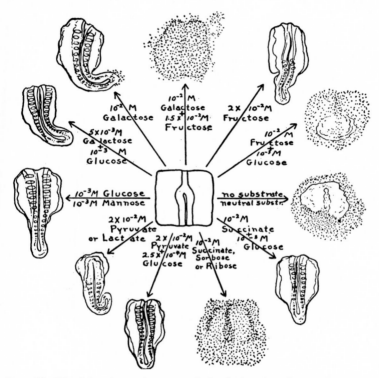

FIG. 82. Nutritional requirement of the isolated node centre area of chick embryos (Spratt, 1955).

Autoradiography methods have, once more, proven useful in studies on the incorporation of $^{14}CO_2$ into nucleic acids and proteins during amphibian development. As shown by Brachet and Ledoux (1955), incorporation is much stronger in the nuclei than in the cytoplasm during cleavage. In fact, as much as 90 per cent of the tracks which can be seen on autoradiographs of cleaving eggs, when $^{14}CO_2$ is used as the precursor, originate from the nuclei. Further work by Tencer (1958) has led one step further. She was able to show that, at gastrulation, cytoplasmic activity becomes more and more conspicuous and that gradients in radioactivity, similar to those described by Flickinger (1954), become apparent. Incorporation of $^{14}CO_2$ into proteins and cytoplasmic RNA follows the already familiar gradient (animal–vegetal and dorso-ventral) pattern. During this period, the nuclei still incorporate the label more actively than does the cytoplasm, but they show no conspicuous gradient activity. In the late gastrula, the cytoplasmic gradients apparently exert an influence on the nuclei; the latter now show the same changes in radioactivity as the cytoplasm (i.e. nuclear radioactivity decreases from the animal to the vegetal pole and from the dorsal to the ventral end). More will be said about these observations in the next chapter, which will deal with nucleo-cytoplasmic interactions during development. For our present purpose, it is enough to remember that nucleoprotein synthesis, in the cytoplasm as well as in the nuclei, follows the same gradient pattern as the energy-producing mechanisms.

(f) ATP Production and Utilization

Many important facts and interesting details can be found in the book of Barth and Barth (1954) on the energetics of development in frog eggs. From extensive studies on phosphorus metabolism, in aerobiosis and in anaerobiosis, the authors have come to the conclusion that phospho-proteins, which are the main constituents of the yolk platelets, can serve to build up ATP during development. Phosphoprotein phosphatase, an enzyme which splits inorganic phosphate from phosphoproteins and which is present in the yolk platelets themselves, may play an important role in these phosphate transfer processes. In anaerobiosis, according to Barth and Barth (1954) and to Brachet (1954b), a measurable breakdown of ATP takes place: it looks as if development stopped when the ATP content drops below a certain threshold value. However, more recent work by Gregg and Kahlbrock (1957) indicates that, in the *Rana pipiens* eggs already studied by Barth and Barth (1954), the situation might be somewhat more complicated than was thought previously. According to Gregg and Kahlbrock (1957), dinitrophenol, but not anaerobiosis, reduces the ATP content of these eggs. This discrepancy between the results of Barth and Barth (1954) and Gregg and Kahlbrock (1957) might, however, simply be due to the fact that it is very difficult to place amphibian eggs in *completely* anaerobic conditions: as found by Brachet (1934), frog eggs respire to an almost normal rate if traces of oxygen are still present in the nitrogenous atmosphere. In our more recent (1954b) experiments on *Rana temporaria*, complete anaerobiosis was obtained; under these conditions, the ATP content was found to drop by at least 50 per cent during a 16-hour period. It seems, therefore, that Gregg and Kahlbrock's (1957) experiments do not carry sufficient weight to modify the conclusion that frog eggs, as all other cells, draw the energy they require for anaerobic development from breakdown of ATP.

(g) Distribution of Mitochondria

Since mitochondria play by far the most important role in intracellular energy production, it is adequate to end the present discussion with a brief survey of the facts known about their distribution and structure

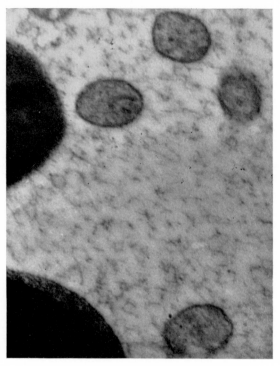

FIG. 83. Electron micrograph (× 28,000) of the ectoderm of a middle gastrula (courtesy of Prof. T. Yamada).

during development of vertebrate eggs. Electron microscopy and biochemical analysis of typical mitochondrial enzymes (cytochrome oxidase, for instance) are obviously the best methods for this type of study. All that can be said is that present evidence points to the conclusion that, in amphibian eggs, both the number and the complexity of the mitochondria increase in a simultaneous fashion (Figs. 83 and 84).

Electron microscopy studies of developing amphibian eggs are barely beginning: the most important paper published so far on the subject is that of Eakin and Lehmann (1954); but this paper is based on work done at a time when resolution of the electron microscope and fixation techniques were not yet at their very best. Fortunately, Yamada and Karasaki (1958), Karasaki (1959), Ranzi (1958), Lanzavecchia and Le Coultre (1959) used the now classical buffered osmium tetroxide as a fixative in their more recent electron microscope studies. Their results agree with those of their predecessors in showing that both mitochondria and endoplasmic reticulum

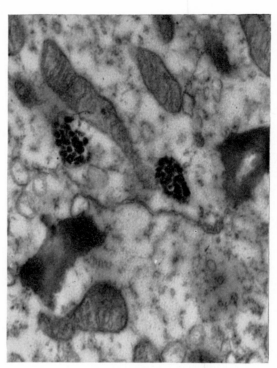

FIG. 84. Electron micrograph ($\times$ 28,000) of the neural area of a late neurula (cf. Fig. 83): note the increase in length and complexity (formation of *cristae*) of the mitochondria and the transformation of particulate into vesicular ergastoplasm.

are unusually simple in the gastrula; in the neural plate mitochondria are already longer and more complex in structure. The number of the 'cristae mitochondriales' increases more and more when differentiation progresses, while the initially coarse and vesicular endoplasmic reticulum becomes denser. A higher frequency of elongated mitochondriae, with many *cristae* and a greater abundance of Golgi elements characterizes the organizer.

An interesting point, which has already been mentioned in Chapter I, is that a close relationship seems to exist between mitochondria and yolk platelets in developing eggs. Studies by R. Bellairs (1958) on chick embryos and by Ranzi (1958)* on amphibian eggs indicate intimate contact between mitochondria and yolk platelets or droplets. It really looks as if yolk could be converted into mitochondria during development; but, as in all purely morphological studies, a definite conclusion can hardly be reached about dynamic processes. The possibility, pointed out by R. Bellairs (1958), that mitochondria might migrate into yolk droplets in developing chick embryos at present cannot be ruled out. It might also be, according to the same author, that mitochondria perform an important function in the digestion of yolk.

The conclusions drawn by Weissenfels (1958), in another electron microscopy study of chick embryos, are rather different: he thinks that mitochondria arise from 'pre-mitochondria', which are built in special regions of the hyaloplasm.

The existence of such discrepancies in the interpretation of electron micrographs (which are probably mainly due to technical reasons) suffices to prove the need of much more extensive studies on mitochondrial origin and structure in embryological material.

On the biochemical level, very careful studies by Boell and Weber (1955) and Weber and Boell (1955) on the distribution of cytochrome oxidase in homogenates of frog eggs have led to conclusions which are in excellent agreement with the main data obtained from electron microscopy.

These workers found that both the number of mitochondria and their cytochrome oxidase content (or specific activity) increase as development proceeds. It is unfortunate, however, that nobody has so far tried to establish the cytochrome oxidase distribution in the different regions of developing amphibian eggs.

Finally, it should be recalled that Spratt (1955) found (using cytochemical methods) increased cytochrome oxidase activity in the node area of chick embryos. He studied both the indophenoloxidase (Nadi) reaction and Janus Green staining and reduction. These results of Spratt (1955) strongly suggest that mitochondria are accumulated in this all important node area of the chick embryo; independent confirmation, with the electron microscope as a tool, would of course be very welcome.

Summing up, this analysis of energy production mechanisms in developing vertebrate eggs leads to a few important conclusions: (1) carbohydrate metabolism is of fundamental importance in early embryonic stages of development, as was clearly shown by J. Needham, as early as 1930; (2) mitochondria, which contain important enzymes for oxidative phosphorylations, are distributed along animal–vegetal and dorso-ventral (reduction) gradients; they either arise from yolk breakdown or are instrumental in breaking down the yolk reserves. In any event, development is closely

* See also the papers of Lanzavecchia and Le Coultre (1958) and Karasaki (1959).

linked to increase in number and complexity of mitochondria at both the biochemical and the morphological levels.

2. The chemical nature of the inducing substance

We have presented in detail elsewhere (Brachet, 1944) the earlier work in this important field; we shall summarize it briefly here and concentrate on the most recent results.

As soon as it was shown by Bautzmann *et al.* (1932) that organizers killed with alcohol, heating or freezing are still capable of inducing a neural tube, it was realized that induction must be a chemical process and attempts have been made to identify and isolate the 'active' inducing substance in pure form. Experiments by Wehmeier (1934) and Holt-freter (1935) gave considerable hope that such a goal might be reached. They found that the 'inducing substance' (also called the 'evocator') is a very widespread one. Almost all tissues of adult Vertebrates and Inverte-brates, especially if they have been killed beforehand, induce neuralization of the ectoblast if they are grafted into the blastocele cavity of young gastrulae.

The next step, as was quickly realized by Needham, Waddington, F. G. Fischer, Barth and others, was to try to isolate the inducing sub-stance from an adult tissue, liver for instance. The results were, however, disappointing, since it soon became clear that many chemically unrelated substances (sterols, glycogen, nucleotides, fatty acids, etc.) can induce neural differentiation in ventral ectoderm (see Brachet, 1944, for a detailed review of this work).

Further investigations by Waddington, Needham and Brachet (1936) indicated that neuralization could be obtained by treatment with sub-stances of non-biological origin, methylene blue for instance. The con-clusion drawn from this observation was that ectoderm already contains the inducing substance, but in a masked, inactive form. Any unspecific agent which releases the block and unmasks the bound inducing substance will provoke neuralization of the ectoblast. Later work by Barth and Graff (1938), Holtfreter (1945, 1947a), Yamada (1950) and Flickinger (1958) has entirely confirmed the correctness of Waddington *et al.*'s (1936) conclusions. They found, as already mentioned, that a shift in the pH of the surrounding medium is enough to produce the neuralization of pieces of presumptive ectoderm. Ammonia (Holtfreter, 1945; Yamada, 1950), thiocyanate (Ôgi, 1958) and CO_2 (Flickinger, 1958) are especially active in this respect. It is interesting to note that, according to Yamada (1950), a treatment with ammonia does not only induce neuralization in presumptive ectoderm fragments, but can even increase the potentialities of ventral mesoderm, which will differentiate into chorda.

These results, interesting as they are, have been a blow to those who had hoped that it might be possible to find *one* single, specific chemical responsible for neuralization. In fact, induction and parthenogenetic activation of the unfertilized egg have a good deal in common. In both cases, many unrelated physical and chemical agents elicit the biological reaction. In both cases, the common denominator still remains unknown, and many hypotheses have been presented in order to explain the facts. Reversible protein denaturation has been suggested by L. Rapkine (see Brachet, 1944), while Holtfreter (1946) has insisted on the fact that the protein membrane which surrounds lipochondria breaks down at the acid and alkaline pH's which provoke spontaneous neuralization of isolated ectodermic fragments. Another tempting hypothesis is that acids and bases produce the breakdown of the membrane surrounding de Duve's (1957) lysosomes: the hydrolytic enzymes present in these vacuoles are then set free, with deep consequences on the metabolism of the ectoderm, which could ultimately lead to neural differentiation. But, unfortunately, it has so far been impossible to demonstrate the existence of lysosomes in amphibian eggs, although these granules are apparently present in young chick embryos (Brachet *et al.*, 1958). It thus must be admitted that we still do not know why ectoblastic fragments undergo a neural differentiation under the influence of an acid or alkaline shock.

It has been suggested by the author (1944) that ribonucleoproteins might play a leading role in neural induction on the following grounds: ribonucleoproteins extracted from different tissues are better neural inductors than proteins which have a lower RNA content; furthermore, removal of RNA from the active ribonucleoproteins by a ribonuclease digestion leads to a decrease in the inducing activity (Brachet, 1944).

The strong inducing power of ribonucleoproteins (liver microsomes of tobacco mosaic virus for instance) has been confirmed by many workers (Brachet *et al.*, 1952; Kuusi, 1953; Yamada and Takata, 1955a, 1956; Hayashi, 1956; v. Woellwarth, 1956; Yamada, 1958a, b, etc.). But, on the other hand, it has been impossible to confirm the inhibitory effect of ribonuclease on abnormal inductors in later experiments (Brachet *et al.*, 1952; Kuusi, 1953; Yamada and Takata, 1955a, Hayashi, 1955; Engländer and Johnen, 1957; Vahs, 1957). The reason for the discrepancy between the results obtained by Brachet (1944) and those of the more recent workers is now clear. As shown by Hayashi (1958), short treatment of the ribonucleoprotein with proteolytic enzymes, such as pepsin or trypsin, is enough to destroy the inducing power. For the wartime experiments of Brachet (1944), no crystalline ribonuclease was available and there is no doubt that the 'purified' preparations used in these experiments were contaminated with proteolytic enzymes. That the active substance in ribonucleoprotein is protein rather than RNA is further shown by the fact that RNA, isolated by mild methods (Yamada and Takata, 1955b;

M

Tiedemann and Tiedemann, 1956) from various tissues, including embryos, is a mild inductor only. These negative experiments carry, however, no great weight in view of the difficulty often experienced in isolating non-denaturated RNA.

Although there is, as we have just seen, strong evidence for the view that the active portion, in ribonucleoproteins, is protein rather than RNA, the question should not yet be considered as completely answered. Tiedemann and Tiedemann (1955) have reported an inhibitory effect of ribonuclease on tail induction by chick embryo extract. Furthermore, Vahs (1957) found the curious fact that Gram positive bacteria—which are thought to contain more RNA in their membranes than the Gram negative ones—can induce neuralization of presumptive ectoderm, while Gram negative bacteria are inactive in this respect. According to Vahs (1957), treatments with either ribonuclease or U.V. irradiation (which inactivate or destroy RNA easily) suppress the inducing activity of Gram positive bacteria.

Still more important is the work of Niu (1956, 1958a, b), who was able to show that explants of the chordomesoblast (organizer) produce ribonucleoproteins in the surrounding medium; the latter—which Niu (1956) calls a 'conditioned medium'—induces neuralization in explanted ectoblastic fragments. This neuralization, according to Niu (1956), cannot be explained on the basis of a release of an inducing or toxic substance by cytolysing cells. Furthermore, ribonuclease inactivates the neuralizing factor produced by the explanted organizer in axolotl and *Triturus torosus*; the enzyme has no inhibitory action, however, in the case of *Triturus rivularis*. These interesting experiments of Niu (1956), which will be discussed again later on, suggest that RNA may play a direct role in neural induction in certain species of Amphibians, but not in all.

Niu's (1958a, b) most recent papers show how controversial the question of the role of RNA in induction remains: working with small explanted ectoblastic fragments, he studied the inducing activity of ribonucleoproteins and purified RNA extracted from various sources, especially thymus. He found that these preparations were active and that a treatment with trypsin inactivates them; but the effect of trypsin is apparently not on the nucleoprotein, but on the explanted cells themselves, since it can be suppressed by the addition of soya bean trypsin inhibitor. Treatment of the extracts with ribonuclease produced only partial removal (40–70 per cent) of the RNA and reduced the inducing activity. Niu's (1958a, b) conclusion is exactly the opposite of that of Yamada (1958a, b): he believes that there is a correlation between the amount of RNA and the frequency of embryonic differentiation. Obviously, much more work is still required before a definite and general conclusion can be reached.

Work by Ambellan (1955, 1958) has shown also that the addition of ribonucleotides, such as ATP, ADP or AMP, definitely speeds up the closure of the neural plate. This stimulation may be due to an increased and faster RNA synthesis, which would be of importance for the formation of the neural tube.

Several workers have attempted to block, in a specific way, the groups which might be active in the protein part of the ribonucleoprotein inductor; they found that formalin, ketene and nitrous acid, which easily react with amino groups, quickly destroy the inducing activity of killed organizers (Lallier, 1950; Kuusi, 1953; Smith and Schechtman, 1954). However, Evans blue, a dye which should also react with —NH$_2$ groups does not inhibit the inducing capacity of dead organizers; nor does iodine, a fact which, as pointed out earlier by Brachet (1944), demonstrates that the integrity of —SH groups is not required for inducing activity (Lallier, 1956).

Without casting any doubt on the interest of such experiments, the conclusion, which has been drawn by Lallier (1950) and by Kuusi (1953), that the *protein* amino groups are required for successful induction cannot remain unchallenged. Nucleic acids contain amino purines and, in a recent study on the infectivity of tobacco mosaic virus RNA, Schuster and Schramm (1958) found that deamination by nitrous acid of one single nucleotide out of 3300 is enough to inactivate the whole molecule.

In the foregoing discussion, only the facts related to *neural* induction have been presented. The evidence, as we have just seen, suggests that the inductor is a ribonucleoprotein, in which the protein part may be more important than the nucleic acid part. Such a conclusion would not be valid for the induction of *mesodermic* tissues, which is so conspicuous when caudal (and not cephalic) regions are induced. All the available evidence suggests that the caudal organizer is of a purely protein nature. Discussion of this problem will be postponed until the last chapter of this book, which will deal with the biochemical mechanisms of organization and differentiation.

If we wish to summarize present knowledge concerning the inducing substance, all we can say is that its chemical nature remains obscure and that it will be an exceedingly difficult task to try to elucidate it along the lines that have just been discussed. The menace of a non-specific release of a neuralizing substance already present in the ectoblast in a masked form will always loom up before the experimenter. The more complex the experiments become, the more difficult is their interpretation. For instance, inhibition of induction by agents such as ribonuclease, proteolytic enzymes, nitrous acid, ketene, etc., may be due to an effect of the ectoblast cells themselves, rather than to the block of a specific chemical group in the inducing substance. In other words, the reacting system, i.e. the ectoblast, may be directly affected by changes in the surrounding medium in two

opposite ways: stimulation of neural differentiation (spontaneous neuralization) or loss of competence, which would make the ectoblast incapable of
reacting to inducing stimuli.

In view of these uncertainties and the difficulty in solving them, another
approach must be used; this is why many investigators have preferred
to study RNA and protein metabolism in intact, living eggs, either placed
in normal or experimentally changed conditions.

3. RNA and protein metabolism of intact eggs

There is no longer any reason to doubt that RNA plays a major role
in protein synthesis (see Brachet, 1957, for a discussion on this question)
and we shall therefore deal with protein and RNA synthesis together in
the following discussion.

(a) RNA AND PROTEIN SYNTHESIS IN THE WHOLE AMPHIBIAN EMBRYO

The existence of a quantitatively measurable RNA synthesis during
amphibian egg development is now a well-established fact (Brachet, 1941;
Steinert, 1951). Studies on the incorporation of various precursors into
RNA (Kutsky, 1950; Rounds and Flickinger, 1958) have confirmed and
extended the conclusions drawn from the earlier, purely quantitative work.
RNA synthesis is very low, if it exists at all, during cleavage. At gastrulation, a definite transfer of the labile phosphate of ATP to RNA becomes
detectable with tracer (^{32}P) methods. During neurulation, net synthesis of
RNA can be demonstrated (Brachet, 1941; Steinert, 1951). RNA synthesis
occurs, to a measurable extent, only in the dorsal, differentiating regions
of the embryo. Already in the young gastrula, the RNA content of the
dorsal half is about 25 per cent higher than in the ventral half. In the
neurula, there is no appreciable synthesis of RNA in the ventral, non-
differentiating half, whereas RNA is quickly synthesized in the dorsal
half, so that the latter contains, in the young neurula, about twice as much
RNA as the ventral half (Brachet, 1944; Steinert, 1951, 1953; Takata,
1953).

The more recent studies of Rounds and Flickinger (1958) and Grant
(1958) are in substantial agreement with the first reported work of Brachet
(1941, 1944), Steinert (1951, 1953) and Takata (1953). They found RNA
synthesis during the formation of the medullary plate in the mesoderm and
during neural tube formation in the neuroblast. During gastrulation,
according to Rounds and Flickinger (1958), yolk breakdown has already
begun in chordomesoblast and a transfer of yolk RNA to cytoplasmic
granules occurs in this region of the egg.

To summarize, there is no important synthesis of RNA during cleavage.
At gastrulation, the isotope studies of Kutsky (1950), Grant (1958) and
Rounds and Flickinger (1958) show increased RNA metabolism, which is

probably linked to induction processes. When induction has taken place, i.e. in the young neurula, net RNA synthesis can be demonstrated, but only in the differentiating, dorsal parts of the embryo.

If RNA and protein synthesis are really linked, one would expect new proteins to be built during gastrulation and neurulation. This expectation has been confirmed by independent work done on amino acid incorporation into proteins (Friedberg and Eakin, 1949; Eakin et al., 1951), on $^{14}CO_2$ incorporation into proteins (Cohen, 1954; Flickinger, 1954; Tiedemann and Tiedemann, 1954) and on the synthesis of new, serologically recognizable, proteins (Cooper, 1948; Clayton, 1953).

A little more should be said now about all this work, which demonstrates the important fact that appreciable synthesis of proteins only begins at gastrulation: Friedberg and Eakin (1949) found, for instance, that incorporation of glycine into proteins is negligible until gastrulation; similar observations have been made in the case of methionine incorporation into proteins by Eakin et al. (1950), who further found that incorporation of this amino acid is higher in the dorsal than in the ventral half. This additional finding is interesting in view of what has been said earlier about RNA synthesis being stronger in the dorsal than in the ventral half at the gastrula stage. Similar observations have been made, but on toad eggs this time, by Céas and Naselli (1958), who observed stronger incorporation of labelled methionine in the dorsal than in the ventral half of the gastrula.

Autoradiography studies by Sirlin (1955) have disclosed the fact that incorporation of methionine, at the gastrula stage, is particularly high in the nuclei of the organizer. Sirlin's (1955) observations are in general agreement with those of Ficq (1954), Waddington and Sirlin (1954, 1955), Brachet and Ledoux (1955) showing that incorporation of glycine, methionine and $^{14}CO_2$ is always higher in the nuclei than in the cytoplasm during early development of amphibian eggs. As already mentioned, 90 per cent of the incorporation of $^{14}CO_2$ occurs in the nuclei (Fig. 85), a fact which has been confirmed by the more recent and extensive studies of Tencer (1958). However, there is no appreciable difference in the radioactivity of the nuclei in dorsal and ventral parts at the early gastrula stage when a non specific precursor such as $^{14}CO_2$ is used. The interesting phenomenon discovered by Sirlin (1955) certainly deserves further analysis. For instance, the effects of ethionine, which is a well-known analogue of methionine, on morphogenesis and methionine incorporation in amphibian eggs, certainly deserve study.

We have already mentioned the fact that, according to Cohen (1954) and Flickinger (1954), radioactive CO_2 is easily incorporated into nucleic acids and proteins, via the tricarboxylic acid cycle of Krebs. The incorporation into the proteins markedly increases at gastrulation and, as shown by Flickinger (1954), it proceeds according to a double, dorso-ventral and animal–vegetal, gradient.

Coming now to the evidence obtained with serological methods, it can be said that both Cooper (1948) and Clayton (1953) found that new antigens make their appearance between the blastula and the gastrula stage, both in frogs and in newts. According to Clayton (1953), synthesis of new antigens occurs at precise stages during development of newt eggs: between the blastula and the gastrula, before neurulation and between the neurula and tail-bud stages. It has also been reported by Vainio (1956) that the organizer contains an antigen which is absent in presumptive

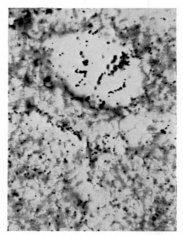

FIG. 85. Strongly labelled nucleus in a blastula treated with $^{14}CO_2$ (Brachet and Ledoux, 1955). Autoradiograph of Dr. A. Ficq.

ectoderm. Such a finding is important and interesting enough to warrant confirmation and extension to other species.

The important work of Ranzi (1957a, b) should now be mentioned. Using both immunological and salting-out techniques, Ranzi and his students (1957) found that at least two proteins which were absent in unfertilized eggs can be detected in tail-bud stages. More will be said about Ranzi's (1957a, b) work when we discuss the effects of lithium ions on both morphogenesis and biochemical processes in amphibian eggs. For the time being, all that should be added is that Ranzi's work (1957a, b) is in very good agreement with results obtained earlier by Flickinger and Nace (1952) in the author's laboratory.

Finally, extensive enzymatic studies by Løvtrup (1955) and Urbani (1955, 1957a, b), although the results obtained differ in several details, have shown clearly that no enzyme synthesis can be detected during segmentation. According to Løvtrup (1955), a few enzymes (amylase and alkaline phosphatase, for instance) undergo synthesis during gastrulation. But Urbani (1957a, b) found, on the contrary, a decrease in the amylase content during development of toad eggs. Regarding other enzymes, he observed a synthesis of lipase during early embryonic development in *Bufo*; proteases and peptidases, according to Urbani (1955, 1957a, b), show a marked increase in activity in late embryonic stages, after hatching of the tadpoles. This increase is presumably linked to the differentiation of the gut, which becomes functional at this time.

Different results have been reported by Deuchar (1958) for cathepsin; she worked on still another species, *Xenopus*, and she observed an increasing proteolytic activity during gastrulation and neurulation, followed by a drop at later stages. As already mentioned, she found that a good deal (40 per cent) of the catheptic activity is present in the yolk itself.

This brief review of the enzymology of amphibian eggs shows that

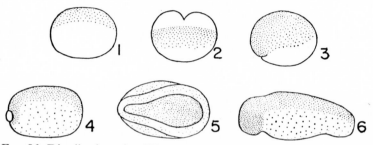

FIG. 86. Distribution of —SH-containing proteins during development of amphibian eggs (Brachet, 1940).

different authors, working on various materials, have obtained widely different results. It is impossible therefore to describe a general pattern for enzyme synthesis in various species. Two general conclusions can be drawn, however: first, protein synthesis (as well as RNA synthesis) cannot be detected during cleavage; both RNA and protein synthesis begin at gastrulation and both become more and more important as development proceeds. Secondly, as pointed out by many authors (Brachet, 1944, 1957; Flickinger, 1957; Deuchar, 1958), conversion of yolk into cytoplasmic proteins and ribonucleoproteins is a very important morphogenetic factor in Amphibians, where yolk itself (which contains cathepsin and phosphoprotein phosphatase) might play an active role. If this is true, one must expect this conversion to be more active in the regions of the egg which are most important from the embryological viewpoint. In other words, the conversion process should be quantitatively more important in the dorsal than in the ventral part. Ribonucleoprotein synthesis, at the expense of the yolk, should thus occur along a dorso-ventral decreasing gradient. We shall now see that this expectation is in fact fulfilled.

(b) GRADIENTS IN RNA AND PROTEIN DISTRIBUTION AND SYNTHESIS

Cytochemical methods were the first to be used to demonstrate regional differences in ribonucleoproteiu distribution in amphibian eggs: Fig. 86 shows the distribution of —SH-containing proteins (after denaturation of the latter) in newt embryos; these proteins are largely associated with RNA (Brachet, 1940). It will be seen that animal–vegetal and dorso-ventral gradients are very conspicuous in early stages (Fig. 86, 1–3); later, a cephalocaudal gradient becomes apparent in the nervous system, which contains many more —SH proteins than the epidermis (Fig. 86, 4–6). On the whole, the results obtained with methods for the detection of —SH-containing proteins are essentially the same as those described by Fischer and Hartwig (1936), Piepho (1938) and Child (1948) for reducing systems in living eggs placed under anaerobic conditions.

Much more precise observations, because of the better quality of the available cytochemical methods, can be made in the case of RNA distribution during amphibian egg development (Brachet, 1942, 1944). As shown in Fig. 87, a polarity gradient is already visible in the unfertilized or freshly fertilized egg; it decreases from the animal to the vegetal pole and remains intact during cleavage (Fig. 88). At gastrulation (Fig. 89), a secondary RNA gradient, decreasing from dorsal to ventral, superimposes itself upon the initial animal–vegetal gradient. As a result of RNA synthesis and morphogenetic movements, the two gradients interact with each other. The outcome is the appearance, in the late gastrula and the early neurula (Figs. 89 and 90) of very well-defined antero-posterior (cephalo-caudal) and dorso-ventral gradients; the latter is especially apparent in the chordomesoblast.

When late gastrulae or early neurulae are examined with a microscope, under high power, a high RNA content is found at the interval separating the young medullary plate from presumptive chorda. It looks as if, at the very time of induction, RNA accumulated precisely at the points where inductor and reacting system are in close contact. Similar observations have been made, more recently, in chick embryos also (Lavarack, 1957).

At later stages of embryonic development, the RNA content of every organ increases just before its differentiation begins. Differentiation itself (for instance, vacuolization of the notochord or formation of neurones in the nervous system) often results in a drop in the RNA content of the individual cells, except when the latter belong to an actively-synthesizing organ (liver or pancreas, for instance).

Considerable experimental work would be required in order to demonstrate the reality of these gradients—which superimpose themselves on the morphogenetic gradients of the experimental embryologists—quantitatively with biochemical methods. The work which has already been done in that direction—and which was mentioned earlier—is sufficient, however,

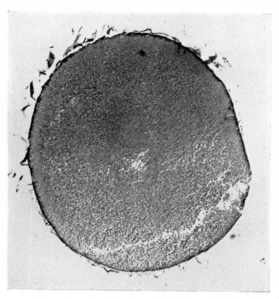

FIG. 87. Distribution of RNA in a fertilized amphibian egg (Brachet 1957).

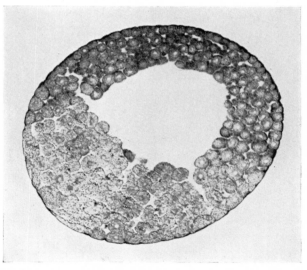

FIG. 88. Distribution of RNA in an amphibian blastula (Brachet, 1957).

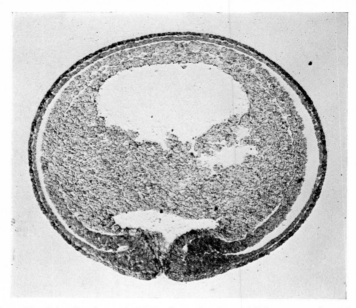

FIG. 89. Distribution of RNA in a late amphibian gastrula. Note stronger basophilia in dorsal (right) than in ventral (left) half (Brachet, 1957).

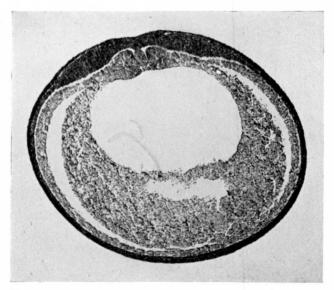

FIG. 90. Distribution of RNA in a young amphibian neurula (Brachet, 1957).

to leave no doubt concerning the existence of the gradients which have been detected with cytochemical methods (Brachet, 1942; Steinert, 1951; Takata, 1953; Blount and Flickinger, 1958).

Less is known about the gradient distribution of proteins, except for the already mentioned case of the —SH-containing proteins. Nevertheless, there is no reason to doubt that several non-yolk proteins are distributed along the same gradient as RNA and the —SH-containing proteins. Such a conclusion is largely based upon the already described work on isotope incorporation in the various parts of the embryo of Friedberg and Eakin (1949), Eakin *et al.* (1951), Flickinger (1954), Tencer (1958), Céas and Naselli (1958): stronger incorporation into the proteins of the dorsal than into those of the ventral regions is a very general rule.

According to d'Amelio and Céas (1957), protease is distributed along the same gradients as RNA: its concentration decreases from the animal to the vegetal pole in the blastula, and from the dorsal to the ventral end in the gastrula. However, Deuchar (1958) found protease, in *Xenopus*, more concentrated in the ventral than in the dorsal half of the gastrula. This discrepancy is not really surprising since the protease studied by Deuchar (1958) is accumulated in the yolk, thus in the ventral and vegetal regions of the gastrula.

In summing up, there is no doubt that amphibian eggs contain RNA and protein gradients; these gradients superimpose themselves on the morphogenetic gradients and, also, on the already described gradients for oxygen consumption and reducing systems. One can, therefore, hardly avoid the conclusion that they represent regions where the yolk reserves are transformed into 'true' cytoplasm (ergastoplasm and mitochondria) at a faster rate than elsewhere. Looking at them from another angle, these gradients should be considered as gradients in the distribution of such cytoplasmic fractions as RNA-rich ergastoplasmic granules or vesicles, and mitochondria.

Before we can consider these gradients as important factors in morphogenesis, two important questions should be answered: are there similar gradients in vertebrate eggs other than those of the Amphibians? What happens to the ribonucleoprotein gradients when morphogenesis is experimentally modified?

(c) RNA Distribution in the Embryos of Vertebrates Other Than Amphibians

The most complete study of RNA distribution in chick embryos is that of Gallera and Oprecht (1948), who showed that node centre cells exhibit greater cytoplasmic basophilia than neighbouring cells; these results have been confirmed by Spratt (1952), who used toluidine blue as a stain for RNA detection. We have already seen that, in the chick as in the amphibian egg, increased basophilia is found at the interface between neuroblast and chordomesoblast, thus at the very site of induction (Lavarack, 1957).

Bird and amphibian eggs are also very similar regarding the distribution of —SH-containing proteins which, as a rule, follows the same pattern as RNA: the existence of a cephalocaudal gradient, in 7–9 somites embryos, was demonstrated by Rulon in 1935. Much more recently, Katayama (1956) found that the primitive streak and, especially, the Hensen node yield very strong reactions for —SH groups bound to proteins. Regarding the latter, autoradiography work by Sirlin and Waddington (1956) on amino acid incorporation into proteins has shown that, as in Amphibians, regions of high morphogenetic activity always show considerable protein anabolism.

It is beyond the scope of the present book to present, in an extensive manner, the results which have been obtained with mammalian eggs, because they are too different from those of the other Vertebrates. A few words should, however, be said about the very interesting results obtained by Dalcq and his co-workers on mammalian material. They have been very adequately summarized by Dalcq himself in a recent book (1957). In the special case of the Mammals, nucleoli are already present in the pronuclei and in early cleavage nuclei. This difference from the eggs of all other Vertebrates and of many Invertebrates is probably due to the slowness of cleavage in mammalian eggs; two to three days are required before the egg divides into a dozen or so cells. It would be very interesting to study this period of exceedingly slow cleavage with auto-radiography methods. We have seen earlier that, during cleavage of amphibian eggs, incorporation of precursors into nucleic acids and proteins is almost completely a nuclear process. But it might well be that, in Mammals, the nuclei already exert a positive influence on *cytoplasmic* syntheses during cleavage, since it is now generally believed that nucleoli play an important role in RNA and protein synthesis (cf. Chapter I).

According to Dalcq (1957), this unusual and remarkable nucleolar activity during cleavage might result in a constant activation of the cytoplasm: mucopolysaccharides and plasmalogen complexes of nuclear origin would arise in the cytoplasm. There would be 'two linked cycles of major activity, one directed outwards from the nucleus and leading to the manufacture of (DNA) precursors, and the other directed towards the nucleus and leading to the synthesis of DNA' (Dalcq, 1957).

The cytochemical studies of Dalcq and his school have clearly shown finite patterns in RNA distribution and synthesis occur during ·elopment of mammalian eggs; Figs. 91–93, which are taken from ɔok (1957) summarize, in a very clear way, the main findings. esis, as in other Vertebrates, is especially marked in the mesoblast and the induced parts of the ectoblast (Fig. 91.) A glance at Fig. 92 will show that there is no parallel synthesis of mucopolysaccharides during mammalian development: metachromatic granules are more abundant in trophoblastic cells than in the embryo itself. On the other hand, the

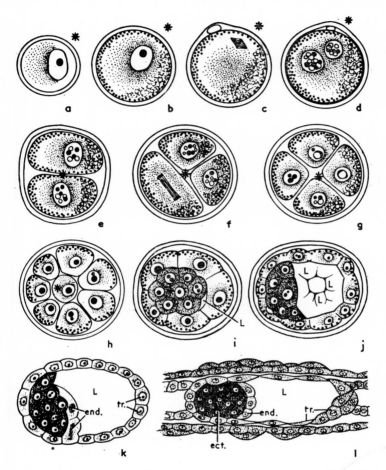

FIG. 91. Distribution of RNA during early development of mammalian eggs (Dalcq, 1957).

distribution of alkaline phosphatase is very similar to that of RNA. As shown in Fig. 93, the primitive streak and the structures which have arisen by induction are especially rich in this enzyme (Mulnard, 1955).

In short, the cytochemical data obtained in the case of Birds and Mammals agree very well with the general conclusions which we have drawn from the study of amphibian eggs: RNA is accumulated and is most actively synthesized in the regions of the embryo which have the greatest importance for morphogenetic processes.

(d) EXPERIMENTAL MODIFICATIONS OF RNA SYNTHESIS AND MORPHO-GENESIS: EFFECTS ON RNA GRADIENTS IN AMPHIBIAN EGGS

If synthesis of RNA along animal and vegetal gradients were really an

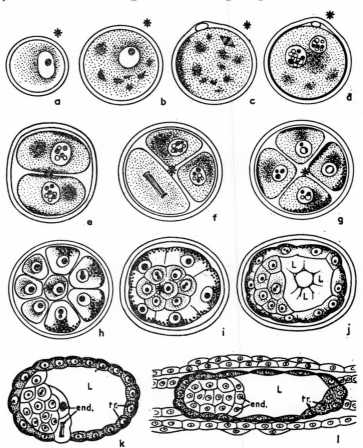

FIG. 92. Distribution of mucopolysaccharides during early development of mammalian eggs (Dalcq, 1957).

essential factor in morphogenesis, inhibition of RNA synthesis by treatment with *chemical analogues* of purines and pyrimidines should lead to the cessation of development or to abnormal development.

This expectation has been fulfilled, as shown by the author (Brachet, 1944), in the cases of barbituric acid, benziminazole and acriflavine.

These early studies have been considerably extended by Bieber (1954), Bieber and Hitchings (1955) and Liedke *et al.* (1954, 1957a, b). They used a considerable number (more than one hundred) of chemical analogues of purines, pyrimidines and nucleosides, and they found, as a rule, inhibition

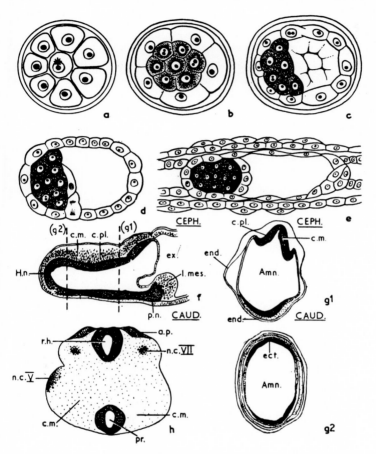

Fig. 93. Distribution of alkaline phosphatase in developing mammalian eggs (Dalcq, 1957).

of development at a definite stage. The number of chemicals studied is so large that no attempt will be made here to discuss this work in any detail. The conclusion is, however, a general one: in the eggs treated with the analogues, development stops at a precise stage, a fact which suggests the possibility that new enzymatic mechanisms for RNA synthesis appear at definite stages of development. Of special interest is the fact, observed by Liedke *et al.* (1957b), that some of the analogues used block development at the gastrula stage. If a piece of the arrested gastrulae is grafted into a normal gastrula, the blocked fragment resumes normal development and differentiation. We shall find, later on, other examples of such '*revitalization*' phenomena, when we study the development of eggs which contain an abnormal paternal nucleus (lethal hybrids) or gastrulae which have been submitted to a heat shock. The most likely explanation for this revitalization phenomenon is the same in all these cases: the fragment of the blocked gastrula can no longer synthesize certain substances, RNA in particular, and its development is thus arrested; if it is grafted into a normal gastrula, substances of an unknown nature, but which are required for RNA synthesis, diffuse from the host to the graft.

In chick embryos, inhibitors of RNA synthesis also impair morphogenesis: for instance, Fox and Goodman (1953) found that abnormal synthetic nucleosides, in which ribose was replaced by another sugar (glucose, for instance), inhibit the development of explanted chick embryos. In more recent studies, Waddington *et al.* (1955) found that the regions which are most sensitive to chemical analogues such as benziminazole or azaguanine are precisely those which show the highest incorporation of methionine into proteins: once more, RNA synthesis, protein synthesis and morphogenesis appear as very closely linked in developing eggs. A later study of Waddington and Perry (1958) has shown, however, that RNA and protein metabolisms can be dissociated, to a certain extent, by the use of more specific analogues of amino acids (ethionine, phenylalanine, for instance) and purines: purine analogues, but not those of amino acids, inhibit mitosis at early prophase. But both types of analogues attack electively tissues which are undergoing differentiation: first the primitive streak, then the neural system. Thus the general conclusion that ribonucleoprotein anabolism and morphogenesis are linked together remains valid.

Finally, Hiroaka and Hopper (1957) have been working on zebra fish eggs and have used barbituric acid as a tool for experimentation; they concluded from these studies that there is a link between morphogenesis and RNA synthesis in fish eggs as well as in those of the Amphibians and the chicks.

Substances other than purine and pyrimidine analogues have comparable effects: for instance, the well-known inhibitors of oxidative phosphorylations, *dinitrophenol* and *usnic acid*, completely inhibit morphogenesis; the inhibition can be largely reversed if the treated eggs are returned to normal medium; however, abnormalities (persistent yolk plug, microcephaly) can often be found in this case (Brachet, 1954a). Cytochemical (Brachet, 1954a) and quantitative (Steinert, 1953) studies have clearly shown that inhibition of development and RNA synthesis always go hand in hand: when the dinitrophenol-treated embryos are brought back to normal medium, RNA synthesis is resumed, but only provided morphogenesis is also taking place.

Another group of interesting substances is that of the steroid hormones (stilboestrol, oestradiol, testosterone), which have been studied by Töndury (1947), Cagianut (1949) and Rickenbacher (1956). These substances, as already mentioned, inhibit cleavage or make it abnormal; furthermore, they also modify the normal gradient of RNA distribution. It seems that, due to alterations of the mitotic apparatus during early cleavage, RNA becomes unevenly distributed in daughter cells. At later stages, strong abnormalities of development can be found, the most conspicuous being unequal differentiation of the medullary folds, with an asymmetry of the nervous system as a result. It is a very interesting fact, which certainly deserves more extensive study, that, according to Cagianut (1949), addition of yeast RNA to the embryos which have been treated with steroid hormones definitely improves their differentiation.

Something should be said about another chemical, which is famous among embryologists for the fact that it inhibits the development of chorda and produces strong microcephaly: we mean *lithium* ions, which have been studied in detail, from the viewpoint of morphogenesis, by Lehmann, (1938), Pasteels (1945) and Hall (1942). It is now generally admitted, as a consequence of this work, that lithium ions exert their primary effect on the organizer itself, which shows reduced capacity for induction. The competence of the ectoblast, i.e. its capacity to react to the inducing stimuli coming out of a normal organizer, is not reduced to the same extent. The results of this situation are well known to all embryologists: the most spectacular are the total absence of the chorda (the somites having fused together under the neural tube) and microcephaly which can be so marked as to lead to cyclopia.

Cytochemical and biochemical studies made on lithium-treated amphibian eggs have yielded a number of important results; first of all, Ficq (1954) has used a very original autoradiography method, based on the nuclear reactions undergone by lithium when it is placed in a neutron flux, to detect lithium in early gastrulae: she found that, in lithium-treated gastrulae, lithium ions are accumulated by the dorsal half. More recent work by Dent and Sheppard (1957) has largely confirmed Ficq's pioneer experiments of 1954; strong accumulation of lithium in the medullary plate was also observed by these authors.

Biochemical and cytochemical work by Lallier (1954) and by Thomason (1957) has clearly shown that lithium interferes with RNA distribution and synthesis in amphibian eggs. According to Lallier (1954), lithium decreases the RNA gradients while, in Thomason's (1957) work, this ion was found to inhibit markedly the incorporation of ^{32}P into the nucleoprotein fraction.

It would, however, be an over-simplification to believe that lithium

N

acts in a *specific* way on nucleic acid distribution and synthesis: for
instance, Lallier (1954) has observed that lithium inhibits the dehydrogenase of the tricarboxylic acid cycle, while Ranzi (1957a, b) has produced
a considerable amount of evidence for the view that lithium considerably
modifies the physical properties of the fibrous proteins present in the egg.
This evidence, which is based on measurements of viscosity and molecular
weight and on the salting-out curves of the fibrous proteins of the egg, has
already been discussed in Chapter IV, in the case of sea urchin eggs. The
general conclusion remains that lithium opposes a resistance to the
demolition of pre-existing protein structures (Ranzi, 1957a, b).

We have seen, in the foregoing, that RNA synthesis and distribution

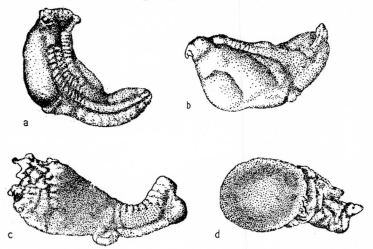

FIG. 94. Increasing reduction of head development, from *a* to *d*,
after centrifugation of fertilized eggs (Pasteels, 1940).

on the one hand and morphogenesis on the other, appear as very closely
linked processes in developing amphibian and chick eggs treated with a
great variety of chemical inhibitors. We shall now consider the effects
of *physical* treatments, such as centrifugation, heating or changing the
pH of the surrounding medium on the RNA gradients.

Centrifuging developing eggs is an easy way to modify both the gradient
distribution of substances or cell organelles and morphogenesis. The most
important experiments in this field are those of Pasteels (1940, 1953), who
worked with amphibian eggs. He found that centrifugation of freshly
fertilized eggs leads to the formation of 'hypomorph embryos'; they show
deficiences in the nervous system, which may go from complete absence
to strong microcephaly (Fig. 94). When gastrulation of these centrifuged
embryos is normal, the result is the production of embryos which have an

almost normal tail, but practically no head. On the other hand, centrifugation of blastulae leads to the formation of double or even triple embryos (Pasteels, 1953).

Unpublished studies of Pasteels and Brachet have shown that the centrifugation of both freshly fertilized eggs and blastulae produces profound changes in the distribution of RNA. As shown in Fig. 95, ribonucleoproteins accumulate at the animal pole when fertilized, but still uncleaved, eggs are centrifuged. If these eggs cleave normally, the blastoporal lip forms in a normal position. But the material which invaginates and which corresponds to the organizer is much poorer in RNA than is

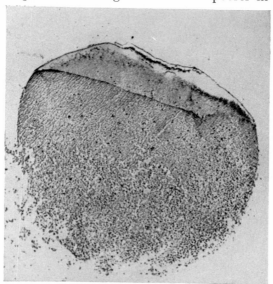

FIG. 95. Stratification of a fertilized egg after centrifugation; from top to bottom: fat; RNA-rich hyaloplasm; pigment and yolk (Brachet, 1957).

the organizer in normal eggs. This reduction in the RNA content of the invaginated material goes together with a marked decrease in its inducing activity; the hypomorphoses described by Pasteels (1940) are the logical result of such a situation.

Very different results are obtained when blastulae are centrifuged: there is first a collapse of the blastocele roof (Fig. 96) and an accumulation of RNA-rich material at the centrifugal pole of the cells. Later on, foci of strong RNA synthesis, which are characterized by their very strong basophilia, make their appearance (Fig. 97). Finally, an accessory nervous system forms in each of these basophilic areas (Fig. 98).

Further investigations, using autoradiography as the major tool, are required in order to analyse further the connections existing between

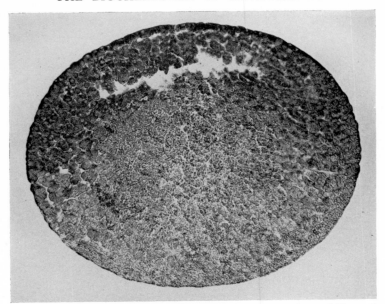

Fig. 96. Centrifuged blastula; collapse of the blastocele roof (Pasteels and Brachet, unpublished).

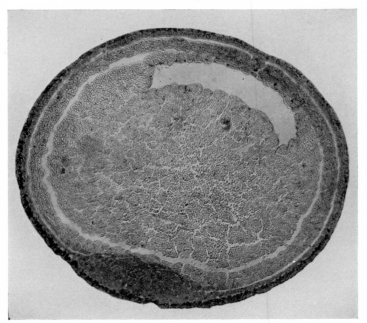

Fig. 97. Development of a RNA-rich mass on the ventral side in a neurula originating from a centrifuged blastula (Pasteels and Brachet, unpublished).

RNA distribution and synthesis on one hand, morphogenesis on the other, in centrifuged eggs. There is no doubt, however, that present evidence confirms the view that RNA and morphogenesis are intimately linked processes.

The same conclusion can be drawn from experiments, in which a young amphibian gastrula is submitted to a 'heat shock' (i.e. heating for one hour at temperatures ranging from 36° to 37°, according to the species). We have shown (Brachet, 1948, 1949a, b) that a mild heat shock produces

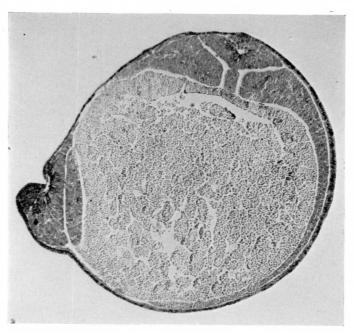

FIG. 98. Differentiation of a RNA-rich secondary embryo from a centrifuged blastula (Pasteels and Brachet, unpublished).

a reversible inhibition of development; when the latter proceeds again, numerous malformations are found. These abnormalities are essentially similar to those produced by a treatment with lithium chloride.

If the temperature chosen is a little higher, the block in development is irreversible, but no cytolysis can be detected for 2–3 days (Fig. 99). If a piece of the blocked gastrula is placed in contact with cells of a normal gastrula, even when they belong to another species, dramatic 'revitalization' of the heated cells occurs. As shown in Fig. 100, the organizer of a heated frog gastrula becomes almost normal again. Differentiation into notochord, somites and archenteron roof occurs in the graft, as well as induction of a secondary nervous system. The inductive power of the heated organizer is, however, subnormal, because it has lost the power of inducing a head, but retained that of spinocaudal induction (Takaya, 1955). 'Revitalization' of ectoblast cells from a heated gastrula can also be demonstrated when they are placed in contact with a normal organizer. These cells, as shown in Fig. 101, can still react to inducing stimuli and differentiate into a neural plate.

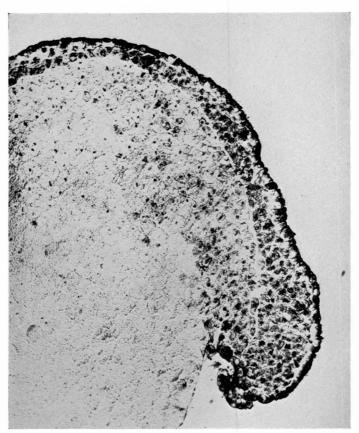

Fig. 99. Dorsal lip from a gastrula blocked after a heat shock (Brachet, 1957).

Cytochemical and biochemical studies of gastrulae which had been submitted to an irreversible or a reversible heat shock have disclosed the fact that the RNA gradients are affected to varying degrees according to the severity of the treatment. These gradients become very irregular, while mitotic activity stops and the achromatic apparatus degenerates. When a fragment of the irreversibly heated gastrula is grafted into a normal host, the first sign of healing is an impressive resumption of mitotic activity. In the reversible heat shocks, the abnormalities found in the distribution of the RNA gradients easily explain why further development becomes abnormal.

Quantitative estimations of the RNA content (Steinert, 1951) have shown that, as suggested by cytochemical observations, RNA synthesis is completely inhibited in the irreversibly blocked gastrulae (Fig. 102); if the heat shock is too severe, cytolysis begins after 3 days and the RNA content begins to drop. Steinert's (1951) results have been confirmed by

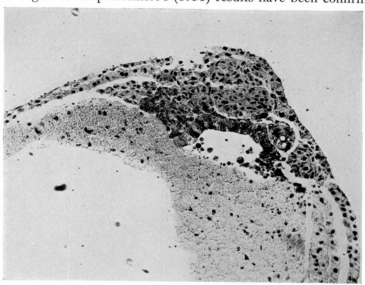

Fig. 100. The organizer of a gastrula blocked by a heat shock has been grafted into a normal host: it has differentiated into chorda and intestinal lumen, and it has induced somites and neural masses (Brachet, (1957).

Hasyawa (1955) who demonstrated that, in amphibian eggs, RNA synthesis is much more sensitive to heating than DNA synthesis. This finding of Hasyawa (1955) is again in excellent agreement with the cytochemical observations.

There is thus no doubt that the ribonucleoprotein structures of the amphibian egg cytoplasm are particularly sensitive to heating. In fact, Brachet (1949a) was able to show that a large proportion of the RNA which is normally found in the microsomes fraction goes in the supernatant when heated gastrulae are homogenized and submitted to differential centrifugation. It would, however, be unwise to believe that heat shocks act in a *specific* way on RNA-containing structures. These shocks also produce, at the gastrula stage, a very appreciable decrease (30–40 per cent) in the oxygen consumption (Brachet, 1949a).

Once again, it is clear that new tools such as electron microscopy and autoradiography should be used in the case of heated amphibian gastrulae; electron microscopy could give very valuable information about the alterations which probably occur in the ultra-fine structure of the mitochondria and the basophilic cytoplasmic constituents. Autoradiography, on the other hand, might throw useful light on the more dynamic aspects of nucleic acid and protein synthesis in heated gastrulae. But, whatever

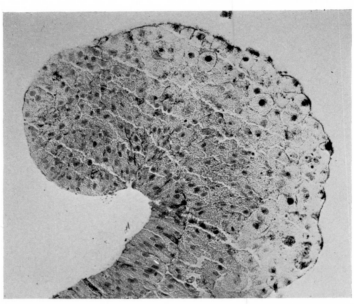

Fig. 101. 'Revitalization' and differentiation into neural plate of a piece of ectoderm from a heated gastrula placed in close contact with a fragment of normal organizer; the cells on the right have not been 'revitalized' and are degenerating (Brachet, unpublished).

the results given by these new methods, the present conclusion will certainly remain valid: changes in morphogenesis and in RNA distribution and synthesis are always parallel in heated embryos.

We saw, earlier in this chapter, that *sublethal cytolysis*, produced by shifts in the pH or removal of the calcium ions of the medium, can provoke the spontaneous neuralization of ectoblastic explants (Holtfreter, 1947): the treatments used by Holtfreter (1947) produce effects which resemble superficially the abnormalities produced by heat shocks, since they are also of short duration and applied at the early gastrula stage. However, heat shocks differ from the acid and alkaline shocks used by Holtfreter (1947) in that they never produce spontaneous neuralization (Mookerjee,

1953). Thus heat shocks decrease the morphogenetic potential of explanted ectoblastic fragments, while acid and alkaline shocks often increase it.

Too little is known as yet about the chemical and ultra-structural changes induced by acid and alkaline shocks to draw any definite conclusions. All that can be said is that they modify the structure of the cells in much the same way as does the centrifugation of blastulae. As shown in Fig. 103, the RNA-rich cytoplasm, in the cells which have been exposed to an acid or alkaline medium, accumulates in the form of a basophilic

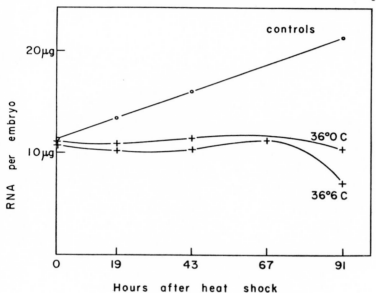

FIG. 102. RNA content of normal and heated embryos (Steinert, 1951).

crescent (Brachet, 1946). As we have already seen, the local concentration of RNA at one pole of the cells is a characteristic feature of both normal induction and formation of additional embryonic axes in centrifuged blastulae; it can thus be supposed that the crescent-shaped accumulation of RNA-rich cytoplasm in cells which have been submitted to acid or alkaline shocks has something to do with spontaneous neuralization.

A good correlation between morphogenesis and RNA synthesis is found also when an egg is fertilized with a spermatozoon belonging to another species (lethal hybrid) or with more than one spermatozoon (polyspermy). These problems will be examined in more detail in the next chapter; for the time being, it is enough to say that RNA synthesis stops when development of a lethal hybrid is blocked; there is a resumption of this synthesis when a fragment of the lethal hybrid becomes 'revitalized' after it has been transplanted into a normal host. Finally, dispermic eggs are usually formed of a diploid and a haploid half. If the two halves are equally well developed, their RNA content is the same; but, when the haploid half is underdeveloped, its RNA content is lower than that of the diploid half. In the case of dispermic eggs, it is clear that RNA synthesis is not linked to the diploid or haploid condition *per se*, but to the degree of morphogenesis which has been attained by diploid and haploid organs.

To sum up, all the evidence we have concerning RNA distribution and synthesis in normal and experimental embryos (action of numerous chemical substances, centrifugation, heating, treatment with acid or alkali, producing of an abnormal nuclear condition, etc.) shows that these

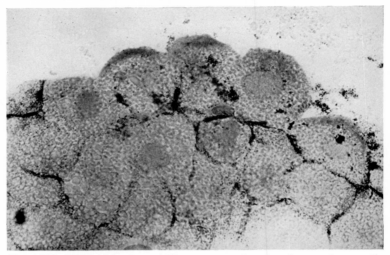

FIG. 103. RNA-rich, basophilic crescents forming in ectoderm cells which have been exposed to an alkaline shock (Brachet, 1957).

phenomena are always closely linked to morphogenesis. One should not forget, however, that RNA is only one of the many constituents of ribonucleoprotein particles. There is no proof, for the time being, that RNA is, in itself, more important for morphogenesis than the proteins and lipids with which it is associated in ergastoplasmic structures. The advantages of RNA, over the other unknown constituents of basophilic structures are the relative ease of its cytochemical detection and its important role in protein synthesis. In any event, experiments designed to demonstrate, in an unambiguous way, the role of RNA itself in morphogenetic processes are highly desirable.

Brachet and Ledoux (1955) and Brachet (1959) have attempted to attack this important point in a direct way, by treating living amphibian eggs with ribonuclease: it was hoped that the enzyme might penetrate into the living cells, inactivate or break down the RNA they contained and exert important morphogenetic effects. As we shall see, these hopes have not been entirely fulfilled because of the poor penetration of ribonuclease into amphibian eggs once cleavage is over.

We have already seen, in Chapter III, that ribonuclease quickly inhibits cleavage in amphibian eggs and that the nuclei are usually blocked in interphase. The penetration of the enzyme is, however, slow and incomplete; therefore, only the blastomeres which form the outer layers of the morula are irreversibly blocked in their development. If the treated

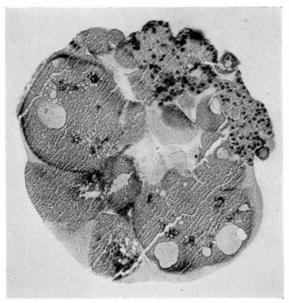

FIG. 104. Formation of atypical ectoderm in an amphibian egg treated with ribonuclease at the morula stage (Brachet and Ledoux, 1955).

morulae are brought back to normal medium, after a few hours of treatment with ribonuclease, the innermost blastomeres, which surround the blastocele, resume cleavage. They finally migrate through the dying or dead outer blastomeres and form an atypical undifferentiated ectoderm (Fig. 104). If the eggs are treated with a mixture of ribonuclease and RNA, or if they are placed in a RNA-containing medium after the ribonuclease treatment, one can occasionally obtain the formation of a nervous system (Fig. 105) which lies on a bed of large, blocked cells. The experiments are, unfortunately, not reproducible enough to allow definite and general conclusions. The fact that we have never obtained a nervous system after treatment with ribonuclease alone, but obtained several 'neurulae' after a ribonuclease–RNA treatment provides, however, a definite indication of a role for RNA in normal induction.

Penetration of ribonuclease at later stages of development is, as a rule, very poor and thus little or no effects on morphogenesis are observed. One can, however, occasionally find ribonuclease preparations which are more active than the others; since their effects can be duplicated by adding small amounts of versene (EDTA) to otherwise inactive preparations of ribonuclease, it is probable that the active preparations contain some chelating agent as a contaminant.

When blastulae or gastrulae are treated with ribonuclease reinforced by

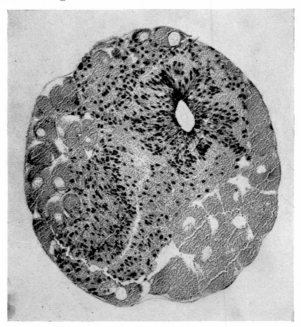

FIG. 105. Formation of a nervous system in an amphibian egg treated with a mixture of RNA and ribonuclease at the morula stage (Brachet and Ledoux, 1955).

the addition of versene (at low concentrations at which the latter is inactive by itself), the first visible result is that the ectoderm cells dissociate, lose their basophilia and finally cytolyse (Brachet, 1959). The consequence is the formation of 'ectodermless' embryos, which have well differentiated chorda and somites, but no nervous system (Figs. 106, 107) or a very reduced one. It was also found, in further experiments, that cells of the organizer exhibit a marked differential susceptibility towards the ribonuclease–versene mixture: an explanted organizer cytolyses much more quickly in this medium than explanted ventral mesoblast.

The fact that it is possible, after gastrulae have been treated with ribonuclease and versene, to obtain embryos which have no nervous system should not be taken as a proof that RNA is necessary for inductive processes in the normal organizer; of course, even a fully active organizer cannot produce its inductive effects unless the ectoderm cells of the reacting system are present. In the experiments of Brachet (1959), just described, the absence of induction is obviously due to the peeling off of the ectoderm cells. Nevertheless, the experiments have some interest in suggesting that

FIG. 106. Ectodermless embryo after treatment of a young gastrula by a mixture of ribonuclease and versene: a chorda has differentiated, but the ectoderm cells are blocked and cytolysing (Brachet, 1959).

the cement or matrix which holds the ectoderm cells together might be of a ribonucleoprotein nature; we shall return to this point a little later in this chapter.

Since it is clear that it will not be an easy task to establish, using ribonuclease as a specific agent, whether RNA is directly involved in induction or not, more indirect methods of attack will have to be employed in the future: studies on the effects exerted by specific analogues (which inhibit RNA or protein synthesis) on the inducing activity of explanted or implanted organizers might be rewarding for that purpose.

4. Other important biochemical factors in morphogenesis

When we studied cleavage in Chapter III, we came to the conclusion that, besides nucleic acids, other substances such as ATP and —SH-containing proteins are of great importance in this process. The suggestion, made by Rapkine (see Chapter III), that reversible denaturation of proteins

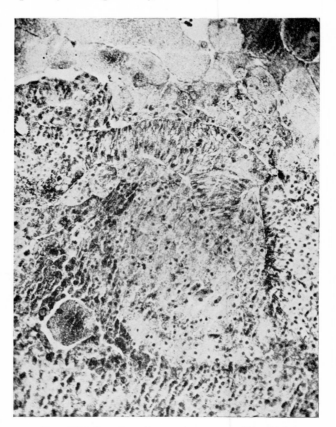

Fig. 107. Ectodermless embryo, as in Fig. 106.

might be an important mechanism in mitosis can be extended to induction (Brachet, 1944; Rapkine and Brachet, 1951). In particular, it is tempting to speculate that closure of the medullary plate is due to the contraction of a fibrous protein under the influence of ATP: in other words, closure of the nervous system and muscle contraction are biochemically similar phenomena.

There is a good deal of evidence in support of such an hypothesis and of the view that both ATP and fibrous —SH-containing proteins play a role in the formation and the closure of the medullary plate. First, the existence of fibrous proteins in amphibian eggs has been clearly demonstrated by Lawrence *et al.* (1944). These proteins have the same solubility characteristics as myosin from muscle and they behave in a similar way in the presence of ATP. As already mentioned, these findings have been confirmed and extended by Ranzi (1957a, b) who has contributed so much to the development of the idea that fibrous proteins play a fundamental role in morphogenesis.

Then, we have already mentioned experiments of Ambellan (1956, 1958), showing that ribomononucleotides accelerate the closure of the medullary plate; the most effective are the adenine nucleotides, with ATP as the most active. It is possible that the other nucleotides are ultimately transformed by the embryo into ATP: the latter would produce a contraction of fibrous proteins, leading to cell deformations and, ultimately, closure of the neural tube. It certainly would be interesting to extend these interesting observations to a more biochemical level: does ATP penetrate into the egg? Is it split inside the cells or on their surface? What is the intracellular distribution of ATPase in amphibian eggs? These are some of the questions which require an answer before one can speculate further.

We would like to mention here two of our own observations which have not yet been published and which have a certain bearing on the problem just discussed: first, we could not detect any measurable ATP breakdown by an 'ecto-ATPase' in amphibian eggs; but the experiments were made at much later developmental stages (hatching) than those used by Ambellan (1955, 1958). Second, we observed that, when such hatched embryos are left continuously in an ATP-containing medium ($15\,\mu g/ml$), their muscles ultimately undergo contraction. Cytological examination of such embryos shows that there is a specific lysis of their somites: the nuclei, in the latter, become pycnotic, while they remain normal in the other parts of the embryo (Fig. 108). It is too early to draw a conclusion from these experiments; they suggest, however, that myosine, when it forms in the differentiating somites, reacts much more strongly to the addition of ATP than the fibrous proteins present at earlier embryonic stages. The specific degeneration of the somites, under the action of ATP, might simply be due to mechanical conditions: continuous contraction of the somites might, for instance, become a block to blood supply. These observations shall serve as a warning for those who might wish to push too far the comparison between muscle contraction and morphogenetic movements.

More will be said about muscle differentiation in the last chapter of this book and we shall now return to our present topic, which is the discussion of the mechanisms of neural system formation and closure. If the hypothesis outlined above is correct, one would expect —SH groups to be involved in this process, since the integrity of —SH groups is known to be important for myosine contraction and since protein denaturation involves the 'unmasking' of —SH groups.

We have already seen that cytochemical methods for the detection of protein-bound —SH groups give a much stronger reaction in the nervous system than in epidermis (Brachet, 1940; Fig. 86). One should be warned again, however, against the wish to draw any conclusion from these observations about the distribution of —SH groups in *living* embryos: all that

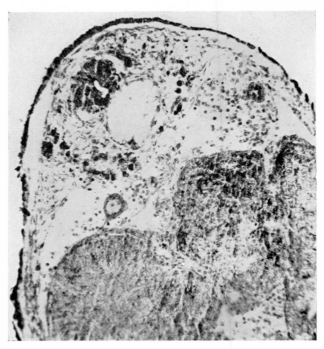

FIG. 108. Specific degeneration of somites in a frog embryo treated, after hatching, with ATP (15μg/ml) for 4 days.

we know is their distribution in fixed embryos, whose proteins have been completely denatured. There is no doubt that our observations of 1940 should be repeated under improved experimental conditions: much better methods for —SH groups detection are now available and fixation by freeze-drying or freeze-substitution greatly reduces the danger of protein denaturation.

But the most impressive evidence we have for an intervention of —SH groups in morphogenesis comes from another direction: the use of specific inhibitors of —SH groups and the study of their effects on development. The results of the earlier work done by Rapkine and Brachet will be found in Brachet (1944), Rapkine and Brachet (1951) and Lallier (1951). They studied the effects of several —SH inhibitors (iodacetamide, chloropicrine, oxidized glutathione, etc.), as well as —SH-containing substances (cysteine, thiomalic acid, etc.) on whole eggs and on isolated dorsal and ventral fragments of gastrulae. The interpretation of the results they obtained remains difficult, because many of the substances used are toxic. Neuralization of ventral ectoblast, which was observed after treatment with cysteine, was probably due to the precytolytic release of a masked inducing substance, rather than to a direct inducing action. In general, —SH inhibitors produce profound alterations in the nervous system, which does not close properly and which remains abnormally thick (Fig. 109). Similar abnormalities have been described in the case of other —SH inhibitors, especially chloracetophenone (Beatty, 1951; Deuchar, 1957) and arseniate (ten Cate, 1957).

More recently, we have studied the effects on amphibian morphogenesis of β-mercaptoethanol, which had given such interesting results in the hands of Mazia (cf. Chapter III) for the *in vivo* study of the mitotic apparatus. It will be recalled that mercaptoethanol is an —SH-containing substance (CH_2OH–CH_2SH), which is very effective in maintaining protein —SH groups in the reduced state. The effects of the oxidized form of mercaptoethanol (dithiodiglycol: HOH_2C–CH_2–S–S–CH_2–CH_2 OH), which easily oxidizes —SH groups of proteins into the —SS— form, were also studied on amphibian eggs.

Here are the main results of these experiments (Brachet, 1958; Brachet and Delange-Cornil, 1959): although mercaptoethanol exhibits very little toxicity in amphibian eggs, it exerts powerful inhibitory effects on morphogenetic movements at gastrulation and neurulation. It also quickly stops mitosis at all stages; finally, cytochemical methods clearly show that it inhibits both DNA and RNA synthesis. The most striking effect of mercaptoethanol is obtained when late gastrulae are treated with 0·01 M solutions of this substance: the medullary plate begins to form, but it remains completely flat for several days (Figs. 110, 111). Partial recovery can be obtained when the eggs are replaced in normal medium after treatment with mercaptoethanol for 1–2 days. There is thus no doubt that neurulation becomes impossible when —SH groups are constantly kept in the reduced form, a fact which suggests that oxidation from —SH to —SS— groups is an important factor for morphogenetic movements. However, the oxidized form of mercaptoethanol is less effective than normal medium for restoring development of mercaptoethanol-treated eggs. Furthermore, dithiodiglycol, in contrast to mercaptoethanol, is very toxic and produces the same types of abnormalities in the nervous system as the other —SH reagents (iodacetamide, chloropicrine and chloracetophenone, for instance), as shown in Fig. 109.

o

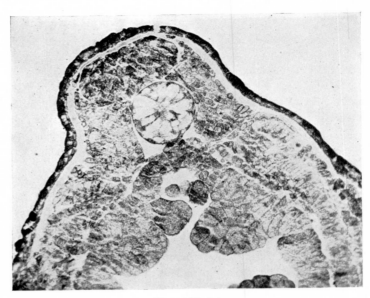

Fig. 109 (*a*)

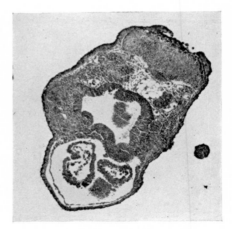

Fig. 109 (*b*)

Fig. 109. Thickened nervous system in a frog embryo treated with
—SH inhibitors; *a*: dithiodiglycol; *b*: monoiodacetamide (*a*: Brachet
and Delange-Cornil, 1959; *b*: Brachet, 1944).

Finally, experiments in which normal ectoderm had been combined with mercaptoethanol-treated organizers and vice versa have shown that a normal equilibrium between —SH and —SS— groups is more important for the *competence* of the ectoderm than for the inducing activity of the organizer. This should by no means be taken as meaning that the importance of —SH groups for morphogenetic processes is a secondary one; response of the competent cells to the inducing stimulus is as important as induction itself.

It would be unwise to go further in the way of conclusions, especially since we know so little about the possible secondary effects of mercaptoethanol and dithiodiglycol on respiration, enzymatic activities, protein and nucleic acid synthesis, etc.

One can thus conclude, from this analysis, that there probably are analogies between muscle contraction and morphogenetic movements, but that these analogies should not be pushed too far; that the reversible denaturation of proteins hypothesis of Rapkine remains very plausible, but that it still is a hypothesis; and that the consequences of a shift in the —SH to —SS— groups equilibrium are greater for the reacting cells than for the inducing ones.

5. Physical properties of the inducing agent

We owe to Raven (1938) the demonstration of the important fact that the inducing principle can diffuse from cell to cell: if a non-inducing fragment of presumptive ectoderm is left for some hours in contact with the living organizer, it acquires inducing capacities. These striking experiments of Raven (1938) have led Dalcq (1941) and Needham (1942) to the very interesting hypothesis that the action of the inducing agent might be similar to that of viruses. The well-known fact that the medullary plate, which has been induced by the organizer, acts as an inductor if it is grafted into the blastocele of a young gastrula leads to the same conclusion: it looks as if the inducing agent can, like a virus, 'infect' the neighbouring cells, propagate and migrate from one cell to another. A further suggestion has been made by the author (1949): the hypothetical virus might be identical with the microsomes, which have dimensions and a RNA-content comparable to those of many viruses, and might therefore possess genetical continuity.

A number of experiments have been performed, in recent years, in order to test these hypotheses: as we shall now see, they have so far failed to give clearcut answers.

The most direct experiment carried out in order to test the 'microsome-virus hypothesis', was the isolation of microsomes by ultracentrifugation of homogenates and the microinjection of these particles into a ventral blastomere of a young morula: such experiments have been attempted by

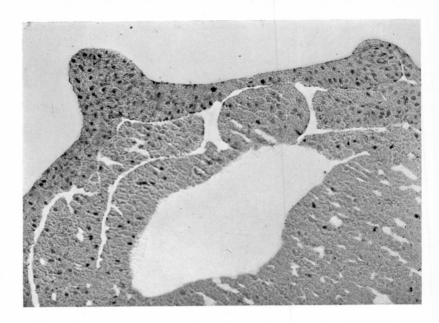

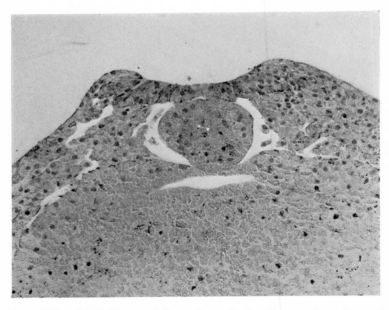

FIGS. 110 and 111. Flat medullary plates obtained by treating advanced gastrulae with mercaptoethanol M/300, for 2–3 days. Chorda and somites are normal (Brachet and Delange-Cornil, 1959).

Brachet and Shaver (1949) and by Brachet *et al.* (1952); but the results were rather disappointing, despite the fact that local increase of basophilia in the injected blastomeres was often observed (Fig. 112). Very few embryos, out of several hundreds, formed a nervous system on the ventral

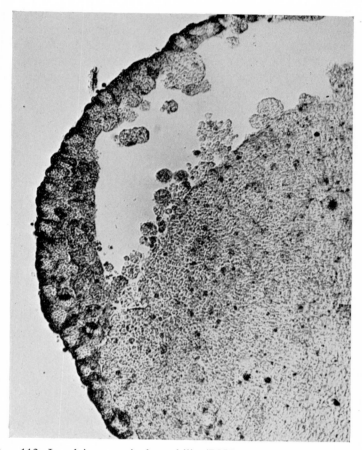

Fig. 112. Local increase in basophilia (RNA content) in an embryo which had been injected, at the young morula stage, with microsomes isolated from tadpoles (Brachet and Shaver, 1949).

side and it is likely that it resulted from purely mechanical troubles of the gastrulation movements rather than true induction. It should, however, be added that the experimental conditions adopted for the isolation of the microsome pellet were far from ideal: the temperature, in the ultracentrifuge, was relatively high and saccharose was not added to the homogeneization medium. It might perhaps be worthwhile to repeat these experiments under the improved isolation conditions which are now available.

Some evidence for the view that substances of high molecular weight can diffuse (if only for a short distance) from cell to cell in amphibian gastrulae can be found in vital staining experiments by Brachet (1950): when ectoblast or chordoblast fragments of a young gastrula are placed in neutral red for some time, only the cytoplasmic granules (yolk platelets, pigment, mitochondria and microsomes) are stained. If such a stained fragment is placed in contact, by its internal face, with an unstained piece, they both stick together and the superficial layer of the unstained fragment quickly becomes coloured. Interposition of a Cellophane membrane (which does not prevent diffusion of free neutral red) completely suppresses the diffusion of the dye from the stained fragment to the other one. The embryological interest of these observations is somewhat decreased by the fact that staining is possible in both directions: stained ectoderm can be used as well as stained organizer for such experiments.

These experiments, also, suffer from the fact that neutral red is of course not a natural constituent of living cells and that its use might lead to a very artificial situation, and thus to misleading conclusions. It is for this reason that similar experiments have been performed by A. Ficq (1954), but with radioisotopes as markers and an autoradiography technique for detection. By grafting into a normal gastrula an organizer in which either RNA or proteins had previously been labelled, appreciable radio-activity was found in the induced neural tube; the experiments suggest a passage of intact ribonucleoproteins from the organizer into the induced tissue. Unfortunately, the primary neural tube of the host also had measurable radioactivity: this observation indicates that part of the radio-active material is broken down (perhaps as a result of limited cytolysis in the implanted organizer) and re-utilized by the host's neural tube. Similar results have been obtained in Waddington's laboratory by several workers (Waddington and Sirlin, 1955; Sirlin et al., 1956; Pantelouris and Mul-herkar, 1957); they conclude that there is no large scale diffusion of macromolecules from the organizer to the induced tissues during induction; their autoradiography experiments, however, cannot exclude a passage of ribonucleoprotein macromolecules from the inducer to the reacting cells, but on a small scale.

This question has been taken up more recently by Rounds and Flickinger* (1958), who worked with chemical and immunological methods. Their experiments indicate that, in explantations, there is a definite (but quantita-tively small) transfer of nucleoproteins from mesoderm to ectoderm. Of special interest are experiments in which *Taricha* ectoderm was cultivated in contact with *Rana* mesoderm: serological tests showed the presence of

* See also Flickinger et al. (1959).

Rana antigens in *Taricha* ectoderm, indicating again a passage of nucleoproteins from mesoderm to ectoderm. It certainly would be very interesting to follow cytochemically this process with methods using labelled antibodies.

These autoradiography and serological experiments are in good agreement with our earlier results with vital dyes, since staining was only visible in cells which were adjacent to those of the stained explant. In this case also, there was no large scale transfer of microscopically visible inclusions. The available results thus strongly suggest that exchanges of substances, even of a macromolecular size, occur at the interface separating the inductor from the reacting cells at the late gastrula stage. All these experiments emphasize the importance for induction of either direct contact between cells (P. Weiss, 1947) or of the intracellular matrix (Grobstein, 1956, 1958). These questions will now be discussed in more detail.

In a very stimulating paper, published in 1947, Weiss has suggested that an intimate contact between the organizer and the presumptive ectoderm is required for successful induction; the cell membranes would be the main site of the inductive processes. Such a conclusion is of course in agreement with all that has just been said about diffusion of vital dyes and labelled ribonucleoproteins during induction.

There is no doubt that neural induction can be completely suppressed when a Cellophane membrane is placed between explants of organizer and ectoblast (Brachet, 1950): as shown in Fig. 113, induction stops abruptly when the membrane has interrupted direct contact between the two fragments. Since the membrane used was easily permeable to mononucleotides and slowly permeable to RNA of a molecular weight of about 10,000, it can be concluded that the induction is not due to the diffusion of a substance of low molecular weight. Either direct contact or passage of macromolecules is thus required for successful induction.

Similar results have been obtained and similar conclusions have been drawn by McKeehan (1951) and by De Vincentiis (1952), who worked on the induction of the lens by the eye cup: again, insertion of a Cellophane membrane between inductor and reactor completely stops lens differentiation.

Since membranes with larger pores, which would allow free passage of macromolecules, also stop lens formation, according to De Vincentiis (1952), it must be admitted that, in this case, direct contact between inductor and reactor, in the sense which P. Weiss (1947) suggests, is the essential factor.* The situation remains more obscure in the case of primary induction: the large pore membranes used for this purpose by Brachet

* However, the inducing substances can diffuse through agar at a distance of 20–100 μ. (McKeehan, 1958). There is a transfer of both small and large molecules, according to Sirlin and Brahma (1959).

and Hugon de Scoeux (1949) often produced spontaneous neuralization of the axolotl ectoderm, probably by provoking a precytolytic condition. No conclusions could thus be drawn from these experiments, which have recently been repeated on *Triton* eggs whose ectoblast is less sensitive to injury than are those of the axolotl (Brahma, 1958): it was found that all the membranes tested, which had pores of $4m\mu$ or $1\cdot45\,\mu$, arrested induction.

But, as shown by the work of Grobstein (1955, 1956), direct contact between inducing and reacting cells is not always required for induction. Working on the induction of tubules in metanephrogenic mesenchyme, he

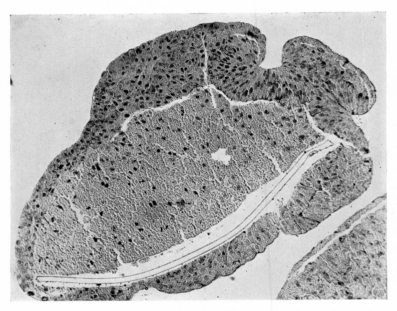

FIG. 113. A Cellophane membrane placed between explants of organizer and ectoblast completely stops induction (Brachet, 1950).

found that the inducing stimulus is not stopped by the interposition of a 'millipore' membrane. Such a membrane has large pores, as compared with those of a Cellophane membrane; its pores are, however, not large enough to allow the passage of free cells; but they can become filled with long pseudopodia which, apparently, never come into direct contact (Grobstein, 1955, 1956; Grobstein and Dalton, 1957). The active substance, which cannot cross a Cellophane membrane, can act at a distance of more than $80\,\mu$ (Grobstein, 1958). For all these reasons, Grobstein (1955, 1956) believes that induction is not mediated through direct contact or diffusion of a small molecular weight substance, but through the matrix uniting the cells. Such a conclusion is probably also valid for induction of cartilage by spinal cord, which remains possible in the presence of a millipore filter (Lash and Holtzer, 1958). We see no reason why it should not be considered as a very possible explanation in the case of the primary organizer as well. Figure 114 summarizes the various possible mechanisms of tissue induction and interaction visualized by Grobstein (1955).

From the embryological viewpoint, the intercellular matrix of Grobstein (1955, 1956) is a development of Holtfreter's (1943) surface coat: this coat is a material which is soluble in alkaline media and which presents a marked

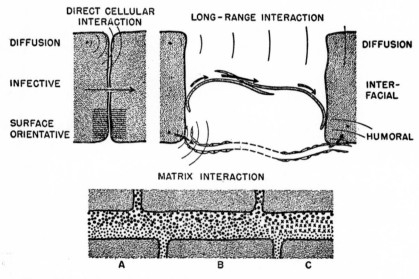

FIG. 114. Schematic description of various possible mechanisms of tissue interaction and induction in development (Grobstein, 1955).

elasticity; it is present in the cell cortex, already in the fertilized egg, and it holds the cells together, thus acting as an intercellular cement. The surface coat becomes reinforced, at the time of gastrulation, in the dorsal lip; it is still further developed in the neural plate, at the neurula stage. Dissolution of the surface coat by weak alkalis (KCN for instance) results in the separation of the cells which form the embryo. This explains why a treatment of gastrulae with relatively concentrated cyanide solutions produces a dissociation of the cells first at the animal pole, then in the dorsal lip. The dissociated cells soon undergo cytolysis. A surface coat, which has the same general properties, has been described in trout eggs by Devillers (1951), who believes that it plays an important role in morphogenetic movements.

202 THE BIOCHEMISTRY OF DEVELOPMENT

Very little is known, unfortunately, about the chemical nature of the surface coat or the intercellular matrix: treatment with the calcium complexing agent versene (EDTA) produces the separation of the gastrula cells. This effect of versene, as we have seen earlier, is greatly enhanced by the addition of small amounts of ribonuclease (Brachet, 1959). It is also known that proteolytic enzymes, trypsin for instance, dissociate easily the cells of the amphibian gastrula. After dissociation by various means, a ribonucleoprotein is liberated (Curtis, 1958): this fact suggests that the intercellular matrix is of a ribonucleoprotein nature, although cytolysis of part of the cells would easily explain the results obtained on dissociated cells by Curtis (1958). Cytochemical studies are, however, in favour of Curtis' conclusion that the intercellular cement is a ribonucleoprotein: in amphibian eggs and embryos, cell membranes give very strong reactions for RNA. Pending further experimental and more precise work, it seems safe to conclude that the intercellular matrix is made of a ribonucleoprotein associated with calcium ions and, possibly, mucopolysaccharides. If RNA is really involved in intercellular matrix composition, its role in induction would become still more probable and easier to understand.

There is, however, a certain amount of evidence for the view that induction of neural structures can be obtained also in ectoblast cells treated with *soluble* agents, without direct contact as in the living organizer or killed tissues: we refer now to the experiments of Niu and Twitty (1953) and Niu (1956), who found that, if chordomesoblastic and ectoblastic fragments are cultivated side by side, but without direct contact of the explants, neuralization of the ectoblast always follows. According to Niu and Twitty (1953), the organizer fragments liberate a diffusible substance, which has the spectroscopic properties of a nucleoprotein. As we have already mentioned, the 'conditioned medium' in which this nucleoprotein has accumulated is neuralizing by itself: in the absence of any chordo-mesoblastic cell, it will produce neural differentiation in ectoblastic explants.

We have already seen that, in the more recent experiments of Niu (1958a, b) the mere addition of ribonucleoprotein or even RNA from thymus can produce the neuralization of ectoderm explants; it is interesting to note that, in the case of RNA, the inducing activity is markedly increased when a protein, which is inactive by itself, is mixed with the nucleic acid. This fact strongly suggests that the uptake and the subsequent neuraliza-tion of the explants is linked to a pinocytosis mechanism, induced by the protein: we have observed that, in organisms which are capable of pinocytosis (amoebae, for instance), the uptake of RNA is greatly increased if a protein is added to the medium in order to produce pinocytosis. A careful study of pinocytosis in ectoderm explants placed in various experi-mental conditions might be rewarding and throw some light on the mechanisms of induction. In agreement with this pinocytosis hypothesis is also the fact that it has been recently reported by Vainio *et al.* (1958) that blood serum and plasma can produce neuralization without any direct contact with a solid substratum.

Interesting as they are, these experiments do not carry entire conviction because of the always present risk of sublethal cytolysis: Niu and Twitty (1953) and their followers were of course aware of this danger and they thought that they could avoid it. But the fragility of gastrula cells is such that, even when one works very carefully, it is very difficult to avoid death or injury of a few of the explanted cells. Furthermore, results obtained with artificial systems such as those used by Niu and Twitty (1953), Niu (1956, 1958a, b) and Vainio *et al.* (1958) can give little information about the processes which occur in a normal embryo. It is important to remember, in this respect, that Holtfreter (1955) found that killed tissues liberate substances which can diffuse through a Cellophane membrane and induce the neuralization of ectoblast fragments in contact with the membrane. The killed tissues of Holtfreter (1955) obviously behave quite differently from the living organizer, whose inductive power is stopped by the insertion of a Cellophane membrane, as we have seen (Brachet, 1950).

6. Conclusions

There is no need to re-discuss here or even to summarize all that has been said: the length of this chapter is enough to show that a wealth of experimental data have already been obtained. These are, however, not sufficient to draw definite conclusions and much more work is obviously required before we are in a position to do so.

All one can say is that there are a few hints about what should be done in the future. There is no doubt that RNA, proteins, —SH groups, ATP are especially important for morphogenesis and that their study deserves more effort than ever. There is no doubt that it would be of the utmost importance to know whether precytolytic agents, such as acid or alkaline shocks, when they induce spontaneous neuralization, exert the same metabolic and morphological effects (especially at the ultra-structural level) as the normal organizer. Again, we are badly in need of a common denominator and the story of induction closely resembles that of fertilization and parthenogenesis. In both cases, the biological characteristic reaction can be elicited by a variety of unrelated physical and chemical agents; in both cases, a co-ordinated attack from the biological, biochemical, cytochemical and ultra-structural viewpoints is required in order to reach a solution, even partial, of the present uncertainties.

REFERENCES

AMBELLAN, E. (1955): *Proc. natl. Acad. Sci., Wash.* **41**, 428.
AMBELLAN, E. (1958): *J. Embryol. exp. Morphol.* **6**, 86.
BARTH, L. G. and L. J. BARTH. (1954): *The Energetics of Development*, Columbia Univ. Press, N.Y.
BARTH, L. G. and S. GRAFF. (1938): *Cold Spring Harbor Sympos.* **6**, 385.
BARTH, L. G. and L. C. SZE. (1951): *Exp. Cell Res.* **2**, 608.
BAUTZMANN, H., J. HOLTFRETER, H. SPEMANN and O. MANGOLD. (1932): *Naturwiss.* **20**, 971.
BEATTY, R. A. (1951): *Proc. Roy. Soc.* B**138**, 575.
BELLAIRS, R. (1958): *J. Embryol. exp. Morphol.* **6**, 149.
BIEBER, S. (1954): *J. cell. comp. Physiol.* **44**, 11.
BIEBER, S. and G. H. HITCHINGS. (1955): *Cancer Res.*, suppl. **3**, 80
BOELL, E. J. (1948): *Ann. N.Y. Acad. Sci.* **49**, 773.
BOELL, E. J., H. KOCH and J. NEEDHAM. (1939): *Proc. Roy. Soc.* B**127**, 374.
BOELL, E. J. and R. WEBER. (1955): *Exp. Cell Res.* **9**, 559.
BRACHET, J. (1934): *Arch. Biol.* **45**, 611.
BRACHET, J. (1935): *Arch. Biol.* **46**, 1.
BRACHET, J. (1939): *Arch. Biol.* **50**, 233.
BRACHET, J. (1940): *Arch. Biol.* **51**, 167.
BRACHET, J. (1941): *Enzymologia* **10**, 87.
BRACHET, J. (1942): *Arch. Biol.* **53**, 207.
BRACHET, J. (1944): *Embryologie chimique.* Desoer. Liège
BRACHET, J. (1946): *C. R. Soc. Biol.* **140**, 1123.
BRACHET, J. (1948): *Experientia* **4**, 353.
BRACHET, J. (1949a): *Bull. Soc. Chim. biol.* **31**, 724.
BRACHET, J. (1949b): *Pubbl. Staz. zool. Napoli* **21**, 71.
BRACHET, J. (1950): *Experientia* **6**, 56.
BRACHET, J. (1954a). *Arch. Biol.* **65**, 1.
BRACHET, J. (1954b): *Experientia* **10**, 492.
BRACHET, J. (1957): *Biochemical Cytology.* Academic Press. N.Y.
BRACHET, J. (1958): *Nature* **181**, 1736.
BRACHET, J. (1959): *Acta Embryol. Morphol. exp.* **2**, 107.
BRACHET, J., M. DECROLY-BRIERS and J. HOYEZ. (1958): *Bull. Soc. Chim. biol.* **40**, 2039.
BRACHET, J. and M. DELANGE-CORNIL. (1959): *Developtl. Biol.* **1**, 79.
BRACHET, J., S. GOTHIÉ and T. KUUSI. (1952): *Arch. Biol.* **63**, 429.
BRACHET, J. and F. HUGON DE SCOEUX. (1949): *J. cyto-embryol. belgo-néerland.* Gand, p. 56.
BRACHET, J. and L. LEDOUX. (1955): *Exp. Cell Res.*, suppl. **3**, 27.
BRACHET, J. and J. NEEDHAM. (1935): *Arch. Biol.* **46**, 821.
BRACHET, J. and J. SHAVER. (1949): *Experientia* **5**, 204.
BRAHMA, S. K. (1958): *J. Embryol. exp. Morphol.* **6**, 418.
CAGIANUT, B. (1949): *Z. Zellforschg.* **34**, 471.
CATE, G. (ten). (1957): *C. R. Assoc. Anatom., 44e réunion*, Leyde.
CÉAS, M. P. and A. NASELLI. (1958): *Arch. Embryol. Morphol. exp.* **1**, 207.
CHILD, C. M. (1948): *J. exp. Zool.* **100**, 79.
CLAYTON, R. M. (1953): *J. Embryol. exp. Morphol.* **1**, 25.

COHEN, A. I. (1954): *Physiol. Zool.* **27**, 128.
COHEN, S. (1954): *J. biol. Chem.* **211**, 337.
COOPER, R. S. (1948): *J. exp. Zool.* **107**, 397.
CURTIS, A. S. G. (1958): *Nature* **181**, 185.
DALCQ, A. (1941): *L'Oeuf et son Dynamisme organisateur.* Paris.
DALCQ, A. (1957): *Introduction to general Embryology.* Oxford Univ. Press.
DALCQ, A. and J. PASTEELS. (1938): *Bull. Acad. roy. Mid. Belg.*, VI, **3**, 261.
D'AMELIO, V. and M. P. CÉAS. (1957): *Experientia* **13**, 152.
DE DUVE, C. (1957): *Sympos. Soc. exp. Biol.* **10**, 50.
DENT, J. N. and C. W. SHEPPARD. (1957): *J. exp. Zool.* **135**, 587.
DEUCHAR, E. M. (1957): *Roux' Arch. Entw. Mech.* **149**, 565.
DEUCHAR, E. M. (1958): *J. Embryol. exp. Morphol.* **6**, 223.
DEVILLERS, C. (1951): *C. R. Acad. Sci. Paris* **232**, 1599.
DEVILLERS, C. (1953): *C. R. Acad. Sci. Paris* **237**, 1561.
DEVILLERS, C., J. COLAS and A. CANTACUZÈNE. (1957a): *C. R. Acad. Sci. Paris* **245**, 1461.
DEVILLERS, C., J. COLAS and L. RICHARD. (1957b): *J. Embryol. exp. Morphol.* **5**, 264.
DE VINCENTIIS, M. (1952): *Soc. oftalmol. ital.* **13**, 3.
EAKIN, R. M., P. B. KUTSKY and W. E. BERG. (1951): *Proc. Soc. exp. Biol. Medic.* **78**, 502.
EAKIN, R. M. and F. E. LEHMANN. (1954): *Roux' Arch. Entw. Mech.* **150**, 177
ENGLÄNDER, J. and A. G. JOHNEN. (1957): *J. Embryol. exp. Morphol.* **5**, 1.
EPHRUSSI, B. (1953): *Nucleo-cytoplasmic Relations in Micro-organisms.* Oxford Univ. Press.
FICQ, A. (1954a): *J. Embryol. exp. Morphol.* **2**, 194.
FICQ, A. (1954b): *J. Embryol. exp. Morphol.* **2**, 204.
FISCHER, F. G. and H. HARTWIG. (1936): *Z. vergl. Physiol.* **24**, 1.
FLICKINGER, R. A. (1954): *Exp. Cell Res.* **6**, 172.
FLICKINGER, R. A. (1958): *Science* **127**, 145.
FLICKINGER, R. A. and R. W. BLOUNT. (1958): *J. cell. comp. Physiol.* **50**, 403.
FLICKINGER, R. A., E. HATTON and D. E. ROUNDS. (1959): *Exp. Cell Res.* **17**, 30.
FLICKINGER, R. A. and G. W. NACE. (1953): *Exp. Cell Res.* **3**, 393.
FOX, J. J. and I. GOODMAN. (1953): *Biochim. biophys. Acta* **10**, 77.
FRIEDBERG, F. and R. M. EAKIN. (1949): *J. exp. Zool.* **110**, 33.
GALLERA, J. and O. OPRECHT. (1948): *Rev. suisse Zool.* **55**, 243.
GRANT, P. (1958): *J. cell. comp. Physiol.* **52**, 227, 249.
GREGG, J. R. (1948): *J. exp. Zool.* **109**, 119.
GREGG, J. R. and M. KAHLBROCK. (1957): *Biol. Bull.* **113**, 376.
GROBSTEIN, C. (1955): In: *Aspects of Synthesis and Order in Growth* (D. Rudnick, ed.), p. 233, Princeton Univ. Press.
GROBSTEIN, C. (1956): *Exp. Cell Res.* **10**, 424.
GROBSTEIN, C. (1958): *Exp. Cell Res.* **13**, 575.
GROBSTEIN, C. and A. J. DALTON. (1957): *J. exp. Zool.* **135**, 57.
HALL, T. S. (1942): *J. exp. Zool.* **89**, 1.
HASYAWA, H. (1955): *Nature* **175**, 1031.
HAYASHI, Y. (1955): *Embryologia* **2**, 145.
HAYASHI, Y. (1956): *Embryologia* **3**, 57.
HAYISHI, Y. (1958): *Embryologia* **4**, 33.
HEATLEY, N. G. (1935): *Biochem. J.* **29**, 5264.
HEATLEY, N. G. and P. E. LINDAHL. (1937): *Proc. Roy. Soc.* B**122**, 395.
HIROAKA, K. K. and A. F. HOPPER. (1957): *Anat. Rec.* **129**, 297.

HOLTFRETER, J. (1931): *Roux' Arch. Entw. Mech.* **124**, 404.
HOLTFRETER, J. (1935): *Roux' Arch. Entw. Mech.* **133**, 367.
HOLTFRETER, J. (1943): *J. exp. Zool.* **93**, 251.
HOLTFRETER, J. (1945): *J. exp. Zool.* **98**, 161.
HOLTFRETER, J. (1946): *J. Morphol.* **101**, 355.
HOLTFRETER, J. (1947a): *J. exp. Zool.* **106**, 197.
HOLTFRETER, J. (1955): *Exp. Cell Res.*, suppl. **3**, 188.
JAEGER, L. (1945): *J. cell. comp. Physiol.* **25**, 97.
KARASAKI, S. (1959): *Embryologia* **4**, 247.
KATAYAMA, H. (1956): *Japan. J. Zool.* **12**, 39
KUTSKY, P. B. (1950): *J. exp. Zool.* **115**, 429.
KUUSI, T. (1953): *Arch. Biol.* **64**, 189.
LALLIER, R. (1950): *Experientia* **6**, 2.
LALLIER, R. (1951): *Bull. Soc. Chim. biol.* **33**, 439.
LALLIER, R. (1954): *J. Embryol. exp. Morphol.* **2**, 323.
LALLIER, R. (1956): *Exp. Cell Res.* **11**, 648.
LANZAVECCHIA, G. and A. LE COULTRE. (1958): *Arch. ital. Anat. Embriol.* **63**, 445.
LASH, J. W. and H. HOLTZER. (1958): *Biol. Bull.* **115**, 322.
LAVARACK, J. O. (1957): *J. Embryol. exp. Morphol.* **5**, 111.
LAWRENCE, A. S. C., M. MIALL, J. NEEDHAM and S. C. SHEN. (1944): *J. gen. Physiol.* **27**, 233.
LEHMANN, F. E. (1938): *Roux' Arch. Entw. Mech.* **138**, 106.
LIEDKE, K. B., M. ENGELMAN and S. GRAFF. (1954): *J. exp. Zool.* **127**, 201.
LIEDKE, K. B., M. ENGELMAN and S. GRAFF. (1957a): *J. Embryol. exp. Morphol.* **5**, 3681.
LIEDKE, K. B., M. ENGELMAN and S. GRAFF. (1957b): *J. exp. Zool.* **136**, 117.
LØVTRUP, S. (1953): *C. R. Trav. Lab. Carlsberg, sér. chim.* **28**, 371, 400.
LØVTRUP, S. (1955): *C. R. Trav. Lab. Carlsberg, sér. chim.* **29**, 261.
LØVTRUP, S. and A. PIGON. (1958): *J. Embyol. exp. Morphol.* **6**, 486.
LØVTRUP, S. and B. WERDINIUS. (1957): *J. exp. Zool.* **135**, 203.
MALAMED, S. (1957): *Exp. Cell Res.* **13**, 391.
MALAMED, S. (1958): *Biol. Bull.* **114**, 226.
MCKEEHAN, M. S. (1951): *J. exp. Zool.* **117**, 31.
MCKEEHAN, M. S. (1958): *Anat. Rec.* **132**, 297.
MOOKERJEE, S. (1953): *Experientia* **9**, 340.
MULNARD, J. (1955): *Arch. Biol.* **66**, 528.
NEEDHAM, J. (1930): *Chemical Embryology*, Cambridge Univ. Press.
NEEDHAM, J. (1942): *Biochemistry and Morphogenesis*. Cambridge Univ. Press.
NELSEN, O. (1947): *Science* **106**, 295.
NIU, M. C. (1956): *Cellular Mechanisms of Differentiation and Growth* (D Rudnik, ed.), p. 155. Princeton Univ. Press.
NIU, M. C. (1958a): *Proc. nat. Acad. Sci. Wash.* **44**, 1264.
NIU, M. C. (1958b): In: *The Chemical Basis of Development*, pp. 256, 625. Johns Hopkins Press. Baltimore.
NIU, M. C. and V. C. TWITTY. (1953): *Proc. nat. Acad. Sci. Wash.* **39**, 985.
O'CONNOR, R. J. (1957): *Internat. Rev. Cytol.* **6**, 343.
ÔGI, K. I. (1958): *J. Embryol. exp. Morphol.* **6**, 412.
PANTELOURIS, E. M. and L. MULHERKAR, (1957): *J. Embryol. exp. Morphol.* **5**, 51.
PASTEELS, J. (1938): *Arch. Biol.* **49**, 629.
PASTEELS, J. (1940): *Arch. Biol.* **51**, 335.
PASTEELS, J. (1945): *Arch. Biol.* **56**, 105.
PASTEELS, J. (1953): *J. Embryol. exp. Morphol.* **1**, 5, 125.

PATERSON, M. C. (1957): *J. exp. Zool.* **134**, 183.
PETRUCCI, D. (1957): *Acta Embryol. Morphol. exp.* **1**, 105.
PETRUCCI, D. (1959): *Arch. Sci. biolog.* **43**, 25.
PIEPHO, H. (1938): *Biol. Zentralbl.* **58**, 90.
RANZI, S. (1957a): In: *The Beginnings of embryonic Development*, p. 291, A.A.A.S., Publ. No. 48, Washington.
RANZI, S. (1957b): *Année biologique* **33**, 522.
RANZI, S. (1958): *Arch. Embryol. Morphol. exp.* 2, 102.
RANZI, S., P. CITTERIO, V. COPES and C. SAMUELLI. (1957): *Acta Embryol. Morphol. exp.* **1**, 78.
RAPKINE, L. and J. BRACHET. (1951): *Bull. Soc. Chim. biol.* **33**, 427.
RAVEN, C. P. (1938): *Roux' Arch. Entw. Mech.* **137**, 661.
RICKENBACHER, J. (1956): *Z. Zellforschg.* **45**, 339.
ROUNDS, D. E. and R. A. FLICKINGER. (1958): *J. exp. Zool.* **137**, 479.
RULON, O. (1935): *Protoplasma* **24**, 346.
SCHUSTER, H. and G. SCHRAMM. (1958): *Z. Naturforschg.* **136**, 697.
SELMAN, G. G. (1958): *J. Embryol. exp. Morphol.* **6**, 448.
SIRLIN, J. L. (1955): *Experientia* **11**, 112.
SIRLIN, J. L. and S. K. BRAHMA. (1959): *Developmental Biol.* **1**, 234.
SIRLIN, J. L., S. K. BRAHMA, and C. H. WADDINGTON. (1956): *J. Embryol. exp. Morphol.* **4**, 248.
SIRLIN, J. L. and C. H. WADDINGTON. (1956): *Exp. Cell Res.* **11**, 197.
SMITH, A. E. and A. M. SCHECHTMAN. (1954): *J. exp. Zool.* **125**, 265.
SPEMANN, H. (1938): *Embryonic Development and Induction.* Yale Univ. Press.
SPRATT, N. T. (1952): *Ann. N.Y. Acad. Sci.* **55**, 40.
SPRATT, N. T. (1955): In: *Aspects of Synthesis and Growth* (D. Rudnick, ed.), p. 209. Princeton Univ. Press,
SPRATT, N. T. (1958): In: *The Chemical Basis of Development*, p. 629. Johns Hopkins Press, Baltimore.
SPRATT, N. T. (1958b): *J. exp. Zool.* **138**, 51.
STEINERT, M. (1951): *Bull. Soc. Chim. biol.* **33**, 549.
STEINERT, M. (1953): Doctorate Thesis. Univ. of Brussels.
SZE, L. C. (1953): *Physiol. Zool.* **26**, 212.
TAKATA, K. (1953): *Biol. Bull.* **105**, 348.
TAKAYA, H. (1955): *Proc. japan. Acad.* **31**, 366.
TENCER, R. (1958): *J. Embryol. exp. Morphol.* **6**, 117.
THOMASON, D. (1957): *Nature* **179**, 823.
TIEDEMANN, H. and H. TIEDEMANN. (1954): *Naturwiss.* **41**, 535.
TIEDEMANN, H. and H. TIEDEMANN. (1955): *Naturwiss.* **42**, 560.
TIEDEMANN, H. and H. TIEDEMANN. (1956): *Z. physiol. Chem.* **306**, 132.
TÖNDURY, G. (1947): *Acta anat.* **4**, 269.
URBANI, E. (1955): *Ricerca scientif.* **25**, 1.
URBANI, E. (1957a): *Ricerca scientif.* **27**, 1549.
URBANI, E. (1957b): *Rendic. Istit. lombardo* **92**, 69.
VAHS, W. (1957a): *Embryologia* **3**, 201.
VAHS, W. (1957b): *Roux' Arch. Entw. Mech.* **149**, 339.
VAINIO, T. (1956): *Ann. Med. exp. et Biol. Fennicae* **34**, 71.
VAINIO, T., S. TOIVONEN and L. SAXÉN, (1958): *Ann. Med. exp. Fenn.* **36**, 285.
WADDINGTON, C. H., M. FELDMAN and M. M. PERRY. (1955): *Exp. Cell Res.*, suppl. **3**, 366.
WADDINGTON, C. H., J. NEEDHAM and J. BRACHET. (1936): *Proc. Roy. Soc.* **B120**, 173.

WADDINGTON, C. H. and M. M. PERRY. (1958): *J. Embryol. exp. Morphol.* **6**, 365.
WADDINGTON, C. H. and J. L. SIRLIN. (1954): *J. Embryol. exp. Morphol.* **2**, 340.
WADDINGTON, C. H. and J. L. SIRLIN. (1955): *Proc. Roy. Phys. Soc. Edinburgh*
     24, 28.
WEBER, R. and E. J. BOELL. (1955): *Rev. suisse Zool.* **62**, 260.
WEHMEIER, E. (1934): *Roux' Arch. Entw. Mech.* **132**, 384.
WEISS, P. (1947): *Yale J. Biol. Med.* **19**, 235.
WEISSENFELS, N. (1958): *Z. Naturforschg.* **136**, 182.
WOELLWARTH, C. VON. (1956): *Roux' Arch. Entw. Mech.* **148**, 504.
YAMADA, T. (1950): *Biol. Bull.* **98**, 98.
YAMADA, T. (1958a): *Experientia* **14**, 81.
YAMADA, T. (1958b): In: *The Chemical Basis of Development.* Johns Hopkins Press,
     Baltimore.
YAMADA, T. and K. TAKATA. (1955a): *Exp. Cell Res.*, suppl. **3**, 402.
YAMADA, T. and K. TAKATA. (1955b): *J. exp. Zool.* **128**, 291.
YAMADA, T. and K. TAKATA. (1956). *Embryologia* **3**, 69.
YAMADA, T. and S. KARASAKI. (1958): *Sympos. Soc. for cell. Chem.* **7**, 153.

CHAPTER VI

Biochemical Interactions Between the Nucleus and the Cytoplasm During Morphogenesis

ONCE more we shall find that there exist too little biochemical data in this field to allow definite conclusions. The problem of nucleo-cytoplasmic interactions during differentiation is now being attacked mostly at the purely biological level and much progress has recently been made in this direction. For a long time, only theoretical ideas had been presented, often inspired by work done on the genetics of micro-organisms. The one gene-one enzyme theory of Beadle (1946), the demonstration of the existence of cytoplasmic particles endowed with genetic continuity by Sonneborn (1947, 1950), by Ephrussi (1953) and by others, the demonstration of genetic recombination in bacteria (Lederberg, 1952) have led to a considerable amount of thinking about how genes and cytoplasmic particles might interact in order to lead ultimately to differentiation. Since these theoretical ideas have been discussed, in the case of the embryo itself, at great length, in two recent books (Waddington, 1956; Brachet, 1957), they will only be summarized briefly here and we shall try to concentrate on the more biochemical aspects of the problem.

1. A brief summary of theories on nucleo-cytoplasmic interactions during morphogenesis

There is no doubt that, for any embryologist, the role of cytoplasmic factors in morphogenesis cannot be dismissed easily: even if we assume that the initial polarity of the oocyte is determined by the nuclear genes present in the germinal vesicle, epigenetic events soon modify the course of ontogenesis. The most impressive of these epigenetic changes is perhaps the formation, in the just fertilized frog egg, of the grey crescent, which later becomes part of the dorsal half of the embryo. As soon as the grey crescent becomes visible, the plane of bilateral symmetry of the embryo can be recognized. Localized destruction of the grey crescent has far-reaching effects on the further development of the egg. And yet, the plane of bilateral symmetry can be determined at will by modifying the orientation

P

of freshly fertilized eggs (Ancel and Vintemberger, 1948). Slight changes in the cortical layer of the egg, which have nothing to do with either genes or even the whole nucleus, are responsible for the early determination of the plane of symmetry and of dorsoventrality. All the classical experiments of 'causal embryology', such as centrifugation, destruction or separation of blastomeres, turning the egg upside down, etc. give results which can be explained on the basis of local cytoplasmic differences (plasms, germinal localization, etc.). Their interpretation does not require the intervention of specific genes. This is why A. Brachet (1910, 1930) drew a distinction between a 'general' heredity and a 'special' heredity: the former controls early morphogenesis and involves the intervention of both cytoplasm and the nucleus; the second, which controls such phenomena as eye colour or hair colour, is the familiar Mendelian, chromosomal heredity.

It would be a mistake, however, to believe that development is possible to a large extent when the genetic constitution of the fertilized egg is abnormal. Aneuploidy (i.e. wide chromosomal unbalance in different blastomeres), as well as the total lack of nuclei leads to a block of development, at the blastula stage in the best cases. Haploidy and introduction of a foreign nucleus (hybridization) often have lethal effects, sooner or later. Even small chromosomal deficiencies, or gene mutations in the X chromosome of *Drosophila* eggs can stop development at the end of cleavage or at later stages (Poulson, 1940, 1945; Ede, 1956; Counce and Ede, 1957). On the whole, there is a considerable amount of evidence for the view that the nuclei—and thus the chromosomal genes—play little part in the cleavage of the fertilized egg. Anucleate blastulae have been obtained by Harvey (1936) in the sea urchin egg and by Stauffer (1945) and others in the amphibian egg. But development in the absence of the nucleus or in strongly aneuploid morulae never proceeds further than the blastula stage (cf. Fig. 35): in fact, these blastulae are usually irregular and abnormal; they never form cilia in the sea urchin egg; real morphogenesis thus requires the presence of a normal nucleus and of a normal genetic constitution. It is probable, as was pointed out by the author in 1949, that the fast-dividing nuclei of the morula and the young blastula exert little influence on the neighbouring cytoplasm. At the late blastula stage, nuclei stop dividing as fast as they did before: they have now 'time' to produce nucleoli during interphase. These nucleoli are a sign of nuclear intervention in nucleic acid and protein synthesis in the embryo.*

In conclusion, there is no doubt that, during cleavage, the cytoplasm is almost autonomous but that, at the gastrula stage, the nuclei (and the genes they contain) come more and more into the picture. The many hypotheses

* For a more precise account of nucleolar differentiation during amphibian development, see the paper of Karasaki (1959), who used the electron microscope.

which have been made in order to explain the relative role of the nucleus and the cytoplasm in morphogenesis have, of course, taken these facts into account; but they vary in placing the emphasis more on the nucleus or on the cytoplasm as the main factor of embryonic differentiation.

Already in 1894, H. Driesch had proposed a theory, which has been made more precise and modernized by Morgan (1934), in order to explain the relative role of the nucleus and the cytoplasm in development. In short, the theory assumes that equipotential nuclei are distributed, during cleavage, in a chemically heterogeneous cytoplasm. As a result of this cytoplasmic inhomogeneity, genetic activity would be stimulated in certain nuclei and decreased in other. This could lead, since genes can control enzymatic reactions, to changes in the chemical composition of the neighbouring cytoplasm. The final result would be a progressive specialization of the various territories of the egg, leading first to organogenesis, then to cytological differentiation.

This theory has been further developed and refined by Waddington (1950, 1956), who has made the further suggestion that activation of certain genes in a certain environment and their inactivation in another environment might be the result of a competition between the genes for certain substrates. Since the gene would ultimately control the synthesis of a specific cytoplasmic protein, it is very likely that RNA, both in the nucleolus and in the ergastoplasm, is involved as an intermediary (Brachet, 1949, 1957).

The theory which has just been presented places the main emphasis on the nucleus and the chromosomal genes, but admits that gene activity is modified by the cytoplasm. In other theories, the emphasis shifts from the nucleus to the cytoplasm; the latter is supposed to contain *plasmagenes*, i.e. cytoplasmic particles endowed with genetic continuity and capable of determining hereditary characters.

As pointed out by Waddington (1956), there is a certain amount of evidence for the existence of four different types of plasmagenes: (1) exogeneous plasmagenes, which are probably identical to viruses and have no obvious embryological interest; (2) true plasmagenes, which would be responsible for cytoplasmic heredity and would be capable of independent multiplication. Nothing is known about their existence in eggs, which cannot of course be excluded; (3) visible cytoplasmic particles with genetic continuity, such as the centrosomes or kinetosomes, which can hardly be expected to play a leading role in morphogenesis; (4) gene-initiated plasmagenes: their initiation, and not only their reproduction, would be dependent on the presence of corresponding nuclear genes.

Gene-initiated plasmagenes are the most interesting ones for the embryologist, as pointed out by Sonneborn (1950), Ephrussi (1953), Poulson (1945), Lehmann (1950), etc.: embryonic differentiation might be controlled by plasmagenes produced under the influence of nuclear genes; as a result of a competition between plasmagenes present in a population of distinct plasmagenes, one type would take over and determine the fate of the corresponding territory.

As pointed out by Waddington (1956), the idea of localized true plasmagenes determining the nature of the organs forming—out of each region of the egg—adds little to the old 'organ-forming substances'. The gene-induced plasmagenes hypothesis has certainly more appeal: these plasmagenes might act as intermediaries between the gene and the protein which is synthesized under its control, and be identical with ribonucleoprotein cytoplasmic particles. In fact, this hypothesis does not exclude at all the Driesch-Morgan hypothesis. The two theories complement each other if we admit, with Waddington (1956), that plasmagenes are initiated by genes which have been activated by differences in the chemical composition of the cytoplasm.

Enough has been said about theories and it is now time to face actual facts. We shall first present and discuss the *nuclear transfer* experiments which have, in recent years, brought the more direct evidence available in favour of the Driesch-Morgan theory. Unfortunately, next to nothing is known about the biochemical effects of nuclear transfers. The biochemical effects of complete removal of the nucleus, of haploidy and polyspermy, of the presence of early lethal genes in the zygote and of lethal hybridization will then be examined.

2. Nuclear transfer experiments

We have already mentioned that nuclei have relatively little importance for cleavage and more detailed evidence in this respect will be presented later. In accordance with this view, it has been found by Spemann (1928) in newt eggs and by Seidel (1932) in insect eggs that, during cleavage, nuclei are *equipotential*: this means that, if the nucleus of a dorsal blastomere, for example, is destroyed, it can be completely replaced by a nucleus originating from the ventral half of the egg. If the Driesch-Morgan theory is correct, one would expect the nuclei to 'differentiate' during development and therefore to lose their initial equipotentiality.

Bold and ingenious experiments by Briggs and King (1952, 1958) have attempted, in a successful way, to answer a number of extremely important questions: are the nuclei really equipotential in early stages? If so, do they lose their equipotentiality and at which stage of development? If a nucleus has become 'differentiated' and has thus lost totipotency, is this a reversible phenomenon?

The method used by Briggs and King (1953) is represented, in a schematic way, in Fig. 115: an unfertilized frog egg is first activated by pricking and its nucleus is removed; a donor cell, removed from a blastula or a gastrula of the same species, is pulled up into a micropipette in such a way that the cell surface is broken down without dispersing the cytoplasm. The broken cell is then injected into the recipient unfertilized, anucleated egg. The operation involves injection of a small amount of cytoplasm with the nucleus; but control experiments have shown that cytoplasmic contamination cannot play any important role in the evaluation of the results.

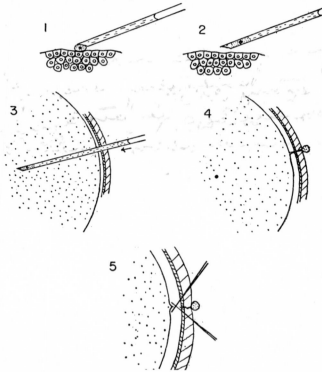

FIG. 115. Method of Briggs and King for transplanting blastula cell nuclei into enucleated eggs. *1*: removal of a blastula cell; *2*: the isolated cell breaks in the pipette; *3*: injection of the nucleus in a previously activated and enucleated unfertilized egg; *4–5*: elimination of exovate (Briggs and King, 1953).

It is clear that, if the injected nucleus is still totipotent, the recipient egg will develop into a normal embryo; if, on the contrary, its potentialities have become more restricted, development will stop sooner or later and lead to the formation of abnormal embryos.

In their first experiments, Briggs and King (1953) used cells taken from the animal half of the blastula or young gastrula as 'donor cells'; the results were the same in both cases: if the transplantation is successful, the recipient unfertilized and enucleated egg develops normally into a tadpole.

The conclusion is clear: the nuclei are not yet differentiated at these young embryonic stages and they are thus still equipotential. This result is not very surprising, since the donor cells from which the nuclei were taken are still undifferentiated at this stage.

In later studies (1954, 1955), King and Briggs have worked with nuclei from cells of late gastrulae (yolk plug stage: Fig. 116), which are more difficult to handle in view of their smaller size. It was found, this time,

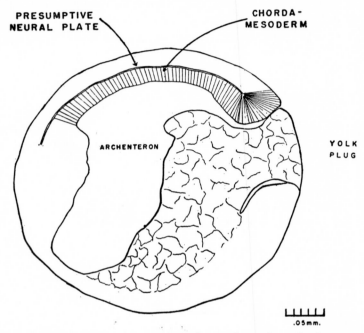

PRESUMPTIVE
NEURAL PLATE

CHORDA-
MESODERM

ARCHENTERON

YOLK
PLUG

.05 mm.

FIG. 116. Schematic representation of gastrula at the yolk plug stage. The arrows indicate the areas from which donor nuclei were taken (King and Briggs, 1954).

that nuclei isolated from late gastrula chordomesoblast no longer allowed the complete development of the recipient eggs: blocked blastulae or gastrulae, and abnormal neurula stages were obtained instead of normal tadpoles; great precautions were taken in order to avoid damage to the transplanted nuclei in these experiments. King and Briggs (1955) were therefore able to conclude that the deficient development of the embryos resulting from transfer of nuclei taken from the chordomesoblast area of late gastrulae reflects a change in the 'differentiation' properties of the nuclei in this area. In other words, the nuclei are no longer totipotent when they are taken out from a region which, as the chordomesoblast, has undergone differentiation.

In a second series of experiments, King and Briggs (1955) and Briggs and King (1957) have studied in great detail the progressive restriction of the potentialities of endoblast nuclei: the nuclei were taken, this time, from cells situated on the floor of the archenteron, i.e. the presumptive mid-gut region (Fig. 116). The result was that some of the nuclei are still totipotent and can thus produce normal and complete development of the recipient eggs; but the majority of the endoblast nuclei is now differentiated, so that the nuclear transfer experiment now yields mostly arrested blastulae, blocked gastrulae and abnormal neurulae. The floor of the archenteron is thus made of a mosaic of cells; some of them have still totipotent nuclei, but the majority of the nuclei have now undergone some sort of differentiation which has restricted their potentialities.

In a later and very important step of their work, King and Briggs (1956) and Briggs and King (1957) have made *serial* transplantations of nuclei, using as hosts embryos which, after a transfer of endoblast nuclei, either developed normally or were arrested at an early embryonic stage. Their conclusion is that, once nuclei have undergone differentiation, this differentiation is *irreversible*. Nuclei taken from embryos whose development, after a nuclear transfer, stops at an early stage do not permit full development of enucleated unfertilized eggs; on the other hand, nuclei taken from embryos which result from a nuclear transfer experiment which can lead to full development are still totipotent: they can produce complete development of the recipient egg.

A few more words should be said about other nuclear transfer experiments which were also made on frog eggs, and also about the evidence concerning other species of Amphibians. We shall soon see, in more detail, that the introduction of an abnormal sperm nucleus into an unfertilized frog egg often results in the production of a '*lethal hybrid*'. If, for instance, eggs of *Rana pipiens* are fertilized with sperm of *Rana catesbeiana* or *Rana sylvatica*, development is perfectly normal at first; but it completely stops at the early gastrula stage. After a few days, the arrested gastrulae undergo rapid cytolysis. The nuclear transfer method is the only one which can give direct clues about the respective role of the nucleus and the cytoplasm in this arrest of development.

Figure 117 represents, in a diagrammatic way, the method used by King and Briggs (1953) for the preparation of hybrid blastulae and for transplantation of their nuclei into enucleated and unfertilized eggs. In the *Rana pipiens* ♀ × *Rana catesbeiana* ♂ combination, development stops after 26 hours; therefore, King and Briggs (1953) transferred hybrid nuclei to enucleated *Rana pipiens* eggs, at the onset of developmental arrest and at various intervals after this time. The result of these experiments was that nuclei of hybrid gastrulae which had just stopped developing can participate again in the whole course of hybrid development: development is normal until the early gastrula stage and then stops completely. On the other hand, nuclei which are taken from a hybrid gastrula which has been arrested for 10–20 hours are irreversibly damaged: they are no longer capable of producing normal cleavage in the recipient eggs.

In a more recent paper, J. A. Moore (1958, 1959) has performed a different type of experiment, which also involves the use of two different frog species; he found that the transfer of a diploid *R. sylvatica* nucleus into an enucleated *R. pipiens* unfertilized egg is followed by a block at the

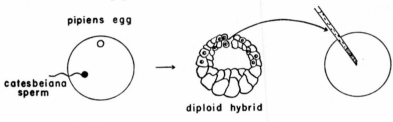

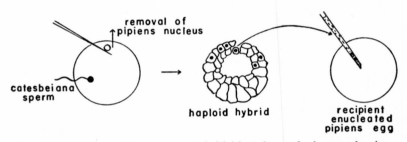

Fig 117. Method of preparing hybrid blastulae and of transplanting their nuclei into enucleated eggs (King and Briggs, 1953).

late blastula stage; the reciprocal combination (i.e. transfer of a diploid *R. pipiens* nucleus into an enucleated *R. sylvatica* egg) gives the same result. But the most important and new experiment made by Moore (1958) is the following one: he took nuclei out of a blocked *R. sylvatica* blastula which had received a *R. pipiens* nucleus and transferred them back to enucleated *R. pipiens* eggs, and he observed a block of development at the early gastrula stage. The experiment clearly shows that the original *R. pipiens* chromosomes have been modified by the *R. sylvatica* cytoplasm in an irreversible way. Moore's (1958, 1959) experiment thus affords a very elegant demonstration of the existence of cytoplasmic effects on nuclei.

Finally, one should mention experiments by Briggs and King (1955) who tried to see whether a nucleus taken from a urodele blastula (*Triturus pyrrhogaster*) could elicit cleavage in an enucleated egg of *Rana pipiens*. All they could obtain was the formation of partial blastulae in 50 per cent of the cases. From their cytological analysis of these partial blastulae, Briggs and King concluded that *Triturus* chromatin had greatly increased in amount. Therefore, the nucleoprotein precursors present in frog eggs must be unspecific and can be used for the synthesis of chromatin of a Urodele.

All the work which has been just described deals with frog eggs; several authors have attempted, with varying success, to extend Briggs and King's work to other species. The attempts made by Waddington and Pantelouris (1953) and Lehmann (1955, 1957) on *Triton* eggs have not been very successful. All they could obtain were blastulae, usually abnormal. There is thus no evidence, in Urodeles, that a blastula nucleus can produce development of unfertilized eggs into normal embryos. These negative results do not necessarily mean that nuclei, in Urodeles, have already lost their totipotency at the blastula stage; it seems more likely that the failure to obtain normal development after nuclear transfer is simply due to the fact that *Triton* eggs, which are normally polyspermic, are not as good a material as frog eggs for this type of experiment.

Entirely different results have been obtained by Fischberg and his co-workers (Fischberg *et al.*, 1958; Gurdon *et al.*, 1958; Fischberg, 1959) who worked on the eggs of *Xenopus*: they performed nuclear transplantation experiments comparable to those of Briggs and King (1953–1957), but without removing the nucleus of the recipient unfertilized eggs. This simplification of the nuclear transplantation method was possible because Gurdon *et al.* (1958) could show that the female pronucleus does not take part as a rule in further development. Under these experimental conditions, Fischberg *et al.* (1958), Gurdon *et al.* (1958) and Fischberg (1959) obtained complete development after transplantation of ectoderm and endoderm nuclei. They even succeeded in obtaining complete development after transfer of nuclei taken at a much later stage than in the Briggs and King (1953–1957) experiments: nuclei taken out of somites, 9 hours before the latter became contractile, still allow complete development if they are injected in unfertilized eggs. One should therefore conclude that, in *Xenopus*, either the nuclei remain totipotent until a late embryonic stage or are able to become totipotent again when they are transferred into an unfertilized egg. Further experiments will of course be required in order to decide whether the rather different results obtained on *Xenopus* and on frog eggs are due to species difference or to the already mentioned fact that, in Gurdon *et al.*'s (1958) experiments, the unfertilized eggs were not enucleated.

Extremely little, unfortunately, is known so far about possible biochemical differences between the nuclei during embryonic development:

the only extensive work in this field is the autoradiography study of Tencer (1958), which has already been mentioned in the last chapter. She found that incorporation of $^{14}CO_2$ into nucleoproteins only occurs in the nuclei until the gastrula stage. During this early period of cleavage, the extent of labelling of the nuclei is essentially the same whatever their localization in the embryo. During gastrulation, RNA and protein synthesis begins in the cytoplasm and follows the animal–vegetal and the dorso-ventral gradients which are now familiar to the readers of the preceding chapter. Simultaneously, the radioactivity of the various nuclei becomes different; it now varies according to the same gradients. It looks therefore as if, during cleavage, all nuclei were very similar from the viewpoint of their metabolic properties. This period, of course, corresponds to that in which nuclei are still equipotential. At gastrulation, biochemical activity increases in both the cytoplasm and the nuclei; the latter apparently undergo changes in their metabolic activity under the influence of the neighbouring cytoplasm. These metabolic changes might be correlated with the biological differentiation of the nuclei, as demonstrated by the nuclear transfer experiments.

The facts are, of course, incomplete and much more work will be needed before we can give definite answers to all the questions we asked at the beginning of this chapter. But, if we take together the work done by Briggs and King (1953–1957), Moore (1958, 1959) and Tencer (1958), one cannot escape the conclusion that a rather satisfactory and coherent picture begins to take shape. This picture is in substantial agreement with the Driesch-Morgan theory, since the cytochemical and biological data agree in demonstrating the following points: (1) the cytoplasm becomes more heterogeneous than it was before, soon after fertilization; (2) the nuclei, during cleavage, are equipotential and totipotential; they are also metabolically indistinguishable; (3) during gastrulation, the nuclei undergo a 'differentiation', which affects both their potentialities for development and their metabolic activity.

We may now shift our interest to other types of experiments, which are perhaps not so meaningful as the nuclear transfers from the biological viewpoint, but which have been better analysed from the biochemical side.

3. Development and metabolism in the complete absence of the nucleus

We have already mentioned several times in this book that cleavage, usually partial and abnormal, can take place in the complete absence of the nucleus. In sea urchin eggs, the standard method to obtain this result is that of E. B. Harvey (1932): fast centrifugation of unfertilized eggs, which have been suspended in a medium which has the same density as their own, results in the sedimentation of the various inclusions present in the egg.

Finally, the eggs break into two parts: the light, clear half contains the nucleus, the fat droplets and most of the clear RNA-rich cytoplasm; the heavy half is anucleate and it contains most of the mitochondria, the yolk and the red pigment granules. If, as was first done by E. B. Harvey (1936), the anucleate (heavy) halves are treated with parthenogenetic agents, so-called 'parthenogenetic merogones' can be obtained. Repeated cleavage occurs, but the typical pattern of segmentation is absent. All one can obtain are irregular morulae or blastulae (Fig. 35) which never form cilia, as was pointed out earlier in this chapter.

Similar, but more elegant experiments, were made by Lorch *et al.* (1953) who removed the nucleus of one of the blastomeres during early cleavage with a micromanipulator: they found that the enucleated blastomere can undergo irregular and abortive cleavages for a while, but that it never takes part in morphogenesis although it is in close contact with normal blastomeres.

In amphibian eggs, development in the absence of the nucleus is generally obtained by fertilizing the eggs with irradiated spermatozoa (which will sooner or later degenerate) and then destroying the maturation spindle by pricking (Dalcq and Simon, 1932; Fankhauser, 1934; Stauffer, 1945; Briggs *et al.*, 1951). Of special interest (but by no means surprising) is the fact, observed by Briggs *et al.* (1951), that non-nucleated 'cells' from arrested blastulae show no sign of differentiation if they are transplanted to inductive sites of normal embryos.

Unfortunately, nobody has studied so far the metabolism of eggs developing in the complete absence of the nucleus, probably because it is difficult to obtain a sufficient number of eggs cleaving under these conditions to make quantitative studies. Autoradiography experiments, which do not require a large number of eggs, might perhaps lead to interesting results with such a material.

Thus the biochemical work has concentrated so far on fragments of *unfertilized* eggs, which had been separated into two halves by centrifugation or ligation, or had been enucleated. Most of the evidence obtained in this field has already been presented in Chapters I and IV. We shall here briefly summarize this work again and compare the main conclusions with those obtained from biochemical studies made on nucleate and anucleate halves of unicellular organisms (*Amoeba proteus* and the giant unicellular alga *Acetabularia mediterranea*).

As early as 1935, Shapiro compared the oxygen consumption of nucleate and anucleate halves of sea urchin eggs separated by E. B. Harvey's (1932) centrifugation method. As shown in Fig. 118, he found that the oxygen uptake of the anucleate (heavy) halves is much higher than that of the nucleate (light) halves. These experiments have been extended by Ballentine (1939), who studied the distribution of the dehydrogenases in the two halves. In accordance with Shapiro's (1935) observations, he found that the anucleate halves possess about 70 per cent more dehydrogenase activity than the nucleate fragments of equal volume. These results are, of course, in excellent agreement with what has been said in Chapter I about the relative importance of the cell nucleus and the mitochondria in energy production.

More recently, Malkin (1954) has studied the incorporation of labelled glycine into the proteins and RNA of nucleate and anucleate fragments of unfertilized sea urchin eggs; using again the centrifugation method for their separation, he observed a stronger incorporation into the RNA of the anucleate halves than in the others. The difference was less striking

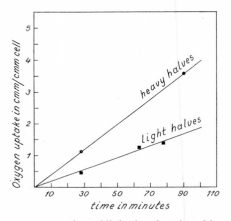

Fig. 118. Oxygen consumption of light (nucleate) and heavy (anucleate) halves of unfertilized sea urchin eggs (Shapiro, 1935).

in the case of the proteins of the two fragments. But the important fact remains that, in unfertilized sea urchin eggs, considerable incorporation of a simple precursor such as glycine into RNA and protein is possible in the absence of the nucleus. Whether this incorporation represents a mere turnover or, as seems less likely, a true synthesis, remains an open question.

For the amphibian egg, the available data are in very good agreement with those which have just been presented for sea urchin eggs: removal of the nucleus from full grown frog oocytes has no effect on the oxygen consumption or CO_2 production; furthermore, the oxygen consumption of isolated germinal vesicles, even in the presence of a number of substrates, is barely measurable and represents less than 5 per cent of the respiration of the intact oocyte (Brachet, 1939). Finally, Tiedemann and Tiedemann (1954) studied the incorporation of $^{14}CO_2$ in *Triton* eggs which had been separated into two by ligation: they found no significant difference between the nucleate and anucleate halves for the incorporation of this very unspecific precursor into several chemical constituents, especially RNA and protein. This means that, in the absence of the nucleus, the tricarboxylic acid cycle and the synthesis or turnover of RNA and protein proceed in a normal manner.

The only conflicting evidence, which suggests a lower metabolic activity of anucleate cytoplasm, is that obtained for polar lobes of *Mytilus*. As we have seen in Chapter IV, the incorporation of precursors into RNA and protein is of a lower magnitude in the anucleate polar lobes than in the other blastomeres (Abd-el-Wahab and Pantelouris, 1957). But the oxygen consumption of the polar lobes (Berg and Kutsky, 1951) and their ^{32}P uptake (Berg and Prescott, 1958) are also lower than in the developing blastomeres. Anyway, the specialized polar lobe material can hardly be taken as a fair sample of 'average' cytoplasm.

It is beyond the scope of the present book to present in any detail the experiments made on the biochemical activities of nucleate and anucleate fragments of unicellular organisms such as amoebae (Brachet, 1955) or *Acetabularia* (Brachet *et al.*, 1955). Their results have been discussed at length recently in another book (Brachet, 1957) and only the most important conclusions will be presented here.

There is no doubt that the nucleus can no longer be considered as the centre of biological oxidations or as a storehouse of enzymes. There is, however, a good deal of evidence for the view that the nucleus is especially active in the synthesis of nucleotides of variable complexity (mononucleo- tides, dinucleotides such as the co-dehydrogenases, RNA and DNA). The nucleus can thus exert a certain control on the oxidative metabolism of the cell via the production of coenzymes; on the other hand, the nucleus is dependent on the cytoplasm, especially on the mitochondria, for the formation of energy-rich compounds such as ATP.

It is also pretty certain now that the nucleus, particularly the nucleolus, is a centre of very active RNA synthesis and that part of the cytoplasmic RNA is of nuclear origin. In this way, the nucleus exerts a more or less direct control on cytoplasmic protein synthesis. But it does not seem probable that the nucleus is by itself a major site of protein synthesis, although proteins are certainly synthesized in the nucleus itself. It is, of course, possible that these nuclear proteins, even if their synthesis is quantitatively not very considerable, have very great importance in view of their possible genetically controlled specificity. Finally, the work done with the micro-organisms agrees with the experiments made on eggs in showing that independent protein synthesis (or at least turnover) can take place in anucleate cytoplasm. The extent of such an independent synthesis varies with the intensity of energy production in the cytoplasm. It is highest in *Acetabularia*, which is capable of photosynthesis in the absence of the nucleus, and lowest in *Amoeba*, which cannot feed any more when the nucleus has been removed. Sea urchin and amphibian eggs, which are rich in reserve materials, occupy an intermediary place.

4. Haploidy—Polyspermy—Polyploidy

Haploidy can be obtained by a variety of means in amphibian eggs: *parthenogenesis* results from pricking and introduction into the egg of a 'second factor', which is required for the formation of a second aster. This 'second factor', according to Shaver (1953), is concentrated in cytoplasmic particles, especially the mitochondria. Other methods used in order to produce haploids are *gynogenesis* (fertilization with irradiated sperm, which will soon degenerate) and *androgenesis* (normal fertilization, immediately followed by removal of the egg nucleus by pricking at the animal pole).

In all cases, the results are the same: cleavage is usually normal, but a few eggs die during gastrulation. The majority develop into abnormal larvae: microcephaly, oedema, ascites and poor development of the blood vessels are the main symptoms of the typical 'haploid syndrome'. Many hypotheses (abnormal nucleo–cytoplasmic ratio, poor utilization of yolk reserves, presence of lethal genes which are not balanced by the normal alleles, insufficient production of the necessary gene products, etc.) have been proposed in order to explain the early death of haploids in Amphibians. None of these theories is entirely satisfactory, or based on enough facts: we must still admit that the real reasons for the development of the haploid syndrome remain unknown, even though Ruhland (1958) has produced fresh evidence for the view that it is related with reduced utilization of yolk.

Whatever these reasons might be, there is no doubt that *polyspermy*, i.e. the penetration of more than one spermatozoon into the unfertilized egg, is also lethal: since only one of the spermatozoa fuses with the female nucleus, the embryo becomes a mosaic of diploid and haploid cells.* As already mentioned in the preceding chapter, cytochemical observations show that haploid regions of polyspermic eggs have an approximately normal RNA content unless, as is often the case, they are underdeveloped (Brachet, 1944).

Finally *polyploidy* is also easy to obtain when amphibian eggs are submitted to cooling or heating soon after fertilization (Fankhauser, 1952): in polyploid organisms, the size of the cells is approximately proportional to the number of chromosome sets, whose multiplication exerts little effect on the basic processes of morphogenesis.

---

* Pantelouris and Jacob (1958) have recently succeeded in injecting haploid nuclei, taken from a neurula, into an unfertilized *Triturus* egg; the result was the production of haploid–diploid chimaerae, which never developed further than the early neurula stage.

If polyspermy and polyploidy have been mentioned in the present chapter, it is because these conditions are very easy to obtain and would certainly deserve careful biochemical studies. But there are no such studies so far. It is only in the case of haploidy that biochemical work has been done or, rather, has been begun (Brachet, 1954). The present results can be summarized in a few sentences. During cleavage, when development remains normal, the oxygen consumption and the DNA content of haploid embryos (obtained by gynogenesis, the eggs being fertilized with U.V.-irradiated sperm) are the same as in diploid controls. At later stages, when the development of haploids becomes progressively more and more abnormal, both their oxygen consumption and their DNA synthesis lag behind those of the controls. We have already pointed out, in Chapter III, that the data obtained in these experiments agree with the view, which has been expressed by Comita and Whiteley (1953), that there is a correlation between the rate of cellular oxidations and that of DNA synthesis. It would, however, be excessive to believe that such a correlation is necessary a causal one. We have no data on the RNA content and the rate of RNA synthesis in haploids, but cytochemical observations (Brachet, 1944, 1954) strongly suggest that the RNA content of the abnormal embryos which display the haploid syndrome is lower than normal, as one would expect. It might thus be that haploidy, at the time it leads to developmental abnormalities, also leads to a general decrease of *all* biochemical activities.

Before leaving the question of the biochemistry of haploid embryos, mention should be made of the quantitative estimations of DNA made by B. C. Moore (1957) on nuclei stained with the Feulgen reaction. She found rather large differences in the DNA content per nucleus of both diploid and haploid frog embryos. In these early embryonic stages, the DNA content per chromosome set is thus far from constant; however, haploids have, of course, less DNA per nucleus than diploids on a statistical basis.

5. Early lethal genes

A tremendous amount of literature exists about developmental abnormalities due to the presence of lethal genes in Insects, Birds and Mammals. The subject has been discussed in great detail in the authoritative book and article of Hadorn (1955, 1958). Since the present monograph deals mostly with biochemical aspects of early development, only a few examples will be presented here.

In *Drosophila*, we have already seen that lack of the X chromosome (Poulson), small chromosomal deficiencies or even gene mutations (Poulson, 1945; Ede, 1956; Counce, 1956; Bull, 1956; Counce and Ede, 1957) can lead to abnormalities and arrest of development in very early embryonic stages (cleavage, gastrulation). The most interesting biochemical work on these early lethals still remains that of Boell and Poulson (1939) and Poulson

(1945), who studied the oxygen consumption of *Drosophila* eggs which lack the X chromosome (nullo-X). The complete absence of the X chromosome leads to early abnormalities of development: the nuclei first divide normally, but their migration towards the periphery, in order to form the blastoderm, is so abnormal that development quickly stops and the embryo dies. Figure 119 shows that the oxygen uptake of the nullo-X embryos first shows a normal increase; but, after one hour, the respiration of the lethal embryos stops increasing, in contrast to the normally developing

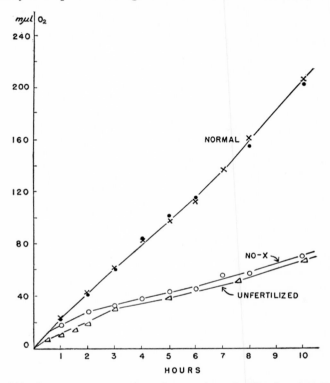

Fig. 119. Oxygen consumption of normal, unfertilized and deficient (no-X) single eggs of *Drosophila melanogaster* (Poulson, 1945).

control embryos, and it becomes almost identical to that of the unfertilized eggs. It certainly would be very interesting to study in more detail the metabolism of the nullo-X embryos and, in particular, to try to find out the reasons for the metabolic block.

The possibilities presented by lethal embryos for biochemical studies are also indicated by the fact, which has been briefly reported by Poulson and Boell (1946), that the cholinesterase content of the embryos is greatly increased in a mutant of *Drosophila* which shows an exaggerated development of the nervous system at the expense of other tissues. The nervous system, in this case, is very abnormal in organization and its mass is greatly increased. The mutation is due to a relatively small deficiency of the X chromosome.

More work, which will be found described in Hadorn (1955, 1958), has been done on *Drosophila* larval lethals: for instance, in *letal meander*, the composition of the amino acid pool is abnormal and the content in protease is decreased in the intestine. Lethality, in this case, is obviously due to trouble in protein metabolism (Chen and Hadorn, 1955). In another *Drosophila* larval lethal studied by Hadorn and Gloor (1942), the so-called *letal 2 gl*, the abnormal larvae contain less DNA than normal embryos at the same stage. A deficiency in DNA synthesis might be responsible for the developmental abnormalities which ultimately lead to the death of the lethal larvae (Welch, 1957).

Another interesting case is that of the *creeper fowl*, which has been extensively studied by Landauer (1932, 1944) from the morphological and experimental viewpoints. The *creeper* mutation is lethal in the homozygous condition and produces a number of abnormalities in heterozygous organisms. A recent cytochemical study of homozygous *creeper* embryos by Loewenthal (1957) has shown that they contain less RNA than the controls. Pycnotic nuclei are also abnormally numerous in the homozygous *creeper* embryos, after 72 hours of development. On the other hand, these lethal *creeper* homozygous embryos give perfectly normal reactions for —SH and —SS— groups, glycogen, alkaline phosphatase and succinic dehydrogenase. It is concluded by Loewenthal (1957) that the mutation exerts its main effect on RNA synthesis and that the developmental block might be linked to an effect on RNA synthesis. Such a conclusion is of course in perfect agreement with all that has been said in the preceding chapter about the close relationships existing between RNA synthesis and distribution on one hand and morphogenesis on the other.

These few examples indicate that lethality is due, in embryos as in micro-organisms, to metabolic blocks. It is very unfortunate that the exact nature of these blocks (absence of a specific enzyme, for instance) remains unknown. The perspectives in this field are obviously tremendous. Although the chemical nature of the biochemical blocks might be more difficult to establish in embryos than in micro-organisms, the former having a marked advantage over the latter, they are the site of complex morphogenesis; thus an extensive biochemical analysis of a number of early lethals might give decisive clues about the biochemical processes which ultimately lead to embryonic differentiation.

It is probably because many chemical embryologists wish to simplify the complicated problems which they are facing in the case of differentiation that they have concentrated their efforts on another type of early lethals,

Q

the so-called 'lethal hybrids', which often undergo a developmental block at the beginning of gastrulation.

6. Biochemical studies on lethal hybrids

The lethal combinations which have been used to the largest extent for biochemical studies are *Paracentrotus* ♀ × *Arbacia* ♂ among the sea urchins, *Rana pipiens* ♂ × *Rana sylvatica* ♂ and *Rana esculenta* ♀ × *Rana temporaria* ♂ among the Amphibians. In the following, we shall first study the Echinoderms, then the Amphibians.

The lethal combinations *Paracentrotus* ♀ × *Arbacia* ♂ and *Psammechinus* ♀ × *Arbacia* ♂ were studied by Baltzer in 1910. Later studies by Baltzer *et al.* (1954) and Baltzer and Bernhard (1955) have shown that they yield true hybrids, with diploid nuclei. Their cleavage is normal, but gastrulation is markedly inhibited and very few plutei (about 1 per cent), which may show a paternal influence, can be obtained.

In an interesting and recent paper, Chen and Baltzer (1958) have studied by chromatography the amino acid and peptide distribution in three different species, belonging to three different families, of sea urchins (*Paracentrotus lividus*, *Arbacia lixula* and *Sphaerechinus granularis*). They also studied, from the same viewpoint, the corresponding chromatographic pattern of the hybrids *Paracentrotus* ♀ × *Arbacia* ♂ and *Sphaerechinus* ♀ × *Paracentrotus* ♂. Their extensive studies show that the patterns of free amino acids differ in the three species which were under investigation and that they show only quantitative changes during development. But no species-specific differences could be found in the amino acid composition of the proteins (after acid hydrolysis of the latter) of the eggs. It is, of course, possible that more refined methods for protein analysis, such as the 'fingerprinting' technique of Ingram (1958), would reveal differences between the proteins in the eggs of various species of sea urchins.

Turning now to the hybrids, the main conclusion of Chen and Baltzer's (1958) paper is that the free amino acids pattern shows an *entirely maternal* character. It is worth noting, in this respect, that while, as we have seen, the *Paracentrotus* ♀ × *Arbacia* ♂ combination is lethal, the *Sphaerechinus* ♀ × *Paracentrotus* ♂ hybrids develop normally to the pluteus stage, where they show paternal and maternal character in the skeleton. Nevertheless, the amino acid pattern remains purely maternal.

However, paternal effects on protein synthesis and metabolism can be detected when methods (immunological or enzymatic) more specific than amino acid composition analysis are used for the study of lethal hybrids in Echinoderms. For instance, Harding *et al.* (1954, 1955), working with the *Paracentrotus* ♀ × *Arbacia* ♂ hybrid, could not detect the paternal antigens 1 hour after fertilization; but these antigens could be detected in hybrid blastulae, thus before development becomes arrested. It would be exceedingly interesting to try to carry the analysis one step further and to establish whether the paternal antigens detected by Harding *et al.* (1954, 1955) in hybrid blastulae are strictly localized in the nuclei or also present in the cytoplasm. In the first case, they would correspond to the repeated reduplication of proteins already associated with the paternal chromosomes in the sperm nucleus; the second eventuality would prove that the egg possesses cytoplasmic mechanisms of protein synthesis capable of reproducing the foreign protein introduced by the paternal nucleus at fertilization. These important questions could probably be answered by using

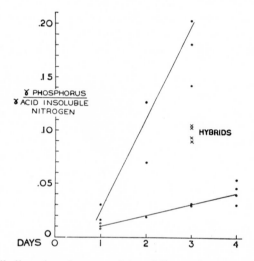

FIG. 120. Alkaline phosphatase activity of *Strongylocentrotus purpuratus*, *Dendraster excentricus* and *Strongylocentrotus purpuratus* ♀ × *Dendraster excentricus* ♂ hybrids. Expressed as the ratio of micrograms of phosphorus released in a 2-hour period per microgram of acid-insoluble nitrogen. Solid dots indicate determinations upon *Dendraster*, open circles are for *S. purpuratus* and X indicates determinations upon hybrids.

such methods as homogeneization and centrifugation, or antigen detection by the Coons fluorescent antibodies technique.

We have just seen that, according to Chen and Baltzer (1958), hybrid plutei which have intermediary characters between the two parents have a strictly maternal free amino acid pool. The situation is different when the enzymatic composition of such plutei is studied. Flickinger (1957), working on the intra-ordinal hybrid *Strongylocentrotus* ♀ × *Dendraster* ♂ (whose plutei are intermediary, as shown by A. R. Moore (1957)) found that the alkaline phosphatase is synthesized in an intermediate way during development (Fig. 120). In this case, there is no doubt that the presence of a foreign nucleus modifies not only the morphological characters of the hybrid, but also the rate of the synthesis of one of its enzymes.*

This fragmentary information about protein metabolism in sea urchin hybrids does not yet allow precise conclusions; but it shows that, thanks to Baltzer and Bernhard (1955), a very useful research material, which can be obtained in large quantities, is now available for studies on biochemical interactions between nucleus and cytoplasm. It is to be hoped and expected that energy production, nucleic acids and protein synthesis will be extensively studied in this material with refined methods, during the years to come.

Much more work has been done with *amphibian hybrids* than with those of sea urchins: a large, detailed amount of biological experiments made on the Urodeles will be found in Baltzer (1952). We owe to J. A. Moore (1955)

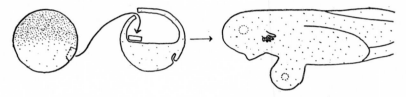

FIG. 121. Schematic representation of J. A. Moore's experiments: the organizer of the lethal hybrid is grafted into the blastocoele of a normal host. It induces a secondary head (J. A. Moore, 1948).

an extensive review on hybridization in Anurans (see also Brachet (1957) for a more complete treatment of the subject). Restricting ourselves here to the combinations which have been studied at the biochemical level, it can be said that the hybrids are diploid and that their development stops, as we have already seen, at the late blastula or early gastrula stage. The failure of gastrulation is essentially due to the absence of one of the important morphogenetic movements, convergent extension of the chordomesoblast (Gregg and Klein, 1955).

Of great interest is the fact that transplantation of a fragment taken from a lethal hybrid into a normal gastrula (even from a foreign species) can 'save' the fragment from lethality: the fragment will develop normally again and, if it is an organizer, it will even induce the formation of a secondary nervous system in the host (Fig. 121). However, both the inducing capacity of the organizer and the competence of the ectoblast are weakened in lethal hybrids as compared with normal gastrulae (Hadorn, 1932, 1934;

---

* The same conclusion can be drawn for the respiration of the *Paracentrotus* ♀ × *Arbacia* ♂ hybrids: in contrast to what has been said for the composition of the amino acid pool, respiration behaves in an intermediate manner (Baltzer *et al.* 1959).

Brachet, 1944; J. A. Moore, 1947, 1948). The reasons for the 'revival' of fragments of lethal hybrids when they are grafted into normal hosts are not yet very clear. It is probable that, as already suggested above for gastrulae treated with a heat shock, the block prior to 'revitalization' is due to the fact that the lethal cells cannot synthesize substances which are required for further development; these substances would be of an unspecific nature and would diffuse from the host into the graft. While this explanation seems to be the more likely, other possibilities, such as a selection of healthy cells in the hybrid (Baltzer, 1952), are not excluded.

It should be added, before we end this short survey of the main biological facts known about early lethal hybrids, that it is easy, in the frog, to obtain

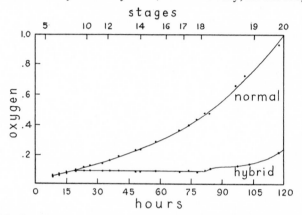

FIG. 122. Oxygen consumption of normal and lethal embryos (Barth, 1946).

a situation which is very similar to lethal hybridization by fertilizing eggs with sperm which has been treated with nitrogen mustard. By choosing an appropriate concentration of mustard, a block of development at the late blastula stage, following normal cleavage, is obtained in all the eggs (Brachet, 1954). The advantage of this type of experiment over lethal hybridization is that a much larger number of blastulae, arrested because they suffered nuclear damage, is made available for biochemical studies.

We shall now examine the metabolism of lethal hybrids and deal first with energy production, then with nucleic acid and protein synthesis.

By far the most important work done on the *metabolism of arrested gastrulae* is that done by Barth and his group on the combination *Rana pipiens* ♀ × *Rana sylvatica* ♂; the main results have been summarized and discussed recently by Gregg (1957).

As indicated in Fig. 122, the oxygen uptake of the lethal hybrids first increases normally and remains constant for a long time as soon as development has stopped. The final rise in the oxygen consumption is probably associated with the onset of cytolysis (Barth, 1946). It is interesting to note, in this respect, that homogenates of normal and hybrid gastrulae have the same oxygen consumption, which is always higher than that of intact gastrulae (Gregg and Ray, 1957). In another study, Sze (1953) made the important observation that the respiration is depressed to the same extent (about 50 per cent) in all parts of the hybrid gastrula: there is thus apparently no tissue-localized block to respiration in these lethal embryos.

Barth (1946) also studied the respiratory quotient (CO_2/O_2) of normal and blocked gastrulae: as shown in Fig. 123, the respiratory quotient first increases in a normal way in both types of embryos. In ageing hybrid gastrulae, however, CO_2 production becomes exaggerated and the R.Q.

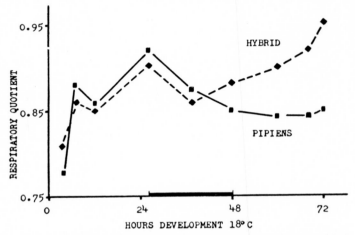

Fig. 123. Respiratory quotients of developing *Rana pipiens* and hybrid embryos (reconstructed from data of Barth, 1946, by Gregg, 1957).

becomes much higher than in the controls. The reason for the over-production of CO_2 by the arrested gastrulae remains uncertain; it might be, as suggested by Barth (1946), that these gastrulae oxidize other substrates than those oxidized by the control embryos.

A study of carbohydrate utilization by Gregg (1948) lends some support to such a hypothesis: he found that normal embryos start using their carbohydrate store at the beginning of gastrulation; hybrid embryos, on the other hand, utilize their carbohydrates from the very beginning of development, but at a slow and almost constant rate. Endogenous carbohydrate utilization is thus subnormal in the hybrid embryos. Estimations of the glycogen content in the various parts of gastrulae, both normal and hybrid, suggest that there is a general depression of glycogenolysis; in particular, there is no measurable glycogenolysis in the organizer of the hybrid gastrulae, in contrast to the appreciable glycogen breakdown which occurs during invagination of the chordomesoblast in normal gastrulae (Jaeger, 1945). Finally, the fact that hybrid embryos produce less lactic acid in anaerobiosis than normal ones (Barth, 1946) confirms the view that there is a block somewhere in the carbohydrate metabolism of the hybrids; the localization of this metabolic block remains unfortunately unknown.

Barth and Jaeger (1947) have also studied the ATP and inorganic phosphate content of normal and hybrid embryos placed in either aerobic or anaerobic conditions: their conclusion is that the hybrid shows a decreased capacity for keeping, in anaerobiosis, ATP in the phosphorylated form. Gregg (1947), who has discussed in detail this question, concludes that 'the evidence thus warrants the conclusion that hybrids meet relatively low anaerobic demands for energy about as well as *R. pipiens* controls, whatever the actual mechanism, but whether they preserve their entire store of phosphate bond energy as well as controls is open to further enquiry'. In fact, a 'further enquiry' by Gregg and Kahlbrock (1957) showed only a slight increase in inorganic phosphate when gastrulae were placed under anaerobic conditions; no measurable difference between normal and hybrid gastrulae could be detected by Gregg and Kahlbrock (1957) in this series of experiments.

As already mentioned, the analysis of the combination *Rana pipiens* ♀ × *Rana sylvatica* ♂ is by far the most complete one on the biochemical level. It would be important to know whether the findings which have just been presented can be generalized to other combinations between Amphibians. The data which will be examined now suggest that there is a good deal of variation in this respect, at least in the case of the oxygen uptake.

For instance, Barth and Barth (1954) have reported on the unpublished work of one of their students, Healy, on the *Rana pipiens* ♀ × *Rana clamitans* ♂ hybrid; in this case, where development also stops at gastrulation, a normal increase in the rate of respiration was found in the hybrids, even after development stopped. The question certainly deserves more careful study, because *Rana pipiens* eggs were used in the two cases we have examined so far. If these eggs are fertilized by *Rana sylvatica* sperm, the respiration stops increasing as soon as the eggs are blocked; but the oxygen uptake increases if *Rana clamitans* sperm is used for fertilization. This means that the introduction of a foreign nucleus into an egg can have very different effects on the respiratory rate, depending on its zoological origin.

In Urodeles, Chen (1953) has studied the oxygen consumption of lethal hybrids between *Triton* ♀ and *Salamandra* ♂; they show a critical phase, characterized by frequent mitotic abnormalities at the blastula stage; development can, however, reach the early gastrula stage. As shown in Fig. 124, the oxygen consumption of the hybrids is already subnormal during the critical phase and increases only slightly (10 per cent) between the blastula and gastrula stages; but this increase is not much less than that found in controls for the same period. It is only later, during gastrulation and neurulation, that the respiration of the normal embryos markedly increases.

As in the case studied by Chen (1953), the oxygen consumption of the *Rana esculenta* ♀ × *Rana temporaria* ♂ hybrid is somewhat lower than in the controls already at the blastula stage, i.e. a few hours before the arrest of development. When gastrulation occurs in the controls, the increase in the oxygen uptake is almost the same in the hybrids, although their

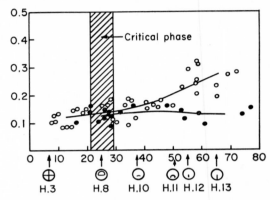

Fig. 124. The rate of oxygen consumption during the early embryonic development of the control eggs (*Triton palmatus* and *taeniatus*) and the lethal hybrid (*Triton palmatus* or *taeniatus* ♀ × *Salamandra atra* ♂). Ordinate: oxygen uptake in c.mm per egg per hour. Abscissa: egg age in hours after fertilization at 18° C with indication of developmental stages according to Harrison's table for *Ambystoma punctatum*. o = control egg; ● = hybrid egg (Chen, 1953).

gastrulation is blocked (Brachet, 1954). In another lethal combination *Bufo vulgaris* ♀ × *Rana temporaria* ♂, in which development stops at the blastula stage, the oxygen consumption of the blocked hybrids increases during one day at the same rate as in the developing controls (Brachet, 1954). Finally, in frog eggs fertilized with nitrogen mustard-treated sperm, the critical phase, from the standpoint of mitotic abnormalities, is cleavage; respiration, at this time, is already lower in the abnormal eggs than in the controls. But, afterwards, the respiration of the arrested blastulae continues to increase, for at least one day, at much the same rate as in controls.

There is thus no doubt that the introduction of a foreign nucleus into an egg does not necessarily stop the normal increase in the oxygen consumption of the embryo when its development becomes arrested. In fact, lethal hybridization, in the cases we studied (1954), provides a good example of a dissociation between morphogenesis and increase in the rate of cellular oxidations.

Species differences certainly also exist in the case of ATP utilization in anaerobiosis by normal and lethal embryos. We have seen that there is no great difference, in this respect, between *R. pipiens* ♀ × *R. sylvatica* ♂ hybrids and normal *R. pipiens* controls. The situation is different when frog eggs fertilized with nitrogen mustard-treated sperm are compared with normal frog eggs (Brachet, 1955). As shown in Fig. 125, the former show a considerably decreased capacity for keeping ATP in its phosphorylated form in anaerobiosis, especially in experiments of relatively short duration (6 hours). It might be that, in frog eggs possessing an abnormal nucleus, glycolysis becomes insufficient to maintain anaerobic synthesis of ATP. It certainly would be important to know the precise localization

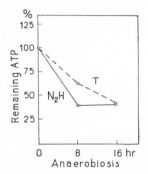

FIG. 125. Anaerobic drop of the ATP content of normal (T) and lethal (N₂H) frog embryos (Brachet, 1955).

of the metabolic block in glycolysis; but Gregg (1957) has pointed out very well how difficult it will be to solve this problem.

We may now turn our attention to the *protein and nucleic acid metabolism* of lethal hybrids. Regarding proteins, about which too little is known to lead to definite conclusions, it should be mentioned first that the incorporation of glycine into the proteins of frog eggs fertilized with nitrogen mustard-treated sperm is well above that found in the controls (Brachet, 1954). But it is doubtful whether this difference is due to increased protein anabolism in the lethal embryos, since similar observations could be made in the case of ^{32}P uptake. It might well be that the presence of an abnormal nucleus merely increases the egg's permeability in an unspecific way; this increase in permeability would facilitate the incorporation of labelled precursors into more complex molecules, proteins or nucleic acids for instance. In fact, studies by Mezger-Freed (1953) on the enzyme phospho-protein-phosphatase (which liberates inorganic phosphate from the yolk phosphoproteins and which is present in the yolk platelets themselves) indicate that protein synthesis is restricted in lethal hybrids. Working with *Rana pipiens* ♀ × *Rana sylvatica* ♂ hybrids, she found that their phosphoprotein-phosphatase content underwent the same changes as normal *Rana pipiens* controls until their development became arrested. At that time, increase in enzymatic activity was less prolonged in the hybrids than in the controls. Of special interest, in Mezger-Freed's work (1953), is the fact that phosphoprotein-phosphatase is much less active in dorsal parts taken from the animal hemispheres of hybrid gastrulae than in the corresponding parts of controls. This deficiency in the liberation of inorganic phosphate from phosphoproteins is the only known tissue-localized metabolic difference between hybrid and normal embryos. But its very existence should encourage further comparative studies on enzymatic activities in lethal and normal embryos, and parts thereof.

Recent experiments by Ranzi *et al.* (1957), who used conventional methods for protein fractionation (salting-out especially), have disclosed the interesting fact that the proteins of the *Bufo viridis* ♀ × *Bufo bufo* ♂ hybrids resemble those of embryos treated with lithium chloride. In a further step of this analysis, Ranzi *et al.* (1958) were able to show, with immunological methods, that the presence of a foreign nucleus in the egg delays the appearance of new maternal antigens. Whether this delay in the synthesis of new specific proteins is linked together with a general retardation of development is, unfortunately, not stated in Ranzi *et al.*'s (1958) paper.

One can conclude, once more, from these studies that, as is too often the case in Chemical Embryology, the little we know about protein metabolism in amphibian lethal hybrids only shows that a large and exciting field is open to the investigator. Enzymatic and immunological studies, because of the high specificity of the methods used, should prove especially rewarding if we wish to get a deeper understanding of nucleo-cytoplasmic interactions in normal embryos and lethal hybrids.

More is known, fortunately, about nucleic acid metabolism in lethal hybrids among Amphibians than about their protein metabolism both from the cytochemical and the quantitative viewpoints.

The cytological and cytochemical picture is apparently the same in the lethal hybrid combinations *Rana esculenta* ♀ × *Rana temporaria* ♂ (Brachet, 1944, 1954), *Rana pipiens* ♀ × *Rana catesbeiana* ♂ (King and Briggs, 1953) and *Rana pipiens* ♀ × *Rana sylvatica* ♂ (B. C. Moore, 1954, 1957): mitotic activity and development both stop together and expulsion of chromatin in the cytoplasm is exceptional. If the arrested gastrulae are stained with methyl green-pyronine, the nuclei form a mosaic: while some are normal, many are characterized by an overload of RNA. Not only are the nucleoli too large, too numerous and too basophilic, but the chromatin itself stains strongly with pyronine. Cytochemical tests show that this exaggerated pyroninophily is not due to a depolymerization of DNA, but to an overload in RNA. As a result of this excessive RNA synthesis in the nuclei, the DNA-containing chromatin is pushed towards the nuclear membrane, where it forms a thin film. It is probable that these cytochemical changes are linked together with the already mentioned fact that nuclei of lethal hybrids progressively lose their activity when they are injected into enucleated unfertilized eggs (King and Briggs, 1953), since the proportion of the pyroninophilic nuclei steadily increases in the arrested gastrulae. It looks as if the nuclei of the arrested hybrid gastrulae synthesized RNA at an exaggerated rate and as if this excess nuclear RNA (which might be abnormal in composition) could not be utilized any more by the cytoplasm for synthetic processes (Brachet, 1954). In any event, there is no cytochemically detectable RNA increase in the cytoplasm of the blocked gastrulae. But, when a fragment of an arrested lethal hybrid gastrula is grafted into a normal host in order to 'revitalize' it, cytoplasmic RNA synthesis soon becomes visible in the graft; simultaneously, the nuclei become more normal and mitotic activity is resumed (Brachet, 1944). There is no doubt that more modern methods of investigation, autoradiography and electron microscopy in particular, might help considerably in our understanding of these puzzling observations.

The cytochemical picture is different in lethals which stop developing in the blastula stage (*Bufo vulgaris* ♀ × *Rana temporaria* ♂; frog eggs fertilized with nitrogen mustard-treated sperm): the nuclei of some of the blocked cells are formed of two hemikaryons; one of them is characterized by a greatly increased content in Feulgen-staining material, while the other forms large RNA-containing nucleoli at a stage where cells of the controls have no nucleoli (Fig. 126). If mitosis occurs in such a blastomere, the chromatin of the hemikaryon which contains a great excess of DNA is eliminated in the cytoplasm, under the form of hundreds of chromosomes (or chromosome fragments) or as a large pycnotic mass (Brachet, 1954). The most likely interpretation of these observations is the following one: the DNA-rich hemikaryon would be of paternal origin; due to the nitrogen-mustard treatment, DNA synthesis and endomitotic reduplication would occur, in an exaggerated fashion. Meanwhile, the maternal (normal) hemikaryon cannot normally divide and, as a result of the mitotic block, it forms nucleoli and accumulates RNA in excess. Admittedly, this explanation is largely hypothetical and is even made somewhat unlikely by the fact that, according to B. C. Moore (1957), nuclei made of two hemikaryons are found in haploid embryos. There is thus no reason to believe that one of them is necessary of paternal and the other of maternal origin. But, whatever the real significance of the facts, it is very striking that, as shown in Fig. 126, two adjacent hemikaryons, which are placed in the same cytoplasm, may be so different in morphology and chemical composition.

The *Rana pipiens* ♀ × *Rana sylvatica* ♂ cross, which has never been studied in detail for RNA localization and content, has been subjected to an extensive analysis of the DNA content of individual nuclei by B. C. Moore (1954, 1957). Her main—and very interesting—conclusion is that DNA synthesis goes on for some time in the arrested gastrulae: cells from the blocked lethal hybrids can synthesize more DNA than is required for the next mitosis. The block in mitotic activity and morphogenesis is thus not due to a total impairment of DNA synthesis. We shall soon see that

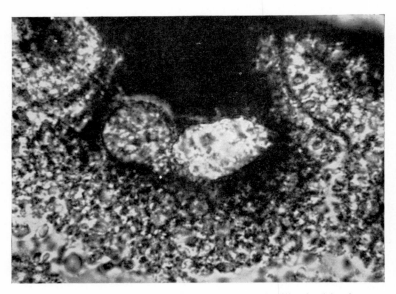

Fig. 126. Adjacent 'hemikaryons' in frog eggs fertilized with nitrogen mustard-treated sperm; their DNA content, as indicated by the Feulgen reaction, is very different (Brachet, 1954).

such a conclusion is in keeping with results obtained from quantitative analysis of the DNA content of blocked lethal hybrids.

Cytochemical studies on nucleic acids distribution have also been made in Urodeles by Schönmann (1938), Baltzer and Schönmann (1951), Baltzer (1952) and Zeller (1956); but the main emphasis, in these studies, has been placed on the mitotic abnormalities, which can be very numerous and varied during the 'critical phase'; they are followed by pycnotic degeneration of the nuclei.

A number of papers have been devoted to quantitative measurements of the RNA and DNA content of lethal hybrids as compared with normal controls. Figure 127 summarizes the results obtained by Steinert (1951) in the case of the lethal *Rana esculenta* ♀ × *Rana temporaria* ♂ hybrids. It will be seen that there is a small RNA synthesis in the hybrids as well as in the controls until the development of the latter stops. At later stages, the controls continue to synthesize RNA, whereas the RNA content of the hybrids drops, as a result of incipient cytolysis. These results agree well with the cytochemical observations already referred to, which showed that no RNA synthesis can be detected in the cytoplasm of the hybrids; the overload in nuclear RNA, which can be demonstrated by cytochemical methods, would of course escape detection when the RNA content of the *whole* egg is estimated quantitatively.

Similar results have been obtained for Urodeles by Chen (1954) and by Zeller (1956): Chen (1954), who worked on the *Triton palmatus* ♀ × *Salamandra* ♂ hybrid, found a normal RNA content of the hybrids during cleavage, followed by a drop; the latter is certainly due to cytolysis

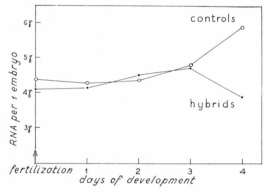

FIG. 127. RNA synthesis in normal eggs and lethal hybrids (Steinert, 1951).

of part of the cells, since dying cells are particularly numerous in this combination. The work of Zeller (1956) has been much more extensive than that of any of his predecessors, since he studied both diploid and merogone hybrids of the *Triton palmatus* ♀ × *Triton cristatus* ♂ type. His conclusions are in excellent agreement with our own cytochemical observations on the *Rana esculenta* ♀ × *Rana temporaria* ♂ hybrids. According to Zeller (1956), RNA is normally built in the nucleus and utilized by the cytoplasm; but, in lethal hybrids, the cytoplasm would be unable to utilize for metabolic purposes the RNA built by the foreign nucleus.

Finally, we have at hand a few valuable indications about DNA synthesis in lethal hybrids. They all strongly suggest that DNA synthesis still continues in the arrested embryos and that the developmental block is thus not due to an interruption of DNA synthesis. For instance, we found (1954) that blocked blastulae originating from frog eggs fertilized with nitrogen mustard-treated sperm have a lower (30 per cent) DNA content than the controls; however, during the next day, the arrested blastulae effect a measurable DNA synthesis. It has also been shown by Chen (1954) that, in *Triton palmatus* ♀ × *Salamandra* ♂ lethal hybrids, a small, but definite, DNA synthesis occurs after development has been blocked. But the best experiments made so far in this field are, without any doubt, those of Gregg and Løvtrup (1955), because the microbiological assay method for DNA estimation they used is much more specific than the techniques used by previous workers. As shown in Fig. 128, DNA is synthesized by the hybrids (*R. pipiens* ♀ × *R. sylvatica* ♂), although they

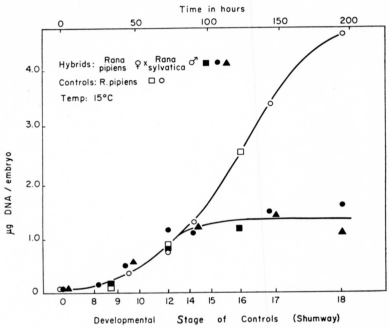

FIG. 128. DNA synthesis in normal and hybrid embryos (Gregg and Løvtrup, 1955).

do not gastrulate at a normal rate, until the controls have reached stage 14, i.e. the early neurula stage (open neural folds). DNA synthesis then completely stops in the hybrids.

These quantitative results are of course in perfect agreement with the already mentioned work of B. C. Moore (1957), who used an entirely different technique (measurement of the DNA content of individual nuclei stained with the Feulgen reaction): there is thus little doubt that DNA synthesis can go on for some time in the nuclei of arrested lethal gastrulae and that the reason for the developmental block must be sought elsewhere.

The reason for this developmental block remains, of course, unknown;

but, as we have seen, valuable indications about the nature of several metabolic blocks have been obtained. We know that the carbohydrate metabolism of the lethal hybrids is reduced; we also know that, in lethal hybrids, there is an unbalance between nuclear and cytoplasmic RNA metabolisms. There is no doubt, as mentioned several times in this chapter, that utilization of methods which have a high resolving power (auto-radiography, for instance) or a high specificity (enzymological and immunological techniques) will lead to considerable progress. But the morphological aspects of the problems raised by the introduction of a foreign nucleus in an egg should not be overlooked: the ultra-fine structure of the cytoplasm, in lethal hybrids, might well be altered. In this field, as in so many others, the last word might be said by an electron microscopist, provided he is also interested in the biochemical aspects of the problem.

REFERENCES

ABD-EL-WAHAB, A. and E. M. PANTELOURIS. (1957): *Exp. Cell Res.* **13**, 78.
ANCEL, P. and P. VINTEMBERGER. (1948): *Bull. biol. France et Belg.*, suppl. **31**.
BALLENTINE, R. (1939): *Biol. Bull.* **72**, 328.
BALTZER, F. (1910): *Arch. Zellforschg.* **4**, 497.
BALTZER, F. (1952): *Sympos. Soc. exp. Biol.* **6**, 230.
BALTZER, F., P. S. CHEN and A. H. WHITELEY. (1959): *Exp. Cell Res.*, suppl. **6**, 192.
BALTZER, F. and M. BERNHARD. (1955): *Exp. Cell Res.*, suppl. **3**, 16.
BALTZER, F., C. HARDING, H. E. LEHMAN and W. BOPP. (1954): *Rev. suisse Zool.* **61**, 402.
BALTZER, F. and W. SCHÖNMANN. (1951): *Rev. suisse Zool.* **58**, 495.
BARTH, L. G. (1946): *J exp. Zool.* **103**, 463.
BARTH, L. G. and L. J. BARTH. (1954): *The Energetics of Development.* Columbia Univ. Press, N.Y.
BARTH, L. G. and L. JAEGER. (1947): *Physiol. Zool.* **20**, 133.
BEADLE, G. W. (1946): *Amer. Scientist* **34**, 31.
BERG, W. E. and P. B. KUTSKY. (1951): *Biol. Bull.* **101**, 47.
BERG, W. E. and D. M. PRESCOTT. (1958): *Exp. Cell Res.* **14**, 402.
BOELL, E. J. and D. F. POULSON. (1939): *Anat. Rec.* **75**, suppl. 1, 65.
BRACHET, A. (1910): *Arch. Zool. exp. génér.*, sér. V, **6**, 1.
BRACHET, A. (1931): *L'Oeuf et les Facteurs de l'Ontogénèse.* Doin. Paris
BRACHET, J. (1939): *Arch. exp. Zellforschg.* **22**, 541.
BRACHET, J. (1944): *Ann. Soc. Roy. Zool. Belg.* **75**, 49.
BRACHET, J. (1949): *Pubbl. Staz. zool. Napoli* **21**, 77.
BRACHET, J. (1954): *Arch. Biol.* **65**, 1.
BRACHET, J. (1955): *Biochim. biophys. Acta* **18**, 247.
BRACHET, J. (1957): *Biochemical Cytology.* Academic Press, N.Y.
BRACHET, J., H. CHANTRENNE and F. VANDERHAEGHE. (1955): *Biochim. biophys. Acta* **18**, 544.
BRIGGS, R., E. U. GREEN and T. J. KING. (1951): *J. exp. Zool.* **116**, 455.
BRIGGS, R. and T. J. KING. (1953): *J. exp. Zool.* **122**, 485.
BRIGGS, R. and T. J. KING. (1955): In: *Biological Specificity and Growth* (E. Butler, ed.), p. 207. Princeton Univ. Press.

BRIGGS, R. and T. J. KING. (1957): *J. Morphol.* **100**, 269.

BULL, A. L. (1956): *J. exp. Zool.* **132**, 467.

CHEN, P. S. (1953): *Exp. Cell Res.* **5**, 275.

CHEN, P. S. (1954): *Experientia* **10**, 212.

CHEN, P. S. and F. BALTZER. (1958): *Nature* **181**, 98.

CHEN, P. S. and E. HADORN. (1955): *Rev. suisse Zool.* **62**, 338.

COMITA, J. J. and A. H. WHITELEY. (1953): *Biol. Bull.* **105**, 412.

COUNCE, S. J. (1956): *Z. indukt. Abstamm.-Vererbgslehre* **87**, 443, 462, 482.

COUNCE, S. J. and D. EDE. (1957): *J. Embryol. exp. Morphol.* **5**, 404.

DALCQ, A. and S. SIMON. (1932): *Protoplasma* **14**, 497.

DRIESCH, H. (1894): *Analytische Theorie der Organischen Entwicklung.*

FANKHAUSER, G. (1934): *J. exp. Zool.* **67**, 349.

FANKHAUSER, G. (1952): *Internat. Rev. Cytol.* **1**, 165.

FISCHBERG, M., J. B. GURDON and T. R. ELSDALE. (1958): *Nature* **181**, 424.

FISCHBERG, M., J. B. GURDON and T. R. ELSDALE. (1959): *Exp. Cell Res.*, suppl. **6**, 161.

FLICKINGER, R. A. (1957): *Biol. Bull.* **112**, 21.

EDE, D. (1956): *Roux' Arch. Entw. Mech.* **148**, 416, 437.

GREGG, J. R. (1948): *J. exp. Zool.* **109**, 119.

GREGG, J. R. (1957): In: *The Beginnings of Embryonic Development*, p. 231, A.A.A.S., Publ. No. 48, Washington, D.C.

GREGG, J. R. and M. KAHLBROCK. (1957): *Biol. Bull.* **113**, 376.

GREGG, J. R. and D. KLEIN. (1955): *Biol. Bull.* **109**, 265.

GREGG, J. R. and S. LØVTRUP. (1955): *Biol. Bull.* **108**, 29.

GREGG, J. R. and F. L. RAY. (1957): *Biol. Bull.* **113**, 382.

GURDON, J. B., T. R. ELSDALE and M. FISCHBERG. (1958): *Nature* **182**, 64.

HADORN, E. (1932): *Roux' Arch. Entw. Mech.* **125**, 496.

HADORN, E. (1934): *Roux' Arch. Entw. Mech.* **131**, 238.

HADORN, E. (1955): *Letalfaktoren in ihrer Bedeutung für Erbpathologie und Genphysiologie der Entwicklung.* G. Thieme, Stuttgart.

HADORN, E. (1958): In: *The Chemical Basis of Development*, p. 779. Johns Hopkins Univ. Press, Baltimore.

HADORN, E. and H. GLOOR. (1942): *Rev. suisse Zool.* **49**, 228.

HARDING, C. V., D. HARDING and J. W. BAMBERGER. (1955): *Exp. Cell Res.*, suppl. **3**, 181.

HARDING, C. V., D. HARDING and P. PERLMANN. (1954): *Exp. Cell Res.* **6**, 202.

HARVEY, E. B. (1932): *Biol. Bull.* **62**, 155.

HARVEY, E. B. (1936): *Biol. Bull.* **71**, 101.

INGRAM, V. M. (1958): *Biochim. biophys. Acta* **28**, 539.

JAEGER, L. (1945): *J. cell. comp. Physiol.* **25**, 97.

KARASAKI, S. (1959): *Embryologia* **4**, 273.

KING, T. J. and R. BRIGGS. (1953). *J. exp. Zool.* **123**, 61.

KING, T. J. and R. BRIGGS. (1954): *J. Embryol. exp. Morphol.* **2**, 73.

KING, T. J. and R. BRIGGS. (1955): *Proc. nat. Acad. Sci. Wash.* **41**, 321.

KING, T. J. and R. BRIGGS. (1956): *Cold Spring Harbor Sympos.* **21**, 271.

LANDAUER, W. (1932): *J. Genetics* **25**, 367,

LANDAUER, W. (1944): *Science* **100**, 1.

LEDERBERG, J. (1952): *Physiol. Rev.* **32**, 403.

LEHMAN, H. E. (1955): *Biol. Bull.* **108**, 138

LEHMAN, H. E. (1957): In: *The Beginnings of Embryonic Development*, p. 231. A.A.A.S., Publ. No. 48, Washington

LEHMANN, F. E. (1950): *Rev. suisse Zool.* **57**, suppl. 1, 141.

LOEWENTHAL, L. A. (1957): *Anat. Rec.* **128**, 201.
LORCH, I. J., J. F. DANIELLI and S. HÖRSTADIUS. (1953): *Exp. Cell Res.* **4**, 253.
MALKIN, H. M. (1954): *J. cell. comp. Physiol.* **44**, 105.
MEZGER-FREED, L. (1953): *J. cell. comp. Physiol.* **41**, 493.
MOORE, A. R. (1957): *J. exp. Zool.* **135**, 75.
MOORE, B. C. (1954): *Science* **120**, 786.
MOORE, B. C. (1957): *J. Morph.* **101**, 209, 227.
MOORE, J. A. (1948): *J. exp. Zool.* **108**, 127.
MOORE, J. A. (1955): *Advances in Genetics* **7**, 139.
MOORE, J. A. (1957): *J. exp. Zool.* **105**, 349.
MOORE, J. A. (1958): *Exp. Cell Res.* **14**, 532.
MOORE, J. A. (1959): *Exp. Cell Res.*, suppl. **6**, 179.
MORGAN, T. H. (1934): *Embryology and Genetics*, Columbia Univ. Press.
PANTELOURIS, E. M. and J. JACOB. (1958): *Experientia* **14**, 99.
POULSON, D. F. (1940): *J. exp. Zool.* **83**, 271.
POULSON, D. F. (1945): *Amer. Naturalist* **79**, 340.
POULSON, D. F. and E. J. BOELL, (1946): *Biol. Bull.* **91**, 228.
RANZI, S., P. CITTERIO, V. COPES and C. SAMUELLI. (1957): *Acta Embryol. Morphol. exp.* **1**, 78.
RANZI, S., P. CITTERIO and C. SAMUELLI (1958): *Rendic. Istit. lombardo* B, **92**, 468.
RUHLAND, G. (1958): *Z. Mikr. anat. Forschg*, **64**, 30.
SCHÖNMANN, W. (1938): *Roux' Arch. Entw. Mech.* **138**, 345.
SEIDEL, F. (1932): *Roux' Arch. Entw. Mech.* **126**, 213.
SHAPIRO, H. (1935): *J. cell. comp. Physiol.* **6**, 101.
SHAVER, J. R. (1953): *J. exp. Zool.* **122**, 169.
SONNEBORN, T. M. (1947): *Advances in Genetics* **1**, 263
SONNEBORN, T. M. (1950): *Heredity* **4**, 11.
SPEMANN, H. (1928): *Z. wiss. Zool.* **132**, 105.
STAUFFER, E. (1945): *Rev. suisse Zool.* **52**, 231
SZE, L. C. (1953): *Science* **117**, 479.
TENCER, R. (1958): *J. Embryol. exp. Morphol.* **6**, 117.
TIEDEMANN, H. and H. TIEDEMANN. (1954): *Naturwiss.* **41**, 535.
WADDINGTON, C. H. (1950): *Rev. suisse Zool.* **57**, suppl 1, 153.
WADDINGTON, C. H. (1956): *Principles of Embryology*. Macmillan, N.Y.
WADDINGTON, C. H. and E. M. PANTELOURIS. (1953): *Nature* **172**, 1050
WELCH, R. M. (1957): *Genetics* **52**, 544.
ZELLER, C. (1956): *Roux' Arch. Entw. Mech.* **148**, 311.

CHAPTER VII

The Biochemistry of Differentiation

THE preceding chapters have been entirely devoted to *primary morphogenesis,* which culminates in the induction of the medullary plate by the organizer. But embryology is only beginning at that time and problems of *secondary morphogenesis* are no less important than those which have been dealt with before. The formation of the various organs, the gradual appearance of their specific functions, the cytological differentiation of their cells, are fascinating problems; but there are so many organs and tissues differentiating in the late embryo that it becomes more and more difficult to give a full account of the biochemical changes which underlie differentiation. Furthermore, since the present author has done very little work himself on these problems, all he will do is to give a few examples, with the hope that one or other of the many embryologists who have devoted more time to thinking and experimental work on the biochemistry of differentiation will some day write a book or monograph on this exciting subject.

In the following, we shall first deal with a problem that is still closely linked with primary induction: the mechanism of head vs. tail formation. We shall then discuss the appearance of new specific proteins during development, since it is often believed (cf. Ebert, 1955) that differentiation is closely linked to synthesis or loss of new proteins. The evidence coming from serological, grafting and enzymological experiments will be the main topic in this chapter.

1. Archencephalic and spinocaudal inductions

Aristoteles (cited by Needham, 1930) was already aware of the fact that morphogenesis is faster in the cephalic than in the caudal end of the chick embryo. The easiest explanation for such a fact is to assume, as did Child (1941) among others, the existence of gradients in the distribution of substances in the embryo: morphogenetic substances or energy-producing mechanisms would have their highest concentration (or activity) at the cephalic end of the embryo and would progressively decrease towards the caudal extremity. Careful comparative morphological study of the head and the tail of the embryo shows, however, that things might be more complicated than that: the head is largely occupied by the brain and the eyes, with relatively little mesoderm between these structures of neural origin and the ectoderm. In the caudal regions, on the other hand, the spinal cord, being much smaller than the brain, the tail is mainly made of structures which originate from the chordomesoblast: chorda, myotomes, mesodermic axis of the fins, etc. It is also well known that, in the gastrula,

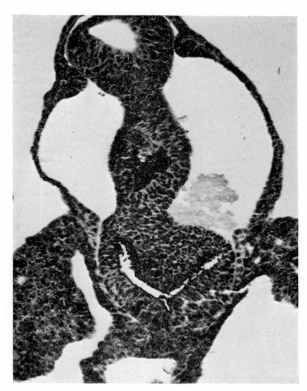

FIG. 129. Archencephalic induction (fore-brain and atypical eyes) obtained with liver ribonucleoproteins (courtesy of Prof. T. Yamada)

a cephalic and a caudal organizer can be distinguished: the former corresponds to the dorsal lip of the early gastrula; if it is implanted in another gastrula, it will induce 'archencephalic'* (brain, eyes, etc.) structures. The spinocaudal organizer is the dorsal lip at the late gastrula stage, when the blastoporus has become circular. If it is grafted into ectoblast fragments, it will induce the formation of a tail, in which, as has just been pointed out,

* As pointed out very rightly to the author by Prof. A. Dalcq, the term 'acrencephalic' should be preferred to 'archencephalic'. But the use of acrencephalic instead of archencephalic might produce confusion in the minds of some of the readers.

mesodermic structures are prevalent over neural ones. In short, archencephalic induction is predominantly neural, while spinocaudal induction
is largely mesodermal (Figs. 129, 130).

The next problem to arise is the following one: are archencephalic and
spinocaudal inductions *quantitatively* or *qualitatively* different? In other
words, is one specific substance responsible for nervous system (brain,

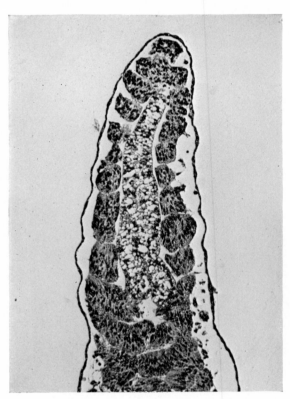

FIG. 130. Purely mesodermal induction (chorda and somites, without
spinal cord) obtained with a protein fraction from bone-marrow
(courtesy of Prof. T. Yamada).

for instance) induction and another one for mesoderm formation in the
tail? Or, on the other hand, are head and tail formation simply due to one
and the same substance, whose concentration would decrease gradientwise
in the cephalocaudal direction?

There has been a good deal of discussion among embryologists about
these questions. It has been one of the many merits of Dalcq and Pasteels
to propose, in 1938, a theory of development entirely based on such ideas

(which are familiar to all embryologists) as gradients, fields and thresholds. The main point was that differentiation depends on 'morphogenetic potentials' which are linked to the concentration, in the various parts of the embryo, of a hypothetical morphogenetic substance, the 'organisine'. The latter would arise from a biochemical interaction between a dorso-ventral cortical 'field' and an animal–vegetal gradient which has its highest activity at the vegetal pole. Regional differentiation of the nervous system, for instance, would result from *quantitative* differences in the 'organisine' content of the various parts; if its content falls under a given threshold, spinal cord would be formed instead of brain.

This hypothesis, which is now 20 years old, appears now as rather unlikely; but it had the very great merit of focusing the attention on a problem (regional differentiation) which had not received as much thought as it deserved. Before leaving the realm of experimental embryology and going into the more biochemical aspects of the problem, a few words should be said about another theory, that of Nieuwkoop (1952, 1955, 1958). According to the Dutch embryologist, the ectoderm would first receive a general 'archencephalic activation' during gastrulation; this activation would tend to produce cephalic structures only. But activation would be immediately followed by a 'transformation' wave which, starting from the caudal end, would progressively change the cephalic structures into caudal ones. This 'transforming' agent would, of course, be a mesoder-malizing one and would be different from the less specific 'activating' factor. Other important theories are those of Yamada (1950), who thinks that regional induction is due to the intervention of two different factors (a dorso-ventral mediator and a cephalo-caudal mediator) and of Toivonen (1950) for whom regional differentiation could be explained on the basis of two qualitatively different inductive actions (archencephalic and spino-caudal), each produced by *specific* inductors.

As we shall now see, there is a considerable amount of evidence, which has been obtained mainly in Yamada's and Toivonen's laboratories, in favour of the idea that archencephalic and spinocaudal inductions can be obtained, in a separate and specific way, when abnormal inductors (killed liver, kidney or bone-marrow cells, for instance) are placed in contact with competent ectoblast. But whether, in the case of *normal* cephalic and caudal organizers, the differences are of a quantitative or a qualitative nature remains unfortunately unknown.

It is impossible to give here a full account of all the work done in Yamada's and Toivonen's laboratories in order to prove that certain organs (or fractions of these organs) are *specific* archencephalic inductors, while others only induce spinocaudal structures.

It is only fair to state that the fundamental observations, in this field, are those of Chuang (1938, 1940). He found that *Triton* liver is a powerful spinocaudal inductor, while mouse kidney essentially induces archencephalic structures. Furthermore, Chuang (1940) discovered the interesting and important fact that heating at 100° for a few minutes destroys the mesoblast-inducing factor without markedly reducing the capacity to induce neural structures. These observations led Chuang (1938, 1940) to the conclusion that mesoblastic structures are induced by a specific substance, which is qualitatively different from the neural inductor. Apparently, the mesoblast inducing substance is more thermolabile than the evocator for nervous system formation.

These conclusions have been confirmed and extended by Toivonen (1940, 1948, 1950, 1953, 1954, 1958) and Kuusi (1953) who studied the inducing abilities of a large number of tissues, either fresh or after heating in boiling water for various times. Only the main results obtained in these extensive experiments will be summarized here. For instance, Toivonen (1940) found that kidney of the guinea-pig is a strictly mesodermal inducer and that guinea-pig thymus can induce lenses. Further analysis of the question by Kuusi (1953) showed the important fact that, as a rule, ribonucleoprotein fractions produce primarily archencephalic inductions (even if RNA is digested away by ribonuclease). Muscle proteins also give mainly archencephalic inductions.

In a later study, Toivonen (1953, 1954) found that the alcohol-treated bone-marrow of the guinea-pig is a very specific inductor of mesodermal structures; but if it is treated for 10 minutes in hot water (80°–90° C), the mesodermal activity of the inductor completely disappears; only epidermal formations such as lenses, lentoids and balancers can now be induced. These experiments suggest that the heat treatment inactivates a thermolabile mesodermal agent; as a result, the epidermal agents which were present in the inductor were enabled to exert their own effect. Furthermore, as shown by Toivonen and Saxén (1955), normal inductions are obtained if ectoderm is treated simultaneously with alcohol-treated liver (an archencephalic inductor) and bone-marrow (a mesodermal inductor) of the guinea-pig. The explants also yielded spinal cord which, in the opinion of Toivonen and Saxén (1955), can only be induced when the inductors contain agents capable of inducing both hind-brain and axial mesoderm. These experiments have led the authors to reject the above-mentioned hypothesis of Nieuwkoop (1955). They find no reason to distinguish between archencephalic induction and a later-occurring transformation. Their results are best explained by assuming the existence of two, qualitatively different, specific inductors.

In a recent study, Kuusi (1957) was able to go one step further and to investigate the properties of the mesoderm inductor: fractions and extracts of bone-marrow, kidney and spleen of the guinea-pig were used for the purpose. Her main results were that all the centrifuge fractions of the bone-

marrow caused almost exclusively mesodermal inductions, the strength
of the reaction increasing with the particle size. In the kidney series, the
archencephalic effect was suppressed by the mesodermal effect: as was
also shown by Takata (1956), mesenchyme can inhibit neural differentiation.
Kuusi's (1957) experiments thus confirm the conclusion of Toivonen and
Saxén (1955) and further show that the neural inductor diffuses more
quickly than the mesodermal inductor, which is dominant, when present.
Archencephalic inductions can thus only be obtained when the more
labile mesodermal inductor has been destroyed.

More recent work from Toivonen's laboratory has further disclosed the
curious fact that, while normal bone-marrow is a strong mesodermal
inductor, bone-marrows of leukaemic rats are practically devoid of inductive
action: thus the factor which induces mesodermal structures and which
is present in normal bone-marrow is inhibited or absent in leukaemic
bone-marrow (Toivonen and Saxén, 1957). If, as we shall see, the
mesodermal factor is a protein, Toivonen and Saxén's (1957) experiments bring additional support for the view, which has been presented
by Miller and Miller (1953), that deletion of key proteins might induce
malignant changes; carcinogenic agents would cause the loss of ability
to synthesize certain 'key proteins' which are essential for the control of
growth. Toivonen and Saxén's (1957) results thus provide very elegant
evidence in favour of the 'deletion of key proteins' hypothesis; their interest
is obvious for embryologists as well as cancerologists.*

Another recent observation of Saxén and Toivonen (1958) is also worth
reporting: they studied the inducing activities of human cancer cells
(HeLa cells) after they cultivated them in various media. They found that
these cells, if cultivated in normal serum, produce deuterencephalic and
spinocaudal inductions. But the inductive properties of the HeLa cells
become changed if they are cultivated on serum which has been heated
at 56°: they no longer induce deuterencephalic and spinocaudal structures,
but instead archencephalic inductions are obtained. The Finnish authors
conclude that their experiments have lead to a decrease in the activity of
the mesodermizing principle without any effect on the neuralizing factor:
what has been changed is the *balance* between the neuralizing and the
mesodermizing factors.

Finally, one should mention a recent study by Toivonen (1958) about
temporal relationship in induction processes. It had been shown earlier
by Johnen (1956), working in Nieuwkoop's laboratory, that when a normal
organizer is placed in an ectoblastic 'sandwich' for various intervals of
time, the reaction is always archencephalic if the implant is removed after

* However, according to a recent paper by Becker *et al.* (1959), the findings of
Toivonen and Saxén (1959)—which could be confirmed—are not valid for *all*
normal and cancerous organs.

4–10 hours. But, if it is removed later than 16 hours, deuterencepoalic differentiations are found. Johnen's (1956) results are in obvious agreement with Nieuwkoop's (1952, 1955, 1958) theory of an activation followed by a transformation into more mesodermal structures. What Toivonen (1958) did was to place alcohol-killed bone-marrow in contact with ectoblast fragments and to remove the inductor after times varying from 4 to 12 hours. He found that the first action of the inductor is a weak mesodermalizing one, without previous archencephalic induction as one would have expected according to Nieuwkoop's (1952, 1955, 1958) theory. But one should point out that experiments such as those of Johnen (1956), which were performed on the living organizer, carry more weight for the embryologist than those which are performed on an abnormal inductor such as alcohol-treated bone-marrow.

Before we leave the work done in Toivonen's laboratory, mention should be made of a recent paper by Vainio (1958); he made the interesting observation that specific rabbit immune serum inhibits the inductive activity of guinea-pig bone-marrow tissue. Normal rabbit serum, which was used as a control, had no appreciable inhibitory effect. Results were, however, much less distinct when liver or kidney of guinea-pigs were treated with the corresponding sera. The interpretation of the results is, of course, complicated by the fact that tissues such as bone-marrow, liver and kidney all contain many distinct antigens. Vainio's (1958) results, however, deserve interest because the method of approach used in his studies is a new one, which might lead to unforeseen results in the future.

The work done, independently, on the same subject, in Yamada's laboratory bears strong resemblances with the just described experiments by Toivonen and his group; but there is no doubt that the Japanese workers have carried the analysis further on the biochemical level than their Finnish colleagues. Two recent papers in which Yamada (1958a, b) summarizes the results obtained by his group and himself will be our main guide, in the following description. It deals with the induction of specific differentiation by purified samples of proteins and nucleoproteins in the isolated ectoderm of *Triturus* gastrulae.

A first study in this direction was made by Hayashi (1956), when he found that a ribonucleoprotein isolated by streptomycin treatment of extracts from guinea-pig liver induces archencephalic structures, which are occasionally accompanied by deuterencephalic structures. In a parallel series of experiments, made on the kidney of the guinea-pig (which is a good spinocaudal inducer, as we have seen), Yamada and Takata (1956) were able to show that the ribonucleoprotein fraction induces spinod caudal and deuterencephalic structures at a high frequency. There is good evidence for the view that the ribonucleoprotein which can be precipitate- by streptomycin corresponds, in fact, to the microsomal fraction. In confirmation of previous results (Brachet, 1944), it was found that the microsomes—which are rich in RNA—show a higher inducing activity than mitochondria and supernatant, which contain less RNA.

Further experiments, in which ribonucleoproteins were isolated by ultracentrifugation instead of streptomycin, confirmed that the ribonucleoprotein of liver has a strong inducing activity for archencephalic and deuterencephalic structures (Fig. 129).

More recent studies by Hayashi and Takata (1958) have shown that it is possible to fractionate further the ribonucleoprotein of guinea-pig liver by differential centrifugation: while the sedimentable fraction has a weak activity for archencephalic induction, the non-sedimentable supernatant has strongly mesodermizing effects.

However, as already discussed in Chapter V, many investigators have clearly shown that the integrity of RNA itself is not required for successful induction of such ribonucleoproteins; on the other hand, limited digestion by proteolytic enzymes such as pepsin and trypsin results in a marked reduction of the inducing ability of these fractions. The latest paper on this subject is that of Hayashi (1958), who reaches the following conclusions: incubation of a ribonucleoprotein from guinea-pig liver (which had strong archencephalic and deuterencephalic inductive effects) with pepsin progressively reduces these inductive effects; but there is no concomitant suppression for the induction of melanophores and mesenchyme. A treatment of the sample with trypsin progressively decreases the archencephalic frequency, producing finally the complete disappearance of all the regional inducing effects. These results strongly suggest that, in liver ribonucleoprotein, the main role in induction is played by the protein-component and not by RNA.

In a further series of experiments, Yamada and his co-workers (cf. Yamada, 1958a, b) have endeavoured to identify the chemical nature of the agent which is responsible for *mesodermal* induction in bone-marrow: various fractionation procedures were used and the result was that the active fraction, in the case of the mesodermal induction, is no longer a ribonucleoprotein, but a *soluble protein*. In the case of bone-marrow, microsomes have little inducing activity, in contrast to what was found for liver (Fig. 130).

Of considerable interest also is the observation made by Yamada (1958a, b, 1959) that heat-treatment produces a progressive shift in the regional inducing effect of bone-marrow: the longer the heating period is, the more cephalic the inductions become. As pointed out by Yamada (1958a, b, 1959), the following sequence of regional types occurs during progressive steaming: trunk-mesodermal ⟶ spinocaudal ⟶ deuterencephalic ⟶ archencephalic. Simultaneously, a gradual suppression of the total induction frequency may occur. Yamada (1958a, b) concludes from all this work that 'it appears not improbable that the protein molecule responsible for the regional induction undergoes a progressive change in configuration under diverse experimental conditions, and this change is reflected in the progressive change in its regional effect'.

The work of Yamada and his group thus strongly suggests that in abnormal inductions, archencephalic induction is mediated by the protein part of ribonucleoproteins, which are probably present in the microsomes; a protein not attached to RNA would, on the other hand, be responsible for spinocaudal (mesodermal) induction.

Similar conclusions have been reached independently by the German school of embryologists; for instance, Mangold *et al.* (1956) have shown that, in the anterior part of the pituitary, the ribonucleoprotein fraction induces deuterencephalic structures, while a protein fraction has spino-caudal activity. According to Tiedemann and Tiedemann (1957a, b), chick embryo extract produces deuterencephalic and spinocaudal inductions; thioglycollic acid inhibits the latter, while trypsin reduces both tendencies. As also found by Yamada (1958), short heating transforms the deuteren-cephalic inducer into an archencephalic one. Finally, according to Vahs (1957), ribonuclease treatment increases the tendency towards archen-cephalic induction, while it has no effect on spinocaudal induction: in particular, there is no shift, in this case, from a spinocaudal to an archencephalic type of induction. All these experiments confirm the general conclusion that proteins play the main role in spinocaudal induction, while ribonucleoproteins are important in archencephalic induction.

The conclusion that RNA by itself plays no role in induction has, as we know, been seriously challenged by Niu (1956, 1958a, b): we have already seen, in Chapter V, that he has some evidence for the view that, at least in some amphibian species, induction might be due to RNA. Later studies (Niu, 1958a, b) suggest that RNA's isolated from different organs of the adult might exert a *specific* inductive effect on the differentiation of small ectodermic explants; for instance, thymus RNA would produce the differentiation into thymus of a large proportion of the explant. This would mean that if there exist, as is often assumed, many different specific RNA's in the various tissues of an organ, these specific RNA's would be, according to Niu (1958), capable of modifying the differentiation of still undifferentiated ectoderm, perhaps by inducing the synthesis of specific proteins. This is a very inviting hypothesis indeed, but one which will require a considerable amount of experimental work before we can take it as demonstrated.

Similar ideas have also been expressed by Benitez *et al.* (1959), who studied the effects of RNA and ribonucleoproteins (extracted from micro-somes) on fibroblasts cultivated *in vitro*. They found that RNA from rat and yeast has a neuralizing effect on rat (but not mouse) fibroblasts. A treatment with ribonuclease abolishes this 'transforming' activity of microsomes or RNA. In confirmation with earlier work by Levi-Montalcini and of Cohen (1956, 1958), Benitez *et al.* (1959) found that a protein extracted from snake venom and salivary glands stimulates the outgrowth of nerve fibres in tissue culture; but this protein, in contrast to RNA, does not *transform* fibroblasts into neurones *in vitro*. These experiments, if correct, would mean that homologous RNA is an active agent in cyto-differentiation. More work is obviously needed before such a conclusion can be accepted without reserve; but it might well be that the improvement of isolation methods will yield more and more samples of 'native' RNA's, still endowed with biological properties and capable, if they are introduced into embryonic cells, of modifying the course of their protein synthesis and, as a result, their fate and morphology. The well known and recent example of the infectivity of tobacco mosaic virus RNA is a good proof that biologically active RNA can indeed be isolated and tested.

However, if one tries to sum up what has been said so far in this chapter, one cannot help feeling that the results obtained with abnormal inductors (such as bone-marrow, liver, etc.) are not necessarily valid for the head and tail organizers of normal gastrulae. One cannot forget, either, that the inducing activities of ribonucleoproteins or proteins extracted from adult tissues have only superficial importance; the main problem remains the same: what does happen in the *reacting* system when it is submitted to the action of such abnormal inducing agents? We do not know as yet and the whole question of specificity in inductive processes will remain unsolved until it is attacked from that angle.

2. Synthesis of new proteins during differentiation

A number of methods are available for the study of the synthesis of new proteins during development; the most specific of them are, of course, the immunological and enzymatic techniques. However, even these refined techniques are not sensitive enough to prove the *total absence* of a given antigen before development starts: as pointed out aptly by Tyler (1957), failure to detect an antigen does not prove its absence. Similarly, an enzyme might be present, before development, in such a low concentration as to preclude detection or estimation. The question has obvious theoretical importance: if, as discussed by Tyler (1957), the specific structure of any antigen is represented by some special feature of a corresponding gene (for instance, a structure complementary to that of the antigen), all antigens would be regarded as preformed in the fertilized egg. On the other hand, the actual appearance of the antigen would be an epigenetic process, controlled by the particular gene. This brief discussion is sufficient to show that the modern chemical embryologist is still faced with the old preformation vs. epigenesis controversy, but at the molecular level.

Since immunological studies on early development have been reviewed extensively by such leading authorities as Tyler (1957) and Ebert (1955, 1958, 1959) in recent years, we shall limit ourselves to a short summary of the problem. We shall then discuss a few biological experiments (explantation, grafting) which have increased our knowledge on biochemical differentiation and we shall end with a brief survey of the work done on enzyme synthesis during development. As already pointed out, the subject of the biochemical mechanisms of differentiation is so vast that a full treatment in the present book is an impossibility.

(a) SEROLOGICAL EXPERIMENTS

A first point, which has already been presented in Chapter I, is that many antigens of the adult are already detectable in the oocyte. It looks as if the yolk proteins were a direct transudate from the maternal serum; but it might also be that the oocyte has a mechanism for resynthesis of antigens from degradation products of serum that pass into the yolk (Nace, 1953; Schechtman, 1955).

A number of workers have prepared antisera against crude saline extracts of early embryos in order to detect, by the precipitin test, the appearance of new antigens at some stage of development. These experiments have clearly shown that in sea urchin (Perlmann and Gustafson, 1948; Perlmann, 1953) as well as in amphibian eggs (Cooper, 1948; Flickinger and Nace, 1952; Clayton, 1953), synthesis of new antigens occurs during development. In several cases, this synthesis can be detected at stages as early as gastrulation; it will be recalled that this is the time when synthesis of new proteins and normal nucleocytoplasmic interactions begin (Chapter VI).

Experiments have also been made by several of the same workers (Flickinger and Nace, 1952; Clayton, 1953; Nace, 1955; Nace and Inoué, 1957) in order to obtain specific inhibition of development or specific cytolysis by treating amphibian embryos by antisera. Since these antisera, even after adsorption, were of a very complex nature, no clearcut results have been obtained when development was studied in the presence of antibodies. For instance, Flickinger and Nace (1952) used antisera directed against the supernatant obtained after high speed centrifugation of tail-bud homogenates and observed lysis of frog embryos at the same stage, along anterio-posterior and dorso-ventral gradients. Clayton (1953), who did comparable experiments on newt eggs, observed an irregular cytotoxic effect of the antisera, besides the production of more specific abnormalities. More specific inhibitory effects seem, however, to have been obtained in the more recent studies of Nace and Inoué (1957): tissues of neurulae, treated with sera directed against neurulae, gave only ectoderm; but these sera also had strong cytotoxic effects.

The reason that the serological experiments so far mentioned have failed to give clearer results is, of course, the high degree of chemical heterogeneity of the extracts which were used as antigens; for this reason, much of the serological work done on embryos has been concentrated, in recent years, on definite organs, which contain characteristic, easy-to-purify proteins; these organs are the lens on one side, the heart and the muscles on the other.

In the case of the *lens*, there are very few studies in which antibodies against *embryonic* lens antigens have been used: Burke *et al.* (1944), using an antiserum against extracts of the lens of an 160-hours chick embryo, found lens antigens in extracts of lenses from embryos aged from 96 to 160 hours. They also used antisera against extracts of the adult-chick lens and were able to prove the presence of adult lens antigens in lens extracts of embryos older than 250 hours. Mention should be made of comparable results obtained by Konyukhov (1957) on duck embryos: he found, with immunological methods, that stage-specific antigens can be detected in the lens, at the time primary fibres differentiate and RNA content strongly increases. These antigens disappear at later stages of lens differentiation.

A good deal of the recent work on the same subject comes from the Dutch school (ten Cate and van Doorenmaalen (1950); Woerdeman (1953, 1955); van Doorenmaalen (1957, 1958); Langman *et al.*, 1956). Of very great interest is the work of ten Cate and van Doorenmaalen (1950) who were able to show, by the use of the precipitin method, the presence of adult lens antigens in the extracts of lens vesicles of chick embryos of 58 hours: this is the time when the lens placode has formed, but is not yet separated from the ectoderm. Similar results were obtained, by the same authors, on frog embryos.

In a later study, Flickinger *et al.* (1955) could not find any lens antigens in very early stages of frog embryos and confirmed ten Cate and van Doorenmalen's (1950) findings: there is a close correlation between the time of appearance of the lens antigen and the lens itself. Flickinger *et al.* (1955) were also able to show that, in frog larvae, only the anterior half reacts with frog lens antisera. Finally, they added lens antiserum to young chick embryos cultivated *in vitro*; in confirmation of earlier work of De Vincentiis (1954), they observed no specific effect upon the development of the eye lens.

Langman *et al.* (1956) found that cultivated eye vesicles with the adjoining ectoderm are injured by antiserum against lens extracts of the adult chick, provided that they were taken from very young chick embryos (5 to 16-17 somite stage). When the explants grew older, no more cytotoxic effect on the lens could be detected.

Another observation which certainly deserves to be repeated and extended is one of Woerdeman (1953, 1955): he found that extracts from the head ectoderm prepared before the appearance of the lens placodes do not react with antiserum against adult lens; neither do extracts of young isolated eye vesicles react with this antiserum. But if the extracts of ectoderm and eye vesicles are mixed together and incubated for 24 hours at 37°, the precipitin reaction with the antiserum against adult lens becomes positive: it seems that the lens antigen can be formed *in vitro* when extracts of the inducer and the reacting tissue are mixed; this interesting finding is, of course, reminiscent of the 'unmasking' of the organizing substance, which has been discussed in Chapter V.

Finally, mention should be made of a recent paper by van Doorenmaalen (1958) who used a fluorescein-labelled anti-adult-lens serum to stain histological sections of embryonic lenses (Coons method for cytological antigen detection). The Dutch author found that, in 5 to 16 days embryos, only the lens was stained. But the specificity of the reaction could not be demonstrated in stages earlier than 5 days: all tissues stained homogeneously in a non-specific way. It should be added that, in agreement with this work of van Doorenmaalen (1958), Flickinger (1958) found that, at early stages of development, the lens antigen is localized in areas other than the lens-forming region. It should also be added that work parallel to that of van Doorenmaalen (1958) has been made simultaneously by Nace and Clarke (1958), who obtained somewhat different results: using fluorescent antibodies against explants of tail-bud as a tool, they were able to detect lens antigens in the optical cup and lens of young frog embryos (stages 19 and 20): the reaction was negative at earlier and later stages, in agreement with Konyukhov's (1957) observations on 'stage-specific' antigens. Good evidence could be presented for the view that the reaction is localized in the nuclei and the cytoplasm of the optic cup, but only in the cytoplasm of the primordial lens.

The situation, as one can see from this brief summary, is still far from clear and further work is needed in order to explain what remains an apparent discrepancy: while the lens antigen can be detected in the lens area by the precipitin method already after 58 hours of incubation in the chick, the cytochemical technique for lens antigen detection shows no specific localization before the 5th day.

Similar difficulties exist in the case of the differentiation of the *muscle proteins*, as we shall now see. Muscles, both in the heart and elsewhere, share the advantage with the lens of possessing a high content in a few proteins which are relatively easy to purify: in the case of muscle, these proteins are the well-known 'contractile' proteins, myosin and actin.

A large amount of biochemical work has already been done on the biochemistry of the differentiating muscle during embryonic development; since our present purpose is to follow the work done with the more specific immunological techniques, all we can do here is to refer the interested reader to the important and recent paper by Herrmann *et al.* (1957): he will find there a detailed quantitative description of the biochemical changes undergone by muscle when it goes from the proliferative to the differentiating stage.

Of greatest importance in the field of 'biochemical myogenesis' is the immunological work of Ebert and his co-workers (1950, 1953, 1955a, b, 1958, 1959) on the chick. In this material, the *heart* arises by the fusion of two primordia which lie on either side of the mid-line; as soon as it is formed, it already begins to beat (on the second day of development).

Development of the cardiac contractile proteins , actin and myosin

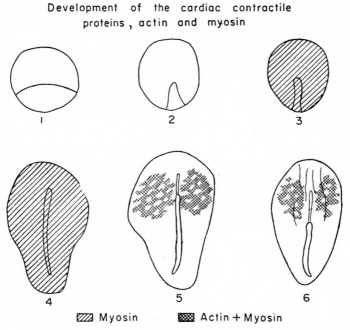

☑ Myosin   ▨ Actin + Myosin

FIG. 131. Distribution of actin and myosin in the chick blastoderm (Ebert, 1954).

Ebert (1950) was first able to show that a positive precipitin reaction could be obtained when an extract of the chick embryo at the primitive streak stage (i.e. well before the heart was formed) is mixed with a serum directed against extracts of adult heart.

In later studies, Ebert (1953, 1955a, b, 1957, 1958, 1959) worked with purified myosin and actin isolated from hearts of adult chicken. The results, which are schematized in Fig. 131, can be summarized as follows: cardiac myosin is already synthesized in the early embryo. At the primitive-streak stage (Fig. 131, 3, 4), the antigen reactive groups of myosin are not localized in any particular part of the embryo. But, at the later 'head fold' stage, cardiac myosin becomes restricted to the heart-forming area. (Fig. 131, 5, 6). The establishment of this area thus involves the disappearance, from a large part of the embryo, of the pre-existing ability to synthesize cardiac myosin. The other important cardiac contractile protein, actin, appears later than myosin (at the head process stage): but, in contrast to myosin, actin is restricted to the heart-forming areas from the very beginning (Fig. 131, 5, 6).

Independent work by Johnson and Leone (1955) has confirmed that actomyosin can only be detected after 40 hours of incubation. A soluble muscle protein, myogen, is, on the other hand, already present at the primitive-streak stage. Serum proteins are not found, by immunological methods, before several days of development. Complex results were obtained when Johnson and Leone (1955) added antisera to developing embryos: sera directed against whole embryos already inhibited development at the primitive-streak stage; anti-actomyosin serum inhibited growth of the heart, while anti-myogen serum had stimulatory effects on growth. Finally, sera directed against actin and globulin had no appreciable effect on development. But it is unfortunate, as pointed out by Ebert (1959b), that the antisera were not adsorbed in order to increase their specificity: if this had been done, the results would perhaps have been clearer.

Before we leave cardiac for skeletal muscle, mention should be made of an observation of Duffey and Ebert (1957) which has obvious interest for chemical embryologists: they cultivated early embryos in a medium containing traces of an inhibitor of cellular oxidations, antimycin A, and found that mesodermal derivatives—especially the heart—are much more sensitive than brain and spinal cord to this inhibitor. These experiments strongly suggest that the metabolic pathways operating during the development of the heart and of the brain are different in the embryo. More quantitative work, especially in enzymatic study, is, of course, required before the nature of these metabolic differences is known.

In the case of *skeletal muscle*, a very important work is certainly that of Holtzer et al. (1957) who used fluorescent-labelled antibodies against myosin in order to study the localization of myosin in the differentiating myoblast: the main conclusion of their interesting paper is that specific staining by antimyosin only occurs in differentiating myoblasts. Prior to this stage, the distribution of myosin, as indicated by the fluorescent antibodies method, is a diffuse one. These findings are thus similar to those obtained by van Doorenmaalen (1958) when he used the same method for the localization of the lens antigens. However, it is interesting to note that Holtzer et al. (1957) were able to detect slender fluorescent filaments or fibrils before any appearance of cross striation: unstriated filaments might thus already contain myosin reactive groups.

The work of Holtzer et al. (1957) suggest, as was pointed out by the authors themselves, that 'chemo-differentiation' does not necessarily precede morphological differentiation; this hypothesis, which was presented as a probable one by the author in 1944, would certainly require revision if more facts arose showing that synthesis of new, specific proteins and cellular differentiation are simultaneous events. Recently, Lash and Holtzer (1958) have come to similar conclusions in the case of differentiation of cartilage as in that of striated muscle; they first showed that cartilage is induced by a diffusible agent, originating from the spinal cord. Experiments with ^{35}S further demonstrated that the synthesis of chondroitine sulphuric acid is simultaneous with the differentiation of cartilage.

It is, of course, impossible to draw now a definite conclusion in this respect, because it is too difficult to establish the exact time sequence of such events as radiosulphate incorporation and cartilage differentiation, or appearance of cytochemically detectable myosin and muscle fibril formation: too much depends obviously upon the sensitivity of the methods used for the detection of organ-specific substances such as chondroitine sulphate or myosin. We thus regard the question of whether chemo-differentiation precedes cytological differentiation or whether the two processes are simultaneous as an open question; but this question is an exciting and important one, and it is to be hoped and expected that more experimental data, obtained with still more refined methods, will ultimately lead to an unambiguous answer.*

Finally, it should be emphasized that conclusions which are valid for one type of embryonic organ and material might not apply for another: recent work by Ogawa et al. (1958) and Ogawa (1958) suggests that this word of caution might be necessary. The Japanese workers studied, with immunological methods, the appearance of myosin and actin in heart and skeletal muscle of the chick and the newt embryo: in the former, myosin precedes actin in heart muscle (as already found by Ebert, 1953), but the order is reversed in striated muscle. In the newt embryo, actin also precedes myosin and can be detected after 132 hours (instead of 176 hours for myosin) of development; similar observations can be made on regenerating limbs of *Triturus* (Ogawa, 1958).

We must now leave the intriguing and exciting field of 'immuno-embryology' for other questions. We are leaving it with mixed feelings: there are too many contradictory results, for the time being, to allow us to draw definite conclusions, but there is also no doubt that the use of immunological methods—which are constantly being refined—will lead us a long way towards the ultimate goal: the understanding of the biochemical mechanisms of tissue and cell differentiation. Immuno-embryologists of

---

* In fact, Holtzer et al. (1959) have recently stated that they have now been able to detect, with the Coons method, the existence of myofibrils before the heart starts beating, thus before they can be seen with conventional techniques.

s

today are indeed pioneers and their work commands interest, respect and admiration.

(b) BIOCHEMICAL (NON-ENZYMATIC) STUDIES ON DIFFERENTIATION

In recent years, a few attempts have been made in order to correlate morphogenetic processes with specific biochemical reactions: we have already mentioned the work of Lash and Holtzer (1958) suggesting that chondroitine sulphate synthesis, as indicated by ^{35}S incorporation studies, occurs simultaneously with cartilage differentiation. Unfortunately, this work of Lash and Holtzer (1958) has only been published in very preliminary form so far; it is thus impossible to discuss it further for the time being.

This difficulty does not exist in the case of the very interesting experiments made by C. E. Wilde (1955a, b; 1956) on the role of phenylalanine in the differentiation of neural crest cells. Wilde's (1955a, b) experiments show that the differentiation of these cells, in tissue culture, is controlled by the metabolism of phenylalanine or tyrosine: chemical analogues of phenylalanine (especially o-fluorophenylalanine) inhibit, in a specific way, the differentiation of pigment cells and pigmentation; they do not affect the differentiation of striated muscle from somite mesoderm. Furthermore, the effects of the non-toxic o-fluorophenylalanine analogues are reversed by an equimolecular amount of phenylalanine. Phenyl-lactic acid (in which the a-amino-group of phenylalanine is replaced by an hydroxyl group) also brings up a specific inhibition of pigmentation and pigment cell differentiation, without affecting the differentiation of striated muscle from somite mesoderm. The addition of small amounts of phenylalanine to the nutrient medium elicits the differentiation of pigment cells from pure ventral ectoderm of post-gastrula stages.

In a later paper, Wilde (1956) could definitely show that molecular phenylalanine is required by cells of the early neural crest of Urodeles for their specific differentiations: he could demonstrate that three different groups of precursor molecules would not support the differentiation of explanted neural crest cells. But experiments with the same precursor molecules show that mesoderm cells of the archenteron roof can relieve the inhibition if they can synthesize phenylalanine. Substances in which the β-carbon position of phenylalanine has been altered (such as phenylglycine or phenylserine) inhibit the differentiation of explanted neural crest cells; again, their inhibitory effect can be reversed by addition of equimolecular amounts of phenylalanine. Further experiments on the effects of different analogues of phenylalanine on ventral ectoderm and on mesoderm have led Wilde (1956) to the general conclusion that mesodermal production of phenylalanine is a very important factor for cellular differentiation of the neural crest.

These observations of Wilde (1955a, b, 1956) are very important, even though pigment cell formation might not be regarded as a morphogenetic event of primary importance; they perhaps represent the only case where cell differentiation can be controlled by the addition of a specific substrate, and inhibited by an analogue of this substrate. Since labelled phenylalanine is readily available, it should be an easy task to study, with autoradiography methods, phenylalanine uptake and metabolism in neural crest cells.

Very interesting also is the biosynthesis of connective tissue and inter-cellular matrix components, which has recently been the subject of reviews by Smith (1957) and Edds (1958a, b); it is impossible to discuss this question adequately within the limited scope of this book. Mention should be made, however, of the recent work of Edds (1958a, b) who took advantage of the fact that hydroxyproline is a specific constituent of collagen: working on frog eggs, he could trace back the appearance of collagen to stages 21–22 (i.e. 172 hours after fertilization). It certainly would be most interesting to have these biochemical studies of Edds (1958a, b) supplemented by electron microscopy studies.

One should finally mention the extensive work done in E. Wolff's laboratory, where the nutritional requirements of various chick embryo organs cultivated *in vitro* have been studied. Limiting ourselves to the most recent and complete papers from E. Wolff's group, attention should be drawn on the fact that the syrinx (E. Wolff, 1957) and the gonads (Stenger-Haffen, 1957) have nutritional requirements very different from those of bones (Kieny, 1958) in certain respects; in others, there are similarities between the three organs. For instance, syrinx, bones and gonads all require glucose for survival and growth; among many sugars tested, only mannose could replace glucose. But, while syrinx and gonads absolutely require sulphur-containing amino acids or peptides (cysteine, methionine, glutathione) for satisfactory growth *in vitro*, cysteine is definitely inhibitory in bones. The latter have instead an absolute requirement for glutamic acid. There is no doubt that the organ culture technique worked out in E. Wolff's laboratory affords enormous possibilities for chemical embryologists: metabolic and enzymatic studies on such a material should be very easy.

While growth and differentiation are the main phenomena in which the embryologist is interested, *regression* of organs should not be forgotten here, especially when it is the result of a specific hormonal action. In fact, Glücksman (1951) summarized, a few years ago, the large amount of evidence suggesting that localized cytolysis might be an important event in morphogenesis: dead cells might release substances required for division and for further development of neighbouring cells. Whether this explanation is correct or not, there is no doubt that degenerating cells, with pycnotic nuclei, are always found in apparently normal embryos, at the time their differentiation begins.

In the following, we shall restrict ourselves to two cases where regression of an already differentiated organ, under the influence of a specific hormone, is a normal event: we refer to the regression of the Müllerian ducts in chick embryos and the disappearance of the tail in anuran tadpoles. Both phenomena have recently been studied from the biochemical viewpoint.

It is a well-known fact that, in the chick embryo, the Müllerian ducts degenerate in the male between the 10th and the 13th day of incubation; in the female, the Müllerian duct also degenerates on the right side around the 11th day of development, while it further grows and differentiates on the left side.

Interesting experiments by E. Wolff (1953) have shown that regression of the isolated Müllerian duct, in organ culture, can be obtained by addition of testosterone to the medium. Wolff (1953) could further show, by cytochemical tests, that regressing Müllerian ducts have a higher proteolytic and nucleolytic activity than normal ducts.

The same question has been studied, with more accurate and quantitative methods, by Brachet et al. (1958): they found that the regression of the Müllerian ducts is accompanied by a large increase (up to 800 per cent) in the activity of several enzymes (acid phosphatase, cathepsin and ribonuclease). Since these enzymes are known to be localized, in liver, in the lysosomes (de Duve, 1957, 1958), the hypothesis was made that, under the influence of testosterone, the hydrolytic enzymes contained in these cytoplasmic particles might be released, with extensive cytolysis as a result. Experiments designed to test this possibility indeed showed that, in normal Müllerian ducts, 60 to 85 per cent of the hydrolases which were studied are bound to sedimentable particles; in the regressing ducts, only 20 to 60 per cent of the enzymes can be recovered in the sedimentable fraction. There are no such changes in the solubility of the hydrolytic enzymes in the normally growing left Müllerian duct of the female. The experiments thus strongly suggest that, under the influence of testosterone, the lipidic membrane of the lysosomes breaks down; the hydrolytic enzymes which they contain can then be set free and act on their natural substrates. Intracellular digestion of proteins and RNA, under the influence of the liberated hydrolytic enzymes, would of course lead to cell death and finally to the regression of the whole organ.

It is possible that similar events occur when the tail of the anuran tadpole regresses under the influence of tyroxin. The question has not yet been studied from the viewpoint of the role of the lysosomes: but it is a striking fact that, according to Weber (1957) and Deuchar et al. (1957), the activity of the proteolytic enzyme cathepsin increases several times, in an almost exponential manner, during the regression of the tail in *Xenopus*. It certainly would be very interesting to extend this study to other hydrolytic enzymes and to follow the distribution of cathepsin in various cell fractions after homogeneization and centrifugation of normal and regressing tails. In any event, the work done on both the tail of *Xenopus* tadpoles and the Müllerian ducts of chick embryos clearly shows that cathepsin is essentially a catabolic enzyme, involved in proteolysis; there is no correlation between catheptic activity and protein synthesis in these cases, in contradiction with hypotheses about the mechanisms of protein synthesis which were once prevalent.

(c) BIOLOGICAL (GRAFTING) EXPERIMENTS

Many experiments have been performed as a result of the very interesting theories of growth and differentiation presented by Weiss (1947, 1955) and Rose (1952, 1957). The theory of Weiss (1957, 1955) is essentially based on specific antigen–antibody reactions: growth is supposed to be controlled by the interaction of 'template' and 'anti-template' molecules and would be proportional to the number of 'template' molecules available to the cell. During growth, 'anti-templates', which are complementary to the 'templates' in the immunological sense of the term, are formed. These 'anti-templates', in contrast with the 'templates' which are supposed to be fixed within the cells, would be diffusible and pass freely to the exterior. Growth would stop when a definite equilibrium between 'templates' and 'anti-templates' becomes established. If, for some reason, a smaller number of 'anti-templates' leave the cell, more of them will be able to react, inside the cell, with the 'templates': as a result, growth will be slowed down.

A consequence of this elaborate theory is that removal of part of an organ will reduce the 'anti-template' concentration and thus stimulate the growth of the rest of this organ: the well-known phenomenon of compensatory hypertrophy can thus be easily explained.

Experiments by Weiss (1955) have brought definite support to his theory: he found, for instance, that addition of kidney extract reduces the differentiation of tubules in tissue cultures; since differentiation and growth are antagonistic processes, it was concluded by Weiss (1955) that the kidney extract had produced homologous growth stimulation. Similar results were obtained by Weiss (1955) in the case of heart cultures: again, heart extract depressed the differentiation of myofibrils, as evidenced by retarded pulsation. Weiss (1955) concluded from this work that substances present in cell extracts promote homologous growth either by being incorporated into the corresponding cells or by neutralizing homologous growth inhibitors present in the medium.

The hypothesis of Rose (1952, 1957) is rather different from that of Weiss (1947, 1955): the main point is the assumption of mechanisms of *specific inhibition*. Patterns would arise as the products of differentiating regions acted on other areas and suppressed differentiation there. Differences could arise from a series of such inhibitions. Development would essentially result from a general, unspecific induction plus specific inhibitions.

This hypothesis, as pointed out by Rose himself (1957), is not incompatible with the template–anti-template theory of Weiss (1952, 1957): the latter is more concerned with the control of growth in already differentiated systems than in differentiation itself.

Rose (1955) has tested his hypothesis by cultivating frog eggs in the presence of fragments of adult tissues and cells; in accordance with his inhibition theory, he obtained a specific inhibition of the development of the homologous organ. For instance, eggs developing in the presence of blood from the adult were found to form larvae which had no blood cells, but were otherwise normal. Unfortunately, Rose (1955) says himself that these striking results could only be obtained in a small number of experimental series (4 out of 26). Very recently, experiments of the same type have been repeated by Braverman (1958), who claims to have obtained very specific homologous inhibition when purified extracts of several adult organs are made to act on 1-day chick embryos: extracts of nervous system selectively inhibit nervous system formation, with even such local actions as inhibition of the development of the fore-brain with extracts of the adult fore-brain. Differentiation of mesoderm, in the embryo, is also said to be inhibited by extracts of mesodermic organs. These results, if confirmed, are certainly of the utmost importance for all those interested in the biochemical mechanisms of differentiation; unfortunately, Braverman's (1958) work has so far been only published in the form of a short abstract and it is impossible to judge the value of his experiments until they are presented in more detail. In any case, Braverman's (1958) provocative experiments deserve both repetition and extension.

By far the most precise and extensive work done in this field is that of Ebert (1951, 1954, 1955, 1957); under the influence of the template theory of Weiss (1947, 1955), he studied extensively the effects of chorioallantoic transplants of adult chicken tissues on homologous chicken embryo. Ebert (1951) immediately found that chorioallantoic grafts of adult chicken spleen produce, in agreement with the theory of Weiss (1947, 1955), a marked enlargement of the spleens of the host chicks; furthermore, this effect was found to be class-specific and quantitatively tissue-specific.

In later experiments, Ebert (1954) was able to show, by estimations of the nitrogen content, that the increase in weight of the stimulated embryonic spleens is indeed the result of an increase in protein content. In an attempt to analyse further the phenomenon, Ebert (1954) injected radioactive methionine into adult chicks: he then removed spleen and kidney and grafted them on chorioallantoic membranes. The results can be seen on Fig. 132: if radioactivity of the homologous tissues is followed, it is found that a *specific* transfer of radioactivity occurs from the graft to the homologous host tissue, both for kidney and spleen. It is important to note that grafts of labelled *mouse* spleen, in contrast to chicken spleen, did not produce any selective incorporation of the label (Ebert, 1954): this clearly demonstrates the existence of species-specificity in these transfer experiments. It would be interesting to know the outcome of similar experiments if made with species which are not so distant from each other as mouse and chick: one wonders, for instance, whether the specificity of the reaction discovered by Ebert (1954) is such that it could distinguish between chick and duck.

Ebert (1954) further showed that calculation of his experimental results

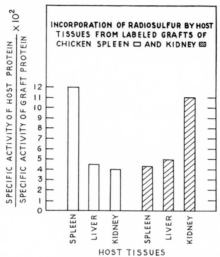

FIG. 132. Specific transfer of radioactivity from graft to homologous tissue (Ebert, 1954).

demonstrates that as much as 15 per cent of the homologous host tissue proteins may be derived from the proteins of the graft, even 3 days after implantation. Cytological observations and analyses of the DNA content of the enlarged spleen clearly established the fact that the transfer of whole cells from the graft to the host is a negligible factor. The conclusion which was drawn by Ebert (1954, 1955) thus seems to be unavoidable: a 'building-block' rather than a 'template' hypothesis should be accepted and there would be a selective incorporation of tissue-specific proteins from grafts into homologous host tissues. We have seen, in Chapter I, that incorporation of proteins into growing oocytes is a highly probable event; there is no theoretical reason to reject the possibility of similar processes at later stages of development. Ebert's (1954, 1955) experiments thus strongly suggest that incorporation of pre-existing proteins can be utilized for the synthesis of new proteins; the incorporation process is a very specific one, since the constituents of one protein are being used preferentially in the synthesis of homologous tissue proteins.

More recently, Ebert (1957, 1958) was able to go one step beyond this general conclusion. Working this time with homogenates of labelled adult tissues, he found that the label is quickly incorporated into the homologous organs of 9 day old embryos. When the homogenates were fractionated by centrifugation at various speeds, it was found that only microsomes and soluble proteins were selectively incorporated into the homologous organs of the embryo. It is too early to draw conclusions from these experiments which have not yet been published in detail. They suggest, however, that only free proteins and small cytoplasmic particles (which might be endowed with a certain degree of genetic continuity, as shown by Le Clerc in 1954) are active in the biological system studied by Ebert (1958). His experiments, as well as those of Le Clerc (1954), further strongly indicate that embryonic cells are capable of assimilating small particles of the size of microsomes, through phagocytic mechanisms perhaps.

The work of Ebert is very convincing; it might, however, be an error to try to generalize its conclusions to other materials, especially to young embryonic stages: the reason for this word of caution is that Waddington and Sirlin (1955) were unable to obtain any evidence for a selective transfer of a labelled protein from one organ to another when they tried to follow, with an autoradiography method, the fate of implanted radio-active organs (eyes and somites, for instance) in young embryos. It is therefore doubtful whether specific incorporation of homologous proteins, as found by Ebert (1951–1957) in the case of late embryonic stages, plays a major role in early development and in primary morphogenesis.

Another interesting approach for the study of tissue specificity is the analysis of 'tissue affinities', which are closely linked to the properties of the cell surface. It has been clearly established by Holtfreter (1939, 1947a,b) that the adhesiveness between membranes of different types of cells is a fundamental factor for cell migration and aggregation. As shown in Fig. 133 (a), ectoderm and endoderm show 'negative' affinity: if they are allowed to fuse together in explantation experiments, they quickly separate from each other and form unorganized gut and epidermic cells. If a piece of mesoderm is inserted between the two types of fragments (Fig. 133, b), a vesicle containing mesenchymatous cells is obtained: ectoderm and endoderm no longer separate, because they both have a 'positive' affinity for mesoderm. Finally, if the mesoderm is entirely surrounded with ecto-derm and endoderm, as shown in Fig. 133 (c), a typical gut, with a normal lumen, is formed. Positive affinities thus exist when the cells stick together as is especially the case for chordomesoblast and neuroblast in the archenteric roof: when affinities are negative, there is no adherence between the cells of the two tissues.

It has been suggested by Weiss (1947, 1955) and by Tyler (1947) that positive or negative affinities, leading to adherence or non-adherence between cells, is controlled by specific reactions of the antigen–antibody type. Experiments of Spiegel (1954) lend some support to this view. He studied the effects of various antisera on the reaggregation of the cells of frog gastrulae which had been dissociated by a short treatment with an

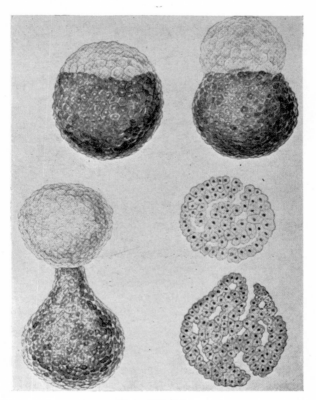

FIG. 133 (a)

alkaline medium. Spiegel (1954) found that an antiserum against frog embryos inhibits the reaggregation of dissociated cells of *Rana* ectoderm and endoderm; this antiserum was species-specific, since it had no effect on the reaggregation of dissociated cells of *Triton* gastrulae. Spiegel (1954) has concluded from his experiments that 'the ability of cells to recognize each other depends on the presence, in their surfaces, of specific antigens which also bring about the normal adhesion of cells, by reciprocal reactions similar to those between antigens and their homologous antibodies.'

It must be admitted that this explanation of Spiegel (1954) remains the most probable one; on the other hand, more serological experiments, involving a larger number of controls, are needed before we can accept Spiegel's (1954) explanation as the only possible one. Treatment of dissociated cells with antisera (thus with proteins) might well produce a number of secondary phenomena: ingestion of the proteins by pinocytosis or non-specific reaction of proteins with substances (mucopolysaccharides or RNA, for instance) present in the cell membranes. Delicate cellular

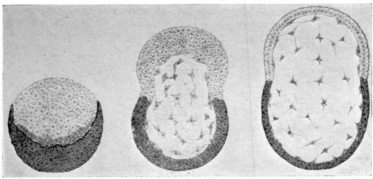

FIG. 133 (b)

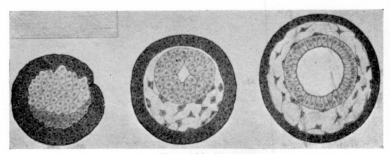

FIG. 133 (c)

FIG. 133. Tissue affinities: explanations in text (Holtfreter, 1939).

reactions occurring in cell membranes are not easily studied with biochemical methods; but indirect techniques, such as treatment of the dissociated cells by chemical agents which have proven their usefulness in chemical embryology (ATP, dinitrophenol, ribonuclease, β-mercaptoethanol, for instance) might yield valuable results in such studies. They might show, for instance, whether the integrity of such important substances as RNA, —SH groups or ATP is required for successful reaggregation of dissociated embryonic cells.

Experiments of the type which has just been suggested might also be useful for an analysis of the curious tissue affinities which can be observed at later stages of development: for instance, Grobstein and Zwilling (1953) could show that the differentiation of *in vitro* cultivated chicken blastoderms largely depends on the degree to which the cells are dispersed: much better development can be obtained when a piece of blastoderm is cultivated as a whole than when it is divided into eighths or sixteenths prior to culture. But dissociation of dorsal spinal cord cells or of metanephrogenic mesenchyme cells, if followed by reaggregation, has no effect on their inducing power (Auerbach and Grobstein, 1958).

The extraordinary specificity of the reaggregation of dissociated cells is well shown in the experiments of Moscona (1957), who worked with mesonephric and limb-bud cells, either isolated or mixed together; even if they had been taken out of embryos at different stages, the various cell types ultimately reappeared in the aggregate to form tissue-like groupings that developed in accordance with their tissues of origin (formation of typical cartilage and mesonephric tubules in the same explant, for instance). Still more impressive is the fact that it is possible to combine in such experiments cells of chick and mouse embryos which form chimeric aggregates. In the course of tissue reconstruction, the dissociated embryonic cells became grouped preferentially, according to their original type identities and regardless of their generic origin.

Another amazing finding, in the same field, is that of Sigel *et al.* (1958), who found that isolated kidney cells can reconstitute kidney tubules when they are grafted in the brain.

Specific cellular interactions can also be studied at earlier stages of development, since the combination of embryonic fragments from different species leads to the formation of 'chimeras' (cf. Chen, 1955, for a discussion of this question). It has been known for a long time that an organizer can produce an induction in a host from a widely different species; but the response is characteristic of the host, so that ectoderm of an Anuran will respond to the same inducing stimulus by the formation of a sucker and the ectoderm of an Urodele by that of a balancer. Nevertheless, chimeras sooner or later show incompatibility reactions, which become more and more important as development proceeds: ultimately, the graft from foreign origin degenerates. It is probable, as suggested by Woerdeman (1952), that incompatibility is often the result of antigen–antibody reactions. In fact, a more recent study by Temme (1956) strongly suggests that, in *adult* Urodeles, a typical antigen–antibody reaction occurs when tissues from an animal belonging to a different species are grafted; this could be clearly shown by the use of precipitin tests.

It is unfortunately not yet known at which embryonic stage this immunity reaction first becomes apparent, although a very large amount of extremely interesting immunological work has been done recently on embryos. Since this work has been extensively reviewed by leading workers in the field (which is well outside the limits of the chemical embryology of present days), the reader will simply be referred to the general papers of Medawar (1957) and Ebert (1959). He will find there a detailed description and discussion of such intriguing phenomena as 'actively acquired tolerance' and the 'graft-against-the-host' immune reaction. It has been shown, for instance, that it is possible to prolong the life of skin homografts in adult mice if the embryos have been injected with living homologous cells (Billingham *et al.*, 1953, 1956). Hašek and Hraba (1955) also succeeded in suppressing antibody formation by the action of homologous cells during embryonic development. The situation regarding antibody formation is thus comparable to that found in X-rayed animals, in which 'radiation chimeras' of hematopoietic tissues have been repeatedly obtained and studied (Ford *et al.*, 1956, 1957; Van Bekkum and Vos, 1957; Makinodan, 1957, etc.).

The problems which have been briefly discussed in the present section are of such a high degree of complexity as to preclude any attempt, for the time being, to attack them by biochemical methods: only the most refined immunological and biological techniques are specific enough for that purpose. But there is no doubt that, ultimately, such questions as differentiation, tissue- and species-specificity will have to be solved in chemical terms. Progress in this complex field might be slow, but it will be made: this is the reason why it was felt necessary to give a glimpse of the fascinating possibilities of 'immuno-embryology' in a book devoted to chemical embryology.

(d) ENZYMATIC STUDIES

The study of enzymes in development should present another approach towards a better understanding of the synthesis of new, specific molecules. It must be admitted that the results so far obtained have been somewhat disappointing, because too much of the work done has been of a purely descriptive or comparative nature. Therefore, a short account of the main results obtained by those who have studied enzyme synthesis in relation to development will be all that is given here; most of this work has already been presented earlier in this book, but from a slightly different angle.

The fact that enzyme synthesis is genetically controlled, in many instances, gives, of course, high hopes that enzymatic studies might throw important light on the intricate relationships between genetics, morphogenesis and biochemistry. Even if the 'one gene, one enzyme' hypothesis of Beadle (1946) might be an over-simplification of the real situation, there is no doubt that enzyme synthesis is genetically controlled in many organisms. There is no reason why a similar situation could not exist in the developing embryo as well. It was therefore perfectly legitimate for

Spiegelman (1948) to present a theory of differentiation based on induced enzyme synthesis: genes would only give the potentiality for the synthesis of enzymes and differentiation would first be a purely cytoplasmic process, not necessarily preceded by any sort of nuclear change. But important changes in the enzymatic composition of the cytoplasm might be produced by the presence of new substrates; such changes might affect the nucleus itself and thus modify the genotype. There is no doubt that Spiegelman's (1948) ideas are interesting enough still to retain all the attention of chemical embryologists; but it is to be admitted that, as we shall soon see, there is so far no evidence for the view that enzyme synthesis, induced or otherwise, can deeply modify morphogenesis. This rather disappointing feeling is shared by many of those who have reviewed the subject in recent years (Boell, 1948, 1955; Moog, 1952; ten Cate, 1953; Shen, 1955; Urbani, 1957a, b; Borghese, 1957).

A number of cases, where enzyme synthesis and development appear to go hand in hand, will now be examined.

For instance, it is impossible to consider as having little interest for Chemical Embryology the already described and discussed work of Gustafson and Hasselberg (1951), of Weber and Boell (1955) and of Boell and Weber (1955), showing that, during development of both sea urchin and amphibian eggs, a marked synthesis of mitochondrial enzymes takes place: such an increase in enzymatic activity is apparently associated with progressive morphological complication of the mitochondria, as well as with an increase in the total number of these cytoplasmic particles.

Cytochemical methods for enzyme detection, because they afford good localization, have an obvious interest for the embryologist, even if their quantitative significance remains open to question for many biochemists. Valuable results have been obtained for alkaline phosphatase in developing sea urchin eggs by Krugelis (1947) and, more recently, by Evola-Maltese (1957): they clearly show that the enzymatic activity increases during gastrulation, especially in the invaginating cells (primary mesenchyme and endoderm). The interesting work of Mulnard (1955) on alkaline phosphatase localization during early development of mammalian embryos has already been mentioned in a previous chapter: let us recall here that the enzyme is first widely distributed throughout the whole embryo and that, at later stages, it becomes electively localized in the areas which are the site of active differentiation (the nervous system in particular) and disappears from the other parts. This peculiar behaviour of alkaline phosphatase is reminiscent of what has been found by Ebert (1954) for myosin in chick embryos.

Many more details about the localization of enzymes in the embryos of Birds and Mammals, as shown by cytochemical methods, will be found in the valuable review of Borghese (1957).

Besides the already mentioned observations by Boell and Weber (1955) on mitochondrial enzymes in amphibian eggs, most of the work done on enzymes in this material is due to Urbani (summarized in Urbani, 1957) and to Løvtrup (1955, 1958). Since this work has already been presented earlier in this book, all that should be recalled here is that, in general, synthesis of hydrolytic enzymes is a rather late process: it can begin already at gastrulation; but, as a rule, synthesis of such enzymes as amylase, protease or lipase does not become really important until the time of hatching. It would, of course, be interesting to study the synthesis of these enzymes in explants, since this synthesis might be closely linked with the differentiation (both morphological and physiological) of the digestive tract.

The work of Moog (1950, 1951) makes such a hypothesis a probable one: she studied, with both cytochemical and quantitative methods, the development of alkaline phosphatase in the duodenum of the mouse and the chick, and found a rapid increase of activity shortly before birth or hatching. Comparable results have been obtained for a number of other enzymes: for instance, Flexner and Flexner (1946) observed an increase in respiratory rate, cytochrome oxidase and succinic dehydrogenase activities when the neurones of the pig cerebral cortex assume their adult characteristics. Still more interesting, because it deals with a more specific enzyme, is the case of cholinesterase: already in 1943, Sawyer demonstrated that neuromuscular development and increase in cholinesterase activity are closely correlated. More details about these relationships existing between cholinesterase synthesis and the differentiation of the nervous system will be found in the reviews of Boell (1955) and Shen (1955, 1958). The latter has, in 1958, presented detailed evidence for the view that, in the case of cholinesterase, specific relations may occur between an enzyme and cytological structures; this evidence is based on studies on cholinesterase distribution in the central nervous system, the neuroretina and the myoneural junctions. In the latter, it could be shown conclusively by Shen (1958) that *in vitro* muscular differentiation of isolated presumptive mesoderm is accompanied by a substantial accumulation of cholinesterase. Synthesis of this enzyme occurs prior to innervation and may thus be a determining factor in the site of motor termination in muscle.

Other recent studies by Markert (1956, 1958) should also be mentioned: he followed the synthetic activities of embryonic cells in culture and found them to be more dependent upon their arrangement into organized tissues than upon the gross chemical composition of the medium. Of special interest for the embryologist is the fact that unique, specific synthetic activities may characterize certain tissues: for instance, the pigmented layer of the retina, at relatively late stages of development, can apparently synthesize some tyrosine—in contrast with other embryonic tissues. Markert (1956) concluded from his experiments that the acquisition of

THE BIOCHEMISTRY OF DIFFERENTIATION 271

distinctive metabolic patterns by cells during the course of differentiation involves three types of changes: qualitative losses in synthetic activity, qualitative gains in synthetic activity and shifts in relative synthetic activity. As a specific example, Markert (1958) especially studied the ontogenesis of a number of specific esterases, which could be separated from one another by electrophoresis in starch gels. He found that 'each adult tissue exhibits its own distinctive repertory of these esterases arranged in characteristic relative concentrations. During embryonic and early post-natal development the esterases appear one after the other as the tissue reaches new stages of differentiation, until finally the repertory is complete at the time the tissue reaches maturity.'

It is not yet known for certain whether young embryos are capable of *induced* enzyme synthesis when a substrate is added to the medium: induced enzyme synthesis of succinic dehydrogenase in amphibian embryos placed in the presence of succinate has been reported by Boell (1948), but the details have never been published and the experiments have still to be repeated. At a late stage of development (one week), injection of adenosine has been said to induce adenosine deaminase synthesis in chicken embryos (Gordon and Roder, 1953). But, despite repeated efforts, it has not been possible to confirm these observations of Gordon and Roder (1953) in our laboratory; the results we obtained were much too variable to allow any conclusion. Without expressing any doubt about the reality of the results published by Gordon and Roder (1953), it must be admitted that it is difficult to duplicate their experiments, for some technical reason probably.

More recently, Dubnau (1958) has published, in abstract form only, a report that adenosine deaminase synthesis can be obtained when adenosine is added to developing sea urchin eggs; this synthesis, however, does not begin until the pluteus stage has been reached.

Especially important and encouraging in this field is a recent report by Stearns and Kostellow (1958), who found that *dissociated* cells of *Rana pipiens* embryos are capable of induced synthesis of tryptophane peroxidase in the presence of tryptophane as an inducer: dissociated gastrulae synthesize the enzyme, at a very appreciable rate, after 4–5 hours of incubation. Entoderm cells, at this stage, are no more active than populations of ectoderm plus mesoderm cells. But it is a very striking and interesting fact that, at a somewhat later stage (just after gastrulation), a strong tryptophane peroxidase activity could only be induced in cultures containing the presumptive gut cells: ectoderm and mesoderm cells now showed very little capacity for induced enzyme synthesis. These results suggest that there is a progressive restriction in the ability of non-endoderm cells to respond to the addition of tryptophane by tryptophane peroxidase synthesis. Synthesis of another inducible enzyme, β-galactosidase, has also been obtained by Stearns and Kostellow (1958), but only in late gastrulae.

The main question, for the embryologist, remains, however, the following one: is induced enzyme synthesis responsible for differentiation? A pessimistic and negative answer to that question has been given a few years ago by Boell (1955), who wrote: 'But it should by no means be concluded that the development of an enzyme is in any way causally linked with the differentiation process with which it appears to be associated. Statement may nevertheless be found in the literature of embryology to the effect that specific enzymes, or the reactions catalysed by them, control such processes as determination, morphogenesis or differentiation. So far this has not been proven for any enzyme.'

All we can do is to agree, for the time being, with the above statement of Boell (1955) and to suggest a slightly different approach to the problem, which might be fruitful: it would be worth finding out whether the addition of a substrate might act as an inducer when *specific* enzymes are synthesized during morphogenetic processes: for instance, acetylcholine in the case of nervous system and phenylalanine in that of pigment cells might be worth trying as inducers.

This brings us to the end of our task and a few words only will be added: the general conclusion of this book is that there is still much to be done in the field of Chemical Embryology. We have tried to show, in this book, that the chemical embryologist, who is faced with problems of such fundamental importance as growth and differentiation, has an enormous field open before him. Possible experiments have been suggested many times and there is no doubt that they only represent a small sample of what can and will be done in a field which is developing at faster and faster speed. If we have succeeded in presenting a few ideas and in suggesting a few meaningful experiments, our task will have been fulfilled: new methods for the approach of developmental problems already exist and there is no doubt that others, still more powerful, will follow.

The emphasis, especially in the last chapter, has been placed on differentiation, which is the most fascinating problem for the embryologist and perhaps even for the general biologist. It should not be forgotten that the study of the mechanisms of differentiation has more than academic interest: we shall not know why cancer cells do not differentiate normally until we understand better normal embryonic differentiation.

In the egg and in the embryo, we meet all the great biological problems: meiosis, fertilization, genetic recombination, mitosis, cell movements and adhesiveness and, above all, the still mysterious differentiation processes, which must be closely linked to the mechanisms of specific protein synthesis. Yet, chemical embryology is a science by itself, which is developing together with other related sciences: morphology, especially at the ultrastructural level, cytochemistry, microchemistry and, above all, causal (experimental) embryology. Chemical embryology still is a young science, but it is growing fast and developing well.

Brussels, November 1958–January 1959.

REFERENCES

AUERBACH, R. and C. GROBSTEIN. (1958): *Exp. Cell Res.* **15**, 384.
BEADLE, G. W. (1946): *Amer. Scientist* **34**, 31.
BECKER, U., V. DOSTAL, H. TIEDEMANN and H. TIEDEMANN. (1959): *Zeitschr. f. Naturforschg.* **14**b, 260.
BEKKUM, D. W. VAN and O. VOS. (1957): *J. cell. comp. Physiol.* **50**, suppl. 1, 139.
BENITEZ, H. H., M. R. MURRAY and E. CHARGAFF. (1959): *J. biophys. biochem. Cytol.* **5**, 25.
BILLINGHAM, R. E., L. BRENT and P. B. MEDAWAR. (1953): *Nature* **172**, 603.
BILLINGHAM, R. E., L. BRENT and P. B. MEDAWAR. (1956): *Phil. Trans. Roy. Soc.* **239**, 357.
BOELL, E. J. (1948): *Ann. N.Y. Acad. Sci.* **49**, 773.
BOELL, E. J. (1955): In: *Analysis of Development* (B. H. Willier, P. A. Weiss and V. Hamburger, ed.), p. 520, W. B. Saunders Co.
BOELL, E. J. and R. WEBER. (1955): *Exp. Cell Res.* **9**, 559.
BORGHESE, E. (1957): *Internat. Rev. Cytol.* **6**, 289.
BRACHET, J. (1944): *Embryologie chimique*, Desoer, Liège.
BRACHET, J., M. DECROLY-BRIERS and J. HOYEZ. (1958): *Bull. Soc. Chim. biol.* **40**, 2039.
BRAVERMAN, M. H. (1958): *Biol. Bull.* **115**, 319.
BURKE, V., N. P. SULLIVAN, H. PETERSON and R. WEED. (1944): *J. infect. Dis.* **74**, 225.
CATE, G. TEN. (1953): *Arch néerl. Zool.* **10**, suppl. 1, 108.
CATE, G. TEN and W. J. VAN DOORENMAALEN. (1950): *Proc. koninkl. Nederl. Akad. Wetensch.* **53**, 849.
CHEN, P. S. (1955): *Vierteljahrschr. Naturforsch. Ges. Zürich* **100**, 232.
CHILD, C. M. (1941): *Patterns and Problems of Development.* Univ. of Chicago Press.
CHUANG, H. H. (1938): *Biol. Zbl.* **58**, 472.
CHUANG, H. H. (1940): *Roux' Arch. Entw. Mech.* **140**, 25.
CLAYTON, R. M. (1953): *J. Embryol. exp. Morphol.* **1**, 25.
COHEN, S. (1958): In: *The Chemical Basis of Development*, p. 665. Johns Hopkins Press, Baltimore.
COOPER, R. S. (1948): *J. exp. Zool.* **107**, 397.
DALCQ, A. and J. PASTEELS. (1938): *Bull. Acad. roy. Méd. Belg.*, 6e série, **3**, 261.
DE DUVE, C. (1957): *Soc. exp. Biol. Sympos.* **10**, 50.
DE DUVE, C. (1958): *Exposés annuels de Biochimie médicale*, 20e série, p. 197, Masson, Paris.
DEUCHAR, E. M., R. WEBER and F. E. LEHMANN. (1957): *Helvet. physiol. et pharmacol. Acta* **15**, 212.
DE VINCENTIIS, M. (1954): *Bollet. di Zool.* **21** 379.
DOORENMAALEN, W. J. VAN. (1957): *Thesis*, University of Amsterdam.
DOORENMAALEN, W. J. VAN. (1958): *Acta morphol. néerl. scand.* **2**, 1.
DUBNAU, D. (1958): *Biol. Bull.* **115**, 350.
DUFFEY, L. M. and J. D. EBERT. (1957): *J. Embryol. exp. Morphol.* **5**, 324.
T

EBERT, J. D. (1950): *J. exp. Zool.* **115**, 351.
EBERT, J. D. (1951): *Physiol. Zool.* **24**, 20.
EBERT, J. D. (1953): *Proc. nat. Acad. Sci., Wash.* **39**, 333.
EBERT, J. D. (1954): *Proc. nat. Acad. Sci., Wash.* **40**, 337.
EBERT, J. D. (1955): In: *Aspects of Synthesis and Order in Growth*, (D. Rudnick, ed.), p. 69, Princeton Univ. Press.
EBERT, J. D. (1958): *Carnegie Inst. Washington Year Book*.
EBERT, J. D. (1958): In: *The Chemical Basis of Development*, p. 526. Johns Hopkins Press, Baltimore.
EBERT, J. D. (1959): *The Cell*, vol. **3**, Academic Press, N.Y. (in press).
EBERT, J. D., R. A. TOLMAN, A. M. MUN and J. E. ALBRIGHT. (1955): *Ann. N.Y. Acad. Sci.* **60**, 698.
EDDS, M. V. (1958a): *Proc. nat. Acad. Sci., Wash.* **44**, 296.
EDDS, M. V. (1958b): In: *The Chemical Basis of Development*, p. 157, Johns Hopkins Press, Baltimore.
EVOLA-MALTESE, C. (1957): *Acta Embryol. Morphol. exp.* **1**, 99.
FLEXNER, J. B. and L. B. FLEXNER. (1946): *J. cell. comp. Physiol.* **27**, 35.
FLICKINGER, R. A. (1958): *Biol. Bull.* **115**, 201.
FLICKINGER, R. A., E. LEVI and A. E. SMITH. (1955)· ? *hysiol. Zool.* **28**, 79.
FLICKINGER, R. A. and G. W. NACE. (1952): *Exp. Cell Res.* **3**, 393.
FORD, C. E., J. L. HAMERTON, D. W. H. BARNES and J. F. LOUTIT. (1956): *Nature* **177**, 452.
FORD, C. E., P. L. T. ILBERG and J. F. LOUTIT. (1957): *J. cell. comp. Physiol.* **50**, suppl. 1, 109.
GLÜCKSMAN, A. (1951): *Biolog. Revs.* **26**, 59.
GORDON, M. W. and M. RODER. (1953): *J. biol. Chem.* **200**, 859
GROBSTEIN, C. and E. ZWILLING. (1953): *J. exp. Zool.* **122**, 259.
GUSTAFSON, T. and I. HASSELBERG. (1951): *Exp. Cell Res.* **2**, 642
HAŠEK, M. and T. HRABA. (1955): *Nature* **175**, 766.
HAYASHI, Y. (1956): *Embryologia* **3**, 57.
HAYASHI, Y. (1958): *Embryologia* **4**, 33.
HAYASHI, Y. and K. TAKATA. (1958): *Embryologia* **4**, 149.
HERRMANN, H., B. N. WHITE, and M. COOPER. (1957): *J. cell. comp. Physiol.* **49**, 227.
HOLTFRETER, J. (1939): *Arch. exp. Zellforschg.* **23**, 169.
HOLTFRETER, J. (1947a): *J. Morphol.* **80**, 57.
HOLTFRETER, J. (1947b): *J. exp. Zool.* **106**, 197.
HOLTZER, H., J. M. MARSHALL and H. FINCK. (1957): *J. biophys. biochem. Cytol.* **3**, 705.
HOLTZER, H., J. ABBOTT and M. W. CAVANAUGH. (1959): *Exp. Cell Res.* **16**, 595.
JOHNEN, A. G. (1956): *Proc. Acad. Sci., Amsterdam*, ser. C, **59**, 652.
JOHNSON, I. S. and C. A. LEONE. (1955): *J. exp. Zool.* **130**, 515.
KIENY, M. (1958): *Arch. Anat. microsc.* **47**, 85.
KONYUKHOV, B. V. (1957): *Bjull. eksper. Biol. Med.* **44**, 96.
KRUGELIS, E. (1947): *Biol. Bull.* **93**, 215.
KUUSI, T. (1953): *Arch. Biol.* **64**, 189.
KUUSI, T. (1957): *Arch. Soc. Zool. Bot. Fenn. 'Vanamo'* **12**, 73.
LANGMAN, J. M., A. M. D. H. SCHALEKAMP, M. P. A. KUYKEN and R. VEEN. (1956): *Acta morphol. néerl. scand.* **1**, 142.
LASH, J. W. and H. HOLTZER. (1958): *Biol. Bull.* **115**, 322.
LE CLERC, J. (1954): *Experientia* **10**, 251.
LEVI-MONTALCINI, R. (1958): In: *The Chemical Basis of Development*, p. 646. Johns Hopkins Press, Baltimore.

LEVI-MONTALCINI, R. and S. COHEN. (1956): *Proc. nat. Acad. Sci., Wash.* **42**, 695.
LØVTRUP, S. (1955): *C. R. Trav. Labor. Carlsberg, sér. chim.* **29**, 261.
LØVTRUP, S. (1958): *Acta Embryol. Morphol. exp.* **2**, 54.
MAKINODAN, T. (1957): *J. cell. comp. Physiol.* **50**, suppl. 1, 157.
MANGOLD, O., H. TIEDEMANN and C. VON WOELLWARTH. (1956): *Roux' Arch. Entw. Mech.* **149**, 45.
MARKERT, C. L. (1956): *Cold Spring Harbor Sympos.* **21**, 339.
MARKERT, C. L. (1958): In: *The Chemical Basis of Development*, p. 10. Johns Hopkins Press, Baltimore.
MEDAWAR, P. B. (1957): *Ann. N.Y. Acad. Sci.* **68**, 255.
MILLER, J. A. and E. C. MILLER. (1953): *Advanc. in Cancer Res.* **1**, 339.
MOOG, F. (1950): *J. exp. Zool.* **115**, 109.
MOOG, F. (1951): *J. exp. Zool.* **118**, 187.
MOOG, F. (1952): *Ann. N.Y. Acad. Sci.* **55**, 57.
MOSCONA, A. (1957): *Proc. nat. Acad. Sci. Wash.* **43**, 184.
MULNARD, J. (1955): *Arch. Biol.* **66**, 525.
NACE, G. W. (1953): *J. exp. Zool.* **122**, 423.
NACE, G. W. (1955): *Ann. N.Y. Acad. Sci.* **60**, 1038.
NACE, G. W. and W. M. CLARKE. (1958): In: *The Chemical Basis of Development*, p. 546. Johns Hopkins Press, Baltimore.
NACE, G. W. and K. INOUÉ. (1957): *Science* **126**, 259.
NEEDHAM, J. (1931): *Chemical Embryology*. Cambridge Univ. Press.
NIEUWKOOP, P. D. (1955): *Exp. Cell Res.* suppl. **3**, 262.
NIEUWKOOP, P. D. (1958): *Acta Embryol. Morphol. exp.* **2**, 13.
NIEUWKOOP, P. D. and others. (1952): *J. exp. Zool.* **120**, 1.
NIU, M. C. (1958a): *Proc. Nat. Acad. Sci., Wash.* **44**, 1264.
NIU, M. C. (1958b): In: *The Chemical Basis of Development*, pp. 256, 625. Johns Hopkins Press, Baltimore.
OGAWA, Y. (1958): *Nature* **182**, 1312.
OGAWA, Y., T. KAWAKARA and J. MIURA. (1958): *Nature* **181**, 621.
PERLMANN, P. (1953): *Exp. Cell Res.* **5**, 394.
PERLMANN, P. and T. GUSTAFSON. (1948): *Experientia* **4**, 481.
ROSE, S. M. (1952): *Amer. Naturalist* **86**, 337.
ROSE, S. M. (1955): *Ann. N.Y. Acad. Sci.* **90**, 1136.
ROSE, S. M. (1957): *Biolog. Revs.* **32**, 351.
SAWYER, C. H. (1943): *J. exp. Zool.* **92**, 1.
SAXÉN, L. and S. TOIVONEN. (1958): *J. Embryol. exp. Morphol.* **6**, 616.
SCHECHTMAN, A. M. (1955): In: *Biological Specificity and Growth* (E. G. Butler, ed.), p. 3, Princeton Univ. Press.
SHEN, S. C. (1955): *Biological Specificity and Growth*. (E. G. Butler, ed.) p. 73 Princeton Univ. Press.
SHEN, S. C. (1958): In: *The Chemical Basis of Development*, p. 416. Johns Hopkins Press, Baltimore.
SIGEL, M. M., T. M. SCOTTI, M. A. WRYK and M. DORSEY JR. (1958): *Nature* **182**, 1034.
SMITH, R. H. (1957): *Progress in Biophysics* **8**, 218.
SPIEGEL, M. (1954): *Biol. Bull.* **107**, 149.
SPIEGELMAN, S. (1948): *Sympos. Soc. exp. Biol.* **2**, 286.
STEARNS, R. N. and A. B. KOSTELLOW. (1958): In: *The Chemical Basis of Development*, p. 448. Johns Hopkins Press, Baltimore.
STENGER-HAFFEN, K. (1957): *Arch. Anat. microsc.* **46**, 521.
TAKAYA, H. (1956): *Proc. Jap. Acad.* **32**, 287.
TEMME, W. (1956): *Verhandl. dtsch. zool. Gesellsch. in Hamburg*, 352.

TIEDEMANN, H. and H. TIEDEMANN. (1957): *Experientia* **13**, 320.

TOIVONEN, S. (1940): *Ann. Acad. Sci. fenn.* **A 55**, No. 6, 1.

TOIVONEN, S. (1950): *Rev. suisse Zool.* **57**, suppl. 1, 41.

TOIVONEN, S. (1953): *J. Embryol. exp. Morphol.* **1**, 97.

TOIVONEN, S. (1954): *J. Embryol. exp. Morphol.* **2**, 239.

TOIVONEN, S. (1958): *J. Embryol. exp. Morphol.* **6**, 479.

TOIVONEN, S. and T. KUUSI. (1948): *Ann. zool. Soc. Zool. Bot. Fenn. 'Vanamo'* **13**, No. 3, 1.

TOIVONEN, S. and L. SAXÉN. (1955): *Exp. Cell Res.*, suppl. **3**, 346.

TOIVONEN, S. and L. SAXÉN. (1957): *J. natl. Cancer Inst.* **19**, 1095.

TYLER, A. (1947): *Growth*, suppl. **10**, 7.

TYLER, A. (1957): In: *The Beginnings of Embryonic Development*, p. 341. A.A.A.S., Publ. No. 48, Washington.

URBANI, E. (1957): *Atti Soc. ital. di Anatom., XVII Convegno sociale*, 26 pp.

VAHS, W. (1957): *Roux' Arch. Entw. Mech.* **149**, 339.

VAINIO, T. (1958): *Exp. Cell Res.* **15**, 184.

WEBER, R. (1957): *Rev. suisse Zool.* **64**, 326.

WEBER, R. and E. J. BOELL. (1955): *Rev. suisse Zool.* **62**, 260.

WEISS, P. (1947): *Yale J. Biol. and Med.* **19**, 235.

WEISS, P. (1955): In: *Biological Specificity and Growth* (E. Butler, ed.), p. 195, Princeton Univ. Press.

WILDE, C. E. JR. (1955): *J. Morphol.* **97**, 313.

WILDE, C. E. JR. (1955): *Ann. N.Y. Acad. Sci.* **60**, 1015.

WILDE, C. E. JR. (1956): *J. exp. Zool.* **133**, 409.

WOERDEMAN, M. W. (1953): *Arch. néerl. Zool.* **10**, suppl. 1, 114.

WOERDEMAN, M. W. (1955): In: *Biological Specificity and Growth* (E. Butler, ed.), p. 33, Princeton Univ. Press.

WOLFF, E. (1953): *Experientia* **9**, 121.

WOLFF, E. (1957): *Arch. Anat. microsc.* **46**, 407.

YAMADA, T. (1950): *Biol. Bull.* **98**, 98.

YAMADA, T. (1958a): *Experientia* **14**, 81.

YAMADA, T. (1958b): In: *The Chemical Basis of Development*, p. 217. Johns Hopkins Press, Baltimore.

YAMADA, T. (1959): *Embryolgia* **4**, 175.

YAMADA, T. and K. TAKATA. (1956): *Embryologia* **3**, 69.

AUTHOR INDEX

SUBJECT INDEX